MOOR
TO
SEA
THE DEVON REAL ALE GUIDE

Published by the Devon Branches of the
Campaign for Real Ale in association with
Westcountry Books

WESTCOUNTRY
BOOKS

British Library Cataloguing in Publication Data
CIP Data for this publication is available from the British Library

ISBN 1 898 38600 5

PUBLISHING AND SALES
Westcountry Books
1 Chinon Court
Lower Moor Way
Tiverton
Devon EX16 6SS
Tel: 0884 243242
Fax: 0884 243325

ACKNOWLEDGEMENTS

The production team on this edition were: Roger Adams; Bruce Ardley (Computer text and maps); Sue Barret; Ian Daniels; Ian Dickinson; Neil Dodd; Rebecca Garland; Mick Gullick; Ray Hodgins; Roger Hulbert; Sean Kelleher; David Lomax; Philip Roberts; David Tooke; Nick Tucker; Ian Ward.

Plus all the members in Devon who also had the unenviable task of carrying out the surveys which enabled this publication to exist.

NOTE

The information presented in this guide, and the opinions expressed, are those of the members of the Devon branches of CAMRA. Every effort has been made to ensure that the information is correct at the time of going to press and the publisher accepts no responsibility for errors.

Printed in Great Britain by BPCC Wheatons Ltd, Exeter

HOW TO USE THIS GUIDE

The map reference which accompanies each entry refers to the grid squares on the maps on the pages following (iv - xi)

A typical pub entry comprises:

ABBOTSKERSWELL ← Town or village

BUTCHERS ARMS ← Name of Pub and map reference
11 - 3; 5 - 11 (M-S) ← Nominal opening times
ABBOTSKERSWELL, NEWTON ABBOT ← Address or location
Tel: (0626) 60731 ← Telephone number and STD

Draught Bass	**(H)**
Eldridge-Pope Hardy Country	**(H)**
Flowers IPA	**(H)**

← Beers and method of dispense

CD (EUCHRE) CP DB DF FA LM ML OD ← Facilities
PG RF
A large village local in a very nice setting. ← Pub description
Old farm tools provide the decor. The Pub
has been pleasantly enlarged. Live Music.

KEY TO SYMBOLS

Method of Dispense:

H	Handpump
G	Gravity
E	Electric Pump

Facilities:

AC	Accommodation		ML	Lunchtime Meals
BB	Bar Billiards		MR	Meetings Room
BR	Near BR Station (within $^1/_2$ mile)		NS	NO SMOKING Area
CA	Camping facilities		OD	Outdoor Area/Garden
CD	Cards		PB	Separate Public Bar
CH	Family Room		PG	Pub Games
CI	Real Cider		PL	Pool
CP	Car Park		QP	Quiet Pub
DB	Darts		RF	Real Coal/Wood Fire (not gas)
DF	Disabled Facilities		RM	Recorded Music
DM	Dominoes		RS	Restaurant
FA	Families Welcome		SH	Shove-halfpenny
GD	Garden		SK	Snooker
LM	Live Music		SN	Snacks
ME	Evening Meals		ST	Skittles

iv

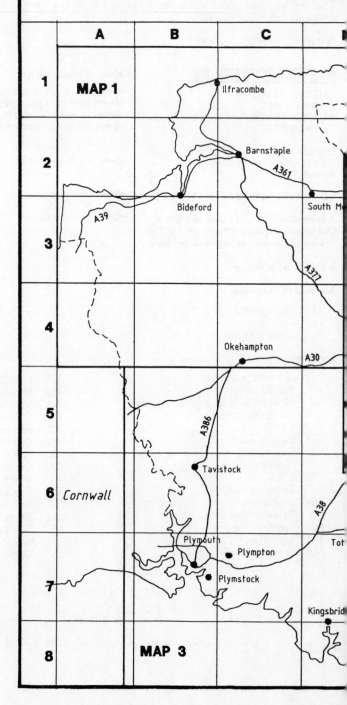

KEY MAP OF THE COUNTY OF DEVON
SHOWING AREAS COVERED BY MAIN MAP

KEY MAP OF THE COUNTY OF DEVON
OWING AREAS COVERED BY MAIN MAPS

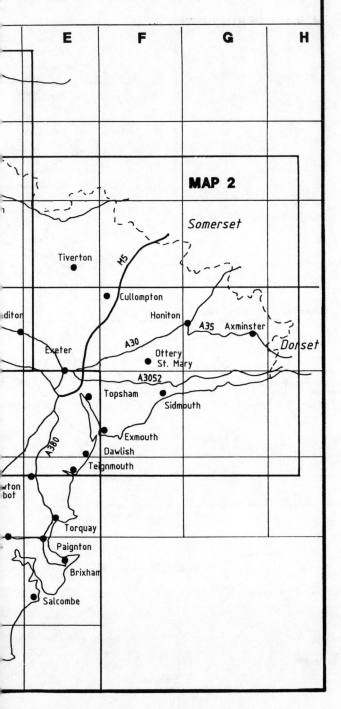

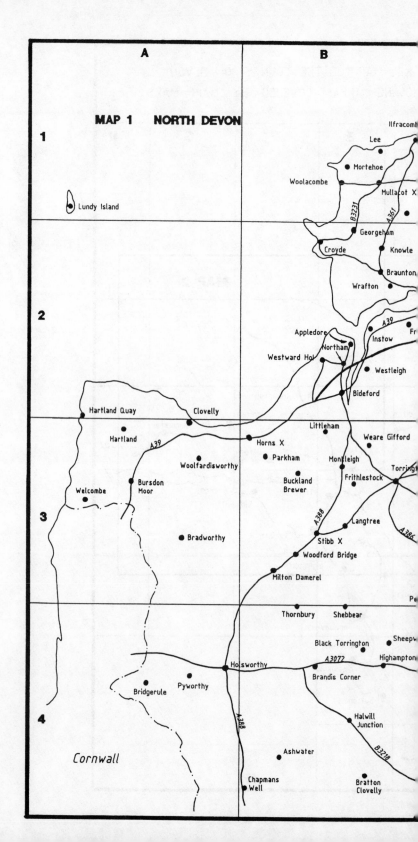

MAP 1   NORTH DEVON

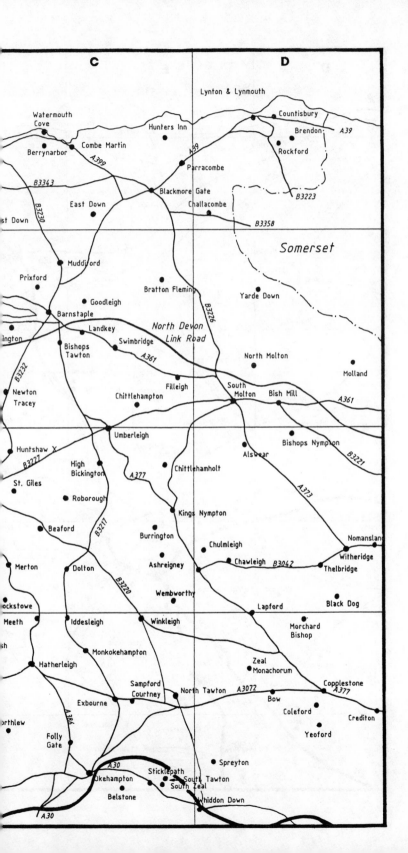

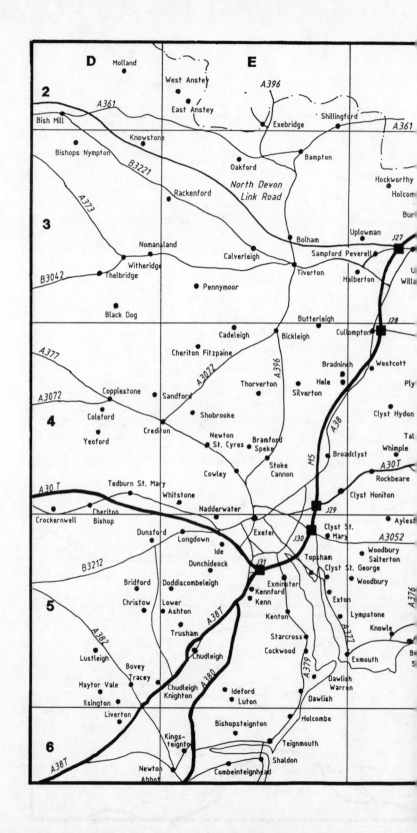

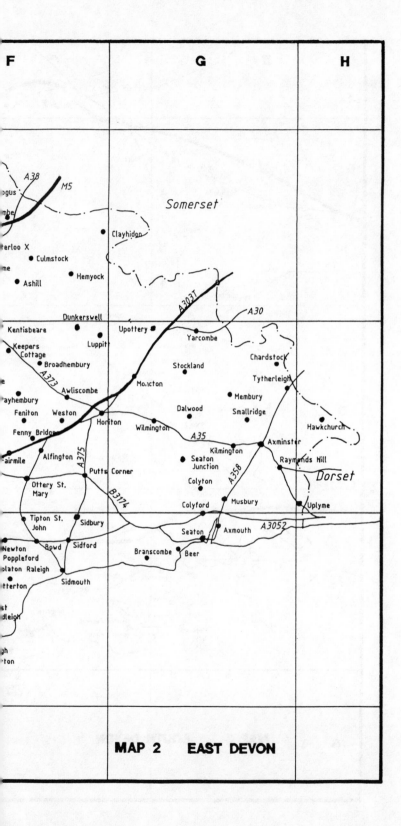

F

G

H

A38 M5

gus

mbe

Somerset

terloo X Clayhidon

• Culmstock

me

• Ashill • Hemyock

A303T

Dunkerswell *A30*

• Kentisbeare Upottery •

Keepers Luppit Yarcombe •
Cottage

• Broadhembury Chardstock •

A373 Stockland • Tytherleigh •

e Awliscombe Mo.icton •

ayhembury • Membury

• Feniton Weston Dalwood Smallridge •
  Horiton •

Fenny Bridge Wilmington Hawkchurch

A35

airmile Alfington Kilmington Axminster

  A375 Seaton Raymonds Hill
  Putts Corner Junction *Dorset*
Ottery St. Colyton • *A358*
Mary *B3174*

Tipton St. Colyford Musbury Uplyme
John Sidbury

Newton Bowd Sidford Seaton Axmouth *A3052*
Poppleford
olaton Raleigh Branscombe • Beer

tterton Sidmouth

st
dleigh

gh
ton

MAP 2   EAST DEVON

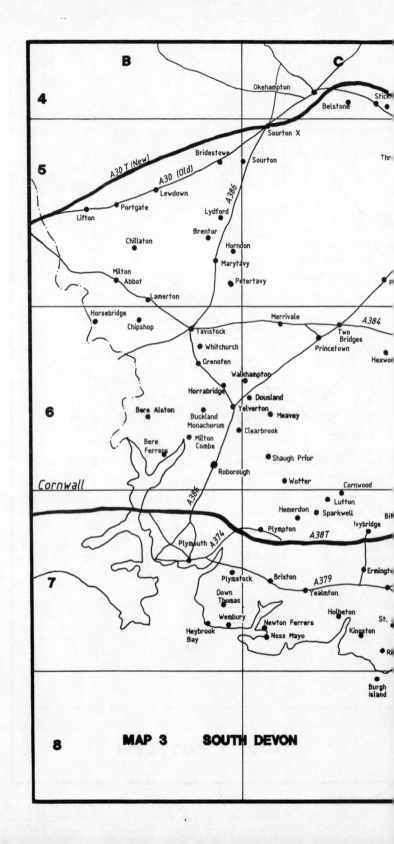

MAP 3   SOUTH DEVON

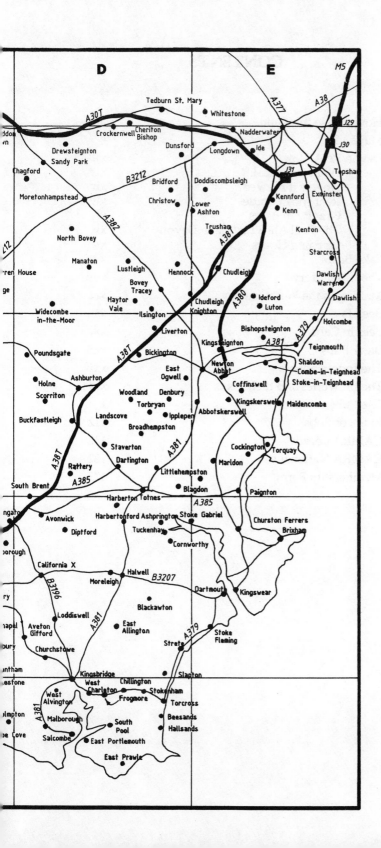

CONTENTS

DEVON REAL ALE

This is the ninth edition of this guide and it is almost three years since the last Devon Real Ale Guide appeared on the bookshelves.

During that time a lot has changed. Out of the MMC report came the Beer Orders which stated that breweries which owned more than 2000 pubs had to free from tie half those owned above 2000. At the time we thought, marvellous, all those pubs owned by the breweries would have to be sold and once in the free trade the choices for real ale drinkers would be dramatically increased. Instead the true position is far from that. The major brewers have formed pub owning companies tied to them for the supply of beer and one of the larger brewers trading in the South West now actually supplies more 'tied' pubs than it did before the Beer Orders.

We have seen an increase in the number of small independent brewers in Devon with the arrival of Summerskills, Otter and Branscombe competing for the free trade market with the established Blackawton, Exe Valley, Mill and Thompsons.

Let us also not forget Furgusons Plympton Brewery who fit into a slot somewhere between the small independent and the national brewer.

At the time of writing we are in what the politicians call the recession. This has resulted in the closure of numerous pubs in Devon and many more are struggling to survive. We must all hope that villages suffering the loss of their only pub will not have to suffer long and that there will be an end to this recession and the village pub will thrive once more. This will only happen if the brewers realise that they cannot put the price of their beer up every five minutes. Have they not heard of the law of diminishing returns?

Finally, since the last guide we have a total of four active CAMRA branches in Devon whereas previously we only had one. This has enabled the compilation of this guide 'Moor to Sea' to be that much easier. We have attempted to list all the outlets serving good real ale however we unfortunately have not been able to visit every outlet so if you are not included in this guide and you feel you should be, my apologies, please get in touch with your local contact listed at the end of this guide.

I should add that all the surveying and work that has gone into the production of this guide has been carried out by unpaid Devon CAMRA members. Notes on pubs, villages and towns are included for the benefit of visitors and locals alike. A profile for all the Devon real ale breweries and of those breweries which supply traditional ales to the area on a regular basis have been included in a separate section.

Traditional cider is mentioned. Cider tends to be more widely available in the summer and as most of our surveying was done over the winter period the number of pubs serving cider will vary.

Updated maps of the county have been included and all outlets entered in the guide are referenced to these maps.

Special thanks should finally be given to Bruce Ardley who has entered the information contained in this guide onto computer so that production costs may be kept to a minimum.

Philip Roberts - Chairman, Devon Real Ale Committee.

WHAT IS REAL ALE?

CAMRA defines real ale as living beer, matured, kept and served under natural conditions without the assistance of extraneous carbon dioxide gas. Fermentation continues slowly after racking into the cask (cask conditioning). After settling, the beer is drawn straight from the cask, or pumped to the bar by hand pump; modern self-priming electric pumps act in the same way as handpumps. However, many publicans serve otherwise real cask ale under pressure of carbon dioxide (even using what look like handpumps, but which are actually valves). The gas dissolves in the beer, disguising the flavour, making it fizzy and sweet. If the gas is used merely to prevent air entering the cask, it is known as blanket pressure (a cask breather is used, and should be a genuine demand valve - a rarity), but if the pressure is sufficient to force the beer to the bar it is known as 'top pressure'.

With keg beers, fermentation is stopped at the brewery (brewery conditioning) by filtration and pasteurisation before filling the keg. This makes the beer sterile, inert and flat, carbon dioxide has then got to be added under pressure to give the beer some life. The result is a clear, long lasting, uniform, easy to serve product, but one which is completely different in character from the type of beer drunk in this country for a score of centuries, and known for 7,000 years.

HOW IS IT BREWED?

Real beer is made from malted barley, free from adjuncts, pure water, dried hops and yeast, with no additives. Long live the Reinheitsgebot, the German purity law which so defines and protects their beer and cares for beer drinkers. Adjuncts used by some brewers include malted or raw grains such as maize, rice, wheat, oats, rye, raw barley and many others, as well as potatoes, processed starches, milks and an infinity of oddities. These include many sugars, which may seem innocent enough, but they contribute negatively to flavour by dilution, and add alcohol to cover deficiencies in malt. Additives include the, again seemingly, innocent caramel (burnt sugar) which darkens the ale (Marston's Merry Monk, Exmoor Dark, Palmers Ales), but can be a euphemism for synthetic colourings like Vandyke brown and other horrors. This is a cheapie substitute for crystal or chocolate malt, which adds flavour as well as colour. There are worse; preservatives and bitters as a substitute for expensive hops, sulphur dioxide, synthetic alpha acid and hop oils; foaming and clinging agents to produce a head and make it stick to a glass, because hops are sparingly measured, and adjuncts deficient in these qualities are used; and many others too technical for the non-specialist. The water used in the mash (liquor in the trade) may be legitimately modified as to its calcium and magnesium content and its acidity, but should not be chlorinated; and the yeast should be a top, not a bottom fermenting variety. Malted barley, water, hops and yeast should be the only ingredients.

REAL ALES IN BOTTLES

Most bottled beers are filtered, pasteurised and carbonated, but some contain remaining or added yeast, giving rise to secondary fermentation. The best known is Worthington White Shield (Bass). Thomas Hardy (Eldridge Pope) is the strongest, Courage Imperial Russian Stout is another strong, but rare, real ale in a bottle. Bottle conditioned ales are beginning to appear from the independents.

GRAVITY OF BEERS

The original gravity, the specific gravity of the wort before fermenation occurs, is a measure of the amount of soluble matter - mainly sugars - extracted from the malt. This is measured by the government gauger and is the basis of the tax levied by the Inland Revenue. Not all the material is fermentable, and not all the sugars are fermented out; the more sugar that is left, the sweeter the ale and the lower the final alcohol content. Nevertheless the O.G. is a guide to the potential alcohol strength of the ale, and roughly speaking bitter is 1030 - 1037, best bitter 1035 - 1042, premium bitter is 1040 - 1050, and strong ale can be up to 1080; beyond that the product is a barley wine. The nearer fermentation is taken to completion, the drier the ale.

THE REAL ALE SITUATION IN DEVON

Real ale is available in the majority of Devon pubs, but sadly most of it still comes from five major national brewers: Whitbread, Courage, Bass, Watneys and Allied in decreasing order of outlets. There are still areas of alleged gross monopoly as in Plymouth (Courage) and Exeter (Whitbread), and as stated elsewhere in this guide some major breweries have even increased the number of 'tied' outlets in the area which serve only their beers.

These major breweries, through the financial tie, also invade our diminishing number of free houses.

Explorers seeking to taste local or independent brews must look among the remaining true free houses. Competition in the free trade (national breweries are fighting in this area too) with so few outlets is fierce, so that new breweries have a hard struggle to establish themselves.

However, 5 pub breweries (possibly soon to be 6) and the small breweries continue to flourish in Devon and so have ales from the neighbouring counties of Cornwall, Dorset, Somerset and Wiltshire to brighten the scene. Activity in the wholesaling of beer to the free trade has also enabled a wider choice of beers from further afield to be available in Devon.

Independents do, of course, produce mediocre beer as well. More important is the fact that the beer is only as good as the quality of the skill and care invested in it by the landlord. A good guvnor' with a good stillage and cellar can convert even a mediocre ale into something worth drinking. With better material to lavish tender loving care on, such an expert can produce ale with the flavour of nectar, showing all the nuances of flavour and condition in the pint one has been seeking all one's life. On the other hand, too high, too low, or widely fluctuating temperatures in the store (a wire cage in the back yard!), and other defects may make a pub unsuitable for real ale. The landlord who uses casks too large for his turn over , forgets the spile, does not observe scrupulous cleanliness, stoops casks jerkily or too much, serves green or stale ale, or does not understand or fails to meet the simple requirements in the care of living ale, does no service to his customers, the ale, or himself, and should either learn the trade properly or give up.

Fortunately, few though our free houses are, there are some gems among them, and we invite you to seek them out and tell us about them .

OPENING HOURS

Whilst every effort has been made to ensure that the opening hours for pubs shown in our guide are correct, it must be pointed out that individual licensees may change their opening hours without notice and for any reason. Exceptions to normal pub opening hours have been noted where these have been supplied by the licensee. A number of pub licensees around tourist centres have stated that they are open all day in summer, but close for an afternoon break in winter. Where this has been repeated in the guide, readers should note that many licensees who say they will be open all day, may, close for an afternoon break 'if there is not sufficient trade'.

No responsibility can be taken by the producers of this guide for pubs not being open at the times shown. If you intend to visit a pub at a particular time, you are advised to check with the pub beforehand to ensure that the pub will be open and that all the facilities you intend to use will be available at the time of your visit.

FAKE BEERS

'Duck Pond Bitter' specially brewed for the Duck and Drake is proudly displayed on the pump clip. You should be well advised to avoid house beers like this fictitious example. With a few exceptions they are not specially brewed for the pub and indeed are likely to be low gravity national brew masquerading as something more unique - with an inflated price to match.

In Devon we have a handful of brew pubs - The Beer Engine, Newton St. Cyres; The Tally Ho, Hatherleigh; The Royal Inn, Horsebridge; The London Inn, Ashburton; The Ship and Plough, Kingsbridge; and the Marisco Tavern on Lundy. These can claim to have beer specially brewed for them, indeed their whole reason for brewing is usually to sell it in their own pub with any surplus going into the free trade.

The practice of stocking a house ale seems, thankfully to be diminishing; whilst we cannot outlaw it, pressure(!) should be put on these pubs to avoid claiming that it is brewed for that pub, implying no one else stocks it. (There are plenty of other places to buy for example, Halls Harvest or Flowers IPA!). It would be good to see trading standards departments taking action against such claims and encouraging the pubs concerned at least to display who brews the 'house special ale', even if the drinker has to work out which brew it is.

It is not only the national brewers who provide these beers, indeed Janners Old Original is often sold under house names, although some of the pump clips do admit to it being brewed by Mill Brewery. In fact where a house beer is provided by a smaller brewer, the publican concerned is usually quite anxious to advertise the fact. Apparently, provided no attempt is made to deceive, a pub can call a beer anything it likes within reason - the brewer cannot stop him except by refusing to supply the beer. Of course, not many brewers like refusing trade!

If your local stocks a house beer and will not admit what it is, try to persuade the local trading standards department to check what you are paying 10p a pint extra for. It could well be taken out of the same cask as the brew on the next pump, is it really worth paying the extra for a fancy name?

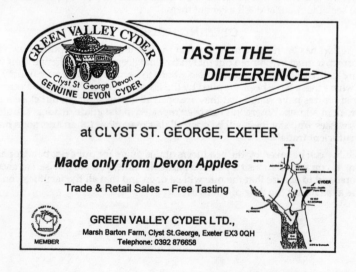

THE CIDER STORY

Traditional cider has long played an important part in Devon's cultural heritage. Along with Somerset and Herefordshire, Devon is one of the top three cider producing counties. At the last count there were 29 cidermakers in the county operating commercially plus an indeterminate number in the sub-commercial area. There is an important distinction here between cidermakers and brewers. For historical reasons, chiefly the former very widespread practice of making cider on farms, those producing less than 1500 gallons per annum do not have to register with HM Customs and Excise. Consequently, on the smaller (duty-free!) scale, there is no clear distinction between commercial and non-commercial production. Some of these small producers make excellent, indeed championship quality, cider, but they may not actively sell it. The true cider enthusiast will hunt them out and strike a deal. It is one of those traditions where the more you look, the more you find.

So, what makes good cider? Good quality apples certainly, simplicity of method, and plenty of tender loving care. The apples deserve a mention. West Country cider apples have a high tannin content which gives them a bitter aftertaste, but, by the same token, imparts body and depth of taste to the cider. A skilful cidermaker will select a balanced blend of Bittersweets (high tannin, low acidity) and Bittersharps (high tannin, high acidity) with probably some Sweets (low tannin, low acidity) and Sharps (low tannin, high acidity) to adjust the acidity. Their picturesque names fire the imagination. Often these are simply descriptive or denote their place of origin. Here are a few: Fair Maid of Devon, Hangy Down, Slack-ma-Girdle, Fillbarrel, Yarlington Mill, Kingston Black, Foxwhelp, Bloody Butcher, Strawberry Norman, Pig Snout, Chisel Jersey, Crimson King, Cap of Liberty, Woodbine, Tremlett's Bitter, Porter's Perfection, Cider Lady's Finger and Sweet Alford. It is reassuring to know that specialists, like the newly established Thornhayes Nursery at Dulford, are still rearing many of these old favourites for replanting so that tradition can be continued.

What about the cider making? The simplest, and in many ways the best, procedure is to take the juice of freshly pressed apples, ferment it using yeast naturally present on the fruit and pressing equipment, and to seal it in oak casks to finish and mature. This is real cider. The chances are that no two batches will taste exactly the same by this method, but it certainly produces some winners. You can understand why cidermaker's yeast is an anathema to the brewers amongst us! These days, pressing is commonly done in cloths with hydraulic equipment, but there are still some traditionalists using straw and single or double screw presses. The search for consistency has led many cidermakers to kill off the natural yeasts in the juice by adding sulphur dioxide before fermentation and then pitching in a commercial yeast. This is rather like the wine producer sacrificing the vintage years to avoid the duff ones. There are several additional processing options: racking and fining are by and large beneficial, but filteration or pasteurisation can radically change the taste of the drink. A natural cider will invariably be dry, and preferred so by the connoisseur, but most cidermakers deviate from the strictly natural and cater to demand by offering medium and sweet versions by the addition of sugar or saccharin - you can always ask about this.

The truth is that much of the cider sold in pubs today is far from traditional. It is made mostly from imported apple juice concentrate and is likely to contain a fair selection of the following additives: artificial colourings, sweeteners, preservatives, added fruit acids, extraneous carbon dioxide and of course water. The 'juice content' of some of these ciders is less than 50%. Some may even use clouding agents to simulate traditional cider! It may seem odd that we import apple juice concentrate to make English cider, but the hard fact is that the current tonnage of cider apples grown in Britain would produce barely 10% of the 84 million gallons of cider consumed here in 1992, 90% of it produced by the Big Three (Bulmers, Taunton and the Gaymer Group). Until more orchards are in production they don't have the choice, but at least in Devon you do. Growing interest is bringing real ciders back, particularly into free houses of course, but increasingly as guest ciders into tied outlets.

Over the last decade or two some famous names have been lost from Devon cidermaking - the Horrells and Hills, the Henleys and Whiteways of this world. Just recently, Farmer John of Newton Poppleford has retired. Against this it is encouraging to see four completely new cidermakers emerging since the last edition of this guide a mere three years ago - Bollhayes, Clawford, Green Valley and Saul's Farm. These and the others are listed below and cross-referenced to the map. It is beyond the scope of this article to go into detail over each one. For this we refer you to the GOOD CIDER GUIDE (available from CAMRA HQ). Suffice it to say that with the exception of Inch's, who now produce well over a million gallons per annum and sell nationally, all operate on the scale of a family business, although some are larger than others.

A final word of advice; remember that real cider is more akin to wine than beer. At 6-8% ABV it is often twice the strength of ordinary bitter or British lager and its effects should be considered before you go ordering pints. We hope you enjoy the wine of Devon.

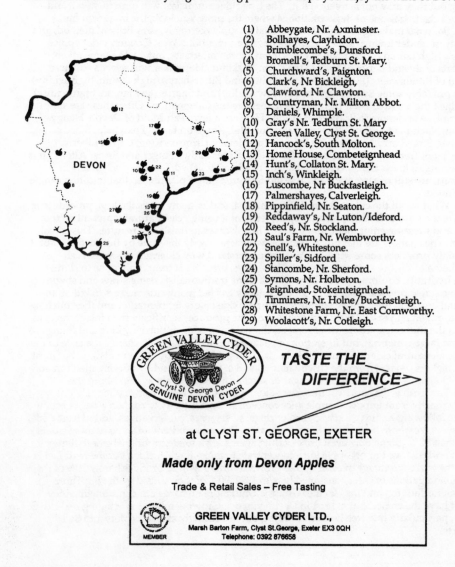

(1) Abbeygate, Nr. Axminster.
(2) Bollhayes, Clayhidon.
(3) Brimblecombe's, Dunsford.
(4) Bromell's, Tedburn St. Mary.
(5) Churchward's, Paignton.
(6) Clark's, Nr Bickleigh,
(7) Clawford, Nr. Clawton.
(8) Countryman, Nr. Milton Abbot.
(9) Daniels, Whimple.
(10) Gray's Nr. Tedburn St. Mary
(11) Green Valley, Clyst St. George.
(12) Hancock's, South Molton.
(13) Home House, Combeteignhead
(14) Hunt's, Collaton St. Mary.
(15) Inch's, Winkleigh.
(16) Luscombe, Nr Buckfastleigh.
(17) Palmershayes, Calverleigh.
(18) Pippinfield, Nr. Seaton.
(19) Reddaway's, Nr Luton/Ideford.
(20) Reed's, Nr. Stockland.
(21) Saul's Farm, Nr. Wembworthy.
(22) Snell's, Whitestone.
(23) Spiller's, Sidford
(24) Stancombe, Nr. Sherford.
(25) Symons, Nr. Holbeton.
(26) Teignhead, Stokeinteignhead.
(27) Tinminers, Nr. Holne/Buckfastleigh.
(28) Whitestone Farm, Nr. East Cornworthy.
(29) Woolacott's, Nr. Cotleigh.

MALTING IN THE WEST COUNTRY

Many people associate Devon with delicious clotted cream teas. Today the county is just as famous for its real ales. During this last decade, many small independent brewers have successfully set up business in the West Country.

Beer has always been considered a subject dear to the hearts of most Englishmen. We all know how to drink it, but how often does one question what actually goes into a pint of real ale? Much is known about hops, yeast and water, but what about malt? Malt is the main raw ingredient in real ale. It gives the flavour, the colour and most importantly, the alcoholic content! But what exactly is it and where does it come from?

Malting is one of the oldest industries known to man, believed to have been first discovered by the ancient Egyptians. In the 19th century thousands of traditional working malthouses existed producing malt from barley for beer. A process which partially germinates the barley converting most of its starches to sugar. Due to modern technology many malthouses were destroyed and today only a few remain in England. Devon brewers have a convenient supply of quality malt made at Newton Abbot in Tucker's traditional floor Maltings - the only one left in the West Country.

Edwin Tucker and Sons have been making malt since 1831. They built Tucker's Maltings in 1900, and today, it is Britain's only working malthouse open to the public. Maltsters still maintain these traditional skills, and the original Victorian machinery is still being used driven by cogs, wheels, belts and pulleys. A guided tour of the Maltings takes well over an hour, and even visitors are set to work by raking the 140ft germinating floors! Certainly, a very different visit for the family!

At the Maltings, there are twelve stages throughout the process. Edwin Tucker's test and buy the best quality malting barley direct from local farmers. If visiting the Maltings, one of the first things you will see is an impressive giant 'Boby' Drum Drier holding 10 tonnes of grain. The barley may lie in storage for up to one year until the following harvest is due. To ensure it does not turn mildewy or grow, drying is essential. The grain is transported along 'corkscrew' conveyors and picked up by wooden bucket elevators. There is very little concession to modern technology!

Once the barley is ready to be malted, it comes out of storage and given a second clean removing damaged grains, dust, mud and straw. This goes through a wooden 1900 Barley Screener which still runs off an old DC electric motor. It is hard to believe such machinery still exists today.

To start germination the barley is soaked in water. 'Steeping' is the first real stage of malting. Six tonnes of grain is soaked in 1500 gallons of water at an ideal temperature of 55 F (13C) for over 2 days. It is similar to a human being. If you left a person in water for $2^{1}/_{2}$ days, eventually they would drown - the same happens to barley. Every alternate 12 hours, the water is drained to allow the grain to breathe with oxygen, and 12 hours later the steeping tanks are replaced with water.

The barley begins to sprout and is emptied onto the 140 ft germinating floors below. After 4-5 days germination is stopped when most of the starches inside the grain have turned to sugar. The 'green malt' is removed from the malting floors and transported by elevator to the enormous Victorian kilns. The grain is baked for 2 days resulting in a fine quality crispy, crunchy and sweet tasting malt - delicious!

Before the malt goes to the brewery it has two further cleans. To prevent it going moist it is carefully stored in a closed container, and as soon as the brewer orders the malt it is weighed and bagged up ready for delivery. Tucker's Maltings supplies over 25 breweries in the West Country. May the art of a traditional forgotten industry continue.

Guided tours of Tucker's Maltings - Every 45 minutes: Open Easter - End October (Sunday - Friday) 10am - 4pm. Restaurant and Gift Shop. Evening and Winter tours by arrangement. Follow brown and white signs from Newton Abbot railway station. Tel: (0626) 334734.

BEER TAX

At the present time the British Government take about four billion pounds a year in tax from beer. This is not just excise duty but V.A.T. as well, the two taxes form about one third the total cost of a pint.

At present the British beer drinker pays twenty four pence in excise duty and twenty pence in V.A.T. on a standard beer. Compared to the continent, this is the second highest rate of taxation behind only the Irish. The rest of the E.E.C. countries have much lower tax rates, some below the new minimum rate of 3.7 pence per which is coming into force sometime in 1993.

With the opening of the borders to free trade within the E.E.C. it means that it is possible to bring in large amounts of canned or bottled beer.

At present our beer tax is twenty five times that of France, eleven times that of Germany and eight times that of the Belgians. Even when the new minimum tax comes into force five of the E.E.C. countries will have tax rates an eighth of our own.

With it so much cheaper to buy beer abroad it is bound to affect the brewing trade in this country. This will lead to the brewers having to raise prices or close pubs to cover their costs.

The aim of the Campaign for Real Ale is to inform the government about these points and to try to get the taxation levels in this country onto a par with our European neighbours. It has been already necessary for the Danish government to drop their tax levels to stop a massive loss in tax revenue and sales to the Germans.

In some quarters it is believed that higher tax on alcohol will help control drink problems, but is this going to stop the person who feels that they need a drink or those that like to go out for a quiet pint, but now find it too expensive, so reducing the number of sales in an already declining trade?

JOIN NOW

BEER IN CANS

CAN YOU TELL THE DIFFERENCE?

After several years of spending huge sums of money (and we mean tens of millions of pounds) the big breweries were no doubt surprised that sales of their overpriced, fizzy, pasteurised 'lager' began to fall quite dramatically. At the same time, Real Ale started to gain more and more of the market - once again, an example of CAMRA's campaigning.

There has been a disappointing response to this trend by the national, and some of the regional breweries. We have not seen the same level of promotion for their own Real Ales as we did for their lagers. Instead, we have seen a massive promotion for what they call 'Draught Beer' or even 'Real Ale' in cans.

Draught beer in a can? What's this I hear you say. Quite right too - how can a beer sold in a can be 'draught' or even more ridiculous 'Real'. My dictionary says that 'draught' means 'stored in bulk, especially in a cask' and I don't think that a 16oz can counts as bulk. 'Real Ale' is a term coined by CAMRA as an ale that undergoes a secondary fermentation in a cask and is therefore neither filtered or pasteurised in any way. Well, the so-called draught beer in a can is different in all these ways since it has been filtered and pasteurised and is also pressurised in the can. So the whole thing is a con. No doubt, as these cans are sold through supermarkets and off licences, these brewers can sell huge amounts of these beers without the overheads of pubs and staff wages.

CAMRA pointed out this misleading practice to the Advertising Standards Authority but sadly this had little effect. To add insult to injury, one national brewer even had the cheek to promote the stuff by an advert which depicted a handpump dispensing ale directly into a can.

CAMRA refused to be defeated on this issue and, after much campaigning, we have just heard, at the time of going to press, that LACOTS, the co-ordinating body for Trading Standards Officers, has decided that draught as a term cannot apply to packaged beer. The decision will hopefully mean we will shortly see an end to the tinned troublemaker.

Whatever the outcome of this matter, don't insult your palate. Drink Real Ale in the pub and support your landlord and independent brewery by enjoying a quality product.

PROTECT YOUR PLEASURE

JOIN CAMRA NOW

BREW PUBS

MARISCO TAVERN

LUNDY ISLAND, BRISTOL CHANNEL
Tel (0237) 431831

Beers:
John O's (OG 1035)
Old Light (OG 1040)
Old Light Special (OG 1055) Winter only

Owned by the National Trust, the three mile long island of Lundy is financed, administered and maintained by the Landmark Trust. The population numbers only 24 but in summertime the island is visited regularly by its own ship, MS Oldenberg, carrying up to 267 passengers on sailings from Ilfracombe and Bideford. Winter sailings are less frequent and only out of Bideford. Journey time is a little over two hours each way.

The island has one pub, the Marisco Tavern, which also doubles as the only shop. In 1984 a two-barrel multi-extract plant was installed in a nearby stable to enable brewer John Olgivie to offer real ale instead of imported keg. The regular brews are named after John himself, and after the now disused lighthouse, built in 1819, the highest in the British Isles at 567 feet above sea level. The ales are brewed using Lundy water, and no additives, and are available only on the island.

Nigel Walker took over as brewer in 1992 and the plant is at present being moved into the Marisco Tavern itself, ready for the 1993 season. It is planned to continue with the same beers for the time being.

ROYAL INN AND HORSEBRIDGE BREWERY

HORSEBRIDGE, TAVISTOCK, DEVON PL19 8PJ
Tel (082 287) 214

Beers:
Tamar (OG 1039, ABV 3.9%)
Horsebridge Best (OG 1045, ABV 4,5%)
Right Royal (OG (1050) Special occasions only
Heller (OG 1060, ABV 6%)

A fifteenth century country pub, once a nunnery, which began brewing in 1981. After a change of hands, and a period of inactivity, the single-barrel plant recommenced brewing in 1984.

THE TALLY HO! COUNTRY INN AND BREWERY

14 MARKET STREET, HATHERLEIGH, NORTH DEVON
Tel (0837) 810306

Beers:
Dark Mild (OG 1034, ABV 2.8%)
Potboilers Brew (OG 1036, ABV 3.5%
Tarka's Tipple (OG 1043, ABV 4.2%)
Nutters (OG 1048, ABV 4.6%)
Janni Jollop (OG 1064, ABV 6.6%)

The Tally Ho! Inn itself has been a pub since the fifteenth century and until 1806 there was a brewery as well. It is recorded that around this time, a fire destroyed both pub and brewery, then known as the New Inn. The pub was rebuilt soon after the fire but, as far as is known, the brewery ceased production until 1990 when the present Landlord, Gianni Scoz, opened the new custom-built brewery at the rear of the inn during 1990.

Tourists and visitors can see two coppers; although only one is a true copper 'kettle', the other, a fermenter, being for show as Gianni admits. Looks aside, it is a very efficient plant.

Now to the important bit! The beers: first Tally Ho!, a dark mild (abv 2.8%), very refreshing on a summer lunchtime - try it as a shandy with ginger ale. Next, Potboiler Bitter (abv 3.5%), light and hoppy (named after inhabitants who once held rights of grazing on Hatherleigh moor). Then there is Tarka Tipple, getting stronger now (abv 4.2%) and more bitter with a pronounced late hop aroma. Or what about Nutters Ale (abv 4.6%), not named after the locals, but after its nutty taste drived from the German hops used

Also available is the winter warmer, Janni Jollop (abv 6.6%) strong and warming, malty yet a good hop finish. Finally, there are two bottle-conditioned bitters, one Thurgia (ancient Greek for 'Natural Magic') is available in the bar in bottle or handpump (abv 5.7%) - buy a bottle to take home and keep it for a few months in the dark for best results. Lastly there is a special brew (abv 6%) made for a delicatessen in Tavistock, N H Greber, not available in the pub at all.

DEVON BREWERIES AND THEIR BEERS

THE BEER ENGINE

The Beer Engine, Newton St. Cyres, Exeter, Devon EX5 5AX.
Tel (0392) 851282

Successful brew pub now serving an expanding free trade. Stands next to the Barnstaple branch railway line. Owns one other pub, the Sleeper in Seaton. Occasionally produces a bottle-conditioned beer.

Rail Ale

(OG 1037, ABV 3.6%) Yellow-coloured beer with a malty aroma and hoppy flavour. Some bitterness in the after taste.

Piston Bitter

(OG 1044, ABV 4.3%) Dark brown in colour; a strong, malty aroma and flavour with a hoppy and malty aftertaste.

Sleeper Heavy

(OG 1055, ABV 5.5%) A pleasant, sweet tasting beer with a strong fruity taste and after taste. Dark brown in colour.

Whistlemas

OG 1068, ABV 6.5%) Produced for Christmas.

BLACKAWTON

Blackawton Brewery, Washbourne, Totnes, Devon, TQ9 7UF.
Tel (0903) 732339

Situated just outside the village of Washbourne, this small family brewery was only founded in 1977 but is the oldest in Devon. It originated in the village of Blackawton, but moved to its present site in 1981 and, despite a change of ownership in 1988, retains a loyal local following. Serves around 50 free trade outlets, having no pubs of its own. Brews from traditional ingredients with no additives.

Bitter

(OG 1037.5, ABV 3.8%) Red in colour, with a malty aroma and a malty and slightly fruity taste. Dry aftertaste.

Devon Gold

(OG 1040.5, ABV 4.1%) A summer brew, available April - October.

44 Special

(OG 1044.5, ABV 4.5%) Mid brown, malty, slightly fruity-tasting beer with a hint of toffee. Malty aroma and aftertaste. Lacks hoppiness, but is still enjoyable.

Headstrong

(OG 1051.5, ABV 5.2%) Tawny-coloured, malty, aromatic beer. Sweet malty taste and finish.

BLEWITT'S

The Ship and Plough Inn, The Quay, Kingsbridge, Devon TQ7 1JD
Tel (0548) 852485

Blewitt's Best Bitter

(OG 1038, ABV 3.8%)

King's Bitter

(OG 1040, ABV 4.0%)

Blewitt's Head Off

(OG 1050, ABV 5.0%) - not dissimilar to Fuller's ESB.

BRANSCOMBE VALE BREWERY

Branscome Vale Brewery, Great Seaside Fram, Branscombe, Seaton Devon EX12 3DP. Tel (029780) 511

One of the newest breweries in Devon, it opened in September 1992. It is housed in a former cow shed, leased on land from the National Trust and run by two ex-dairy industry employees who had been made redundant earlier that year.

After battling with bureacracy for nine months they produced their first brew, Branoc, which immediately became popular. For the Christmas period they evolved a second brew, Old Stoker, which proved so popular that it is still in production and may continue throughout the year.

Branoc

(OG1040, ABV 3.8%)

Old Stoker

(OG1050, ABV 5.4%)

EXE VALLEY BREWERY

• SILVERTON • DEVONSHIRE •

AWARD WINNING TRADITIONAL BREWERS

Contact: Richard Barron or Guy Sheppard
Tel: Exeter (0392) 860406

EXE VALLEY

Exe Valley Brewery, Land Farm, Silverton, Exeter, Devon, EX5 4HF. Tel (0392) 860406

Barron Brewery was set up in 1984 by Richard Barron and the company name changed when he was joined by Guy Sheppard. Operating from an old barn (using the farm's own springwater), new plant was installed in 1993 which has effectively trebled capacity. Some 25 local free trade outlets within a 25-mile radius are supplied on a regular basis (no tied estate).

Bitter
(OG 1039, ABV 4%) Malty pale, brown bitter, with fruity and bittersweet undertones in the aftertaste. A pleasant, malty beer.

Dob's Best
(OG 1039, ABV 4.1%) Pale brown bitter with Bitter a distinctly hoppy/bitter taste. Pleasant malty after taste.

Devon Glory
(OG 1047, ABV 4.7%) Mid brown, with a malty and fruity aroma. A well balanced beer with character.

Exeter Old
(OG 1047, ABV 4.8%) Red/brown-coloured, Bitter with a sweet, fruity taste, a fruity aroma and a malty aftertaste.

FURGUSONS

Furgusons Plympton Brewery, Valley Road, Plympton, Plymouth, Devon, PL7 3LQ. Tel (0752) 330171

Set up in the Halls Plympton depot in 1984, this brewery's business has expanded rapidly over the last four years. It now offers three ales of its own for sale to 29 of Allied's 32 pubs in the area and to free trade in the South-West (about 120 accounts). Brewing capacity was increased by a third in 1991.

Dartmoor Best
(OG 1038, ABV 3.7%) Mid brown to red Bitter beer with a sweet, malty flavour and a strong malty aftertaste.

Dartmoor Strong
(OG 1044, ABV 4,3%) Mid brown, malty yet bitter-flavoured beer.

Cockleroaster
(OG 1060, ABV 5.8%) Winter only. A powerful, golden beer with a strong, near perfect mix of malt and hop flavours, and a fruity nose which dominates the aroma. Not overpowering, but distinctive, with a good, hoppy finish.

| MILL | Mill Brewery, Unit 18c, Bradley Lane, Newton Abbot, Devon, TQ12 4JW. Tel. (0626) 63322 |

Founded in 1983 on the site of an old watermill. Special brews, based on Janner's Old Original, are often sold under local pub names, 'Janner' being the local term for a Devonian. Serves nine regular outlets and the free trade in Devon and Torbay.

Janner's Ale
(OG 1038) Pale brown-coloured, bland beer, without any discernible aroma. The flavour is bitter/hoppy and the aftertaste is also bitter, but it lacks balance.

Janner's Old Dark Ale*
(OG 1040) An occasional brew.

Janner's Old
(OG 1045) A beer malty and sweet in Original character, with a slightly 'thick' consistency. Bitter finish.

Janner's Christmas Ale*
(OG 1050) The festive beer.

| OTTER | Otter Brewery, Mathayes, Luppitt, Honiton, Devon, EX14 0SA. Tel (0404) 891289 |

New brewery which happily exceeded its owners' expectations at the end of its first year in November 1991. Now the brewing capacity has been doubled with the intention of supplying more local houses. At present 30 pubs take the beers which are brewed using local malt and the Brewery's own spring water. Otter Head has recently been introduced and future plans include adding a winter porter to the range.

Bitter
(OG 1036, ABV 3.6%) Amber/pale coloured beer.
Very slightly malty, but a strong hoppy/bitter-tasting beer with a pleasant hoppy, bitter finish.

Otter Ale
(OG 1044, ABV 4.4%) Tawny-coloured with a fruity aroma.
Pleasantly sweet and fruity-tasting, yet a bitter beer with a hoppy, bitter aftertaste.

Otter Head
(ABV 5.5%) Tawny-coloured. The fruity, hoppy aroma and flavour make this a very tasty, yet not oversweet beer for the strength.

| SUMMERSKILLS | Summerskills Brewery, Unit 15, Pomphlett Farm Ind. Estate, Broxton Drive, Billacombe, Plymouth, Devon, PL9 7BG. Tel (0752) 481283 |

Summerskills was initially set up in 1983 in a vineyard, but was only operational for two years. It was relaunched by new owners in 1990, with plant from the old Penrhos brewery, and production has grown at a steady rate. Supplies 20 free trade outlets directly in Plymouth and others nationally via wholesalers. The brewery logo comes from the ship's crest of HMS Bigbury Bay.

Best Bitter
(OG 1042, ABV 4,3%) Mid Brown, strong-flavoured beer with a hoppy bitter finish.

Whistle Belly Vengeance
(OG 1046, ABV 4.7%) Mid brown, multi-flavoured beer - predominantly roast malt and hops, with a hoppy bitter finish. Tastes stronger than it is.

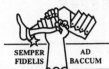

SEMPER FIDELIS · **AD BACCUM**

Established 1983

SUMMERSKILLS BREWERY

PLYMOUTH'S ONLY INDEPENDENT BREWERY

BREWERS OF
SUMMERSKILL'S BEST BITTER (4.3% ABV)
WHISTLEBELLY VENGEANCE (4.7% ABV)
NINJA BEER (5.0% ABV)

UNIT 15 ● POMPHLETT FARM IND. EST. ● BROXTON DRIVE ● PLYMOUTH ● DEVON PL9 7BG ● (0752) 481283

THOMPSON'S

Thompson's Brewery, 11 West Street, Ashburton, Devon, TQ13 7BD. Tel (0364) 52478

Started brewing in 1981 for its own pub, the London Inn, which remains its sole tied house. Free Trade, however, has been increasingly rapidly of late, with 70 outlets throughout the South-West currently supplied, and further growth planned. A major expansion programme is in hand at the brewery, starting with a new brewhouse which opened in early 1992. This now allows a total capacity of 10,000 barrels a year. The beer range tends to change from year to year and 1992 saw the production of a special mild to celebrate CAMRA's 21st birthday.

Best Bitter
(OG 1040, ABV 4.2%) Amber-coloured beer, with a malty, hoppy and fruity aroma, a strong, hoppy, bitter taste and a dry, bitter finish.

Black Velvet
(OG 1040, ABV 4.2%) A black porter with a strong roast chocolate malt aroma. The flavour and aftertaste have roast malt and bitterness.

IPA
(OG 1044), ABV 4.6%) Pale brown ale with malt and fruit in the aroma and a distinct hoppy, fruity flavour with a dry, bitter finish. A well-rounded beer.

Bodwright's Man-of-War
(OG 1050, ABV 5%) Straw-coloured strong beer featuring a slightly fruity and bitter flavour and finish. Too bland for a winter ale.

Yuletide Tipple
(OG 1050, ABV 5.3%) A fruity, copper-red Christmas beer, enjoying a distinctive contrast of roast and hop flavours, and a bitter finish. Hops and fruit in the aroma.

OTHER BREWERIES AND THEIR BEERS

Only those ales known to be available in Devon at the time of our survey are listed here, although a wide range of 'Guest Beers' may be found across the country.

ALLIED BREWERIES

Head office: 107 Station Street, Burton-on-Trent, Staffs. DE14 1BZ.

Allied Breweries was formed in 1961 by the merger of Ansells, Ind Coope and Tetley Walker and is now part of the vast Allied-Lyons Group. The Group own about 6,700 pubs across the country, but relatively few of these are in Devon.

IND COOPE BITTER (OG 1037, ABV 3.5%)

Dark copper in colour, with a faintly hoppy aroma, and a creamy sweet flavour. Light hoppy finish.

IND COOPE BURTON BITTER (OG 1048, ABV 4%)

Tremendously aromatic beer, with a fruity malt and hop nose. The promise is borne out by a powerful burst of malt and Styrian hops, rich and fruity. Dryish finish.

TETLEY BITTER (OG 1035)

When it's good it's very very good, but off its home patch, in the free trade, it is more than a bit hit and miss. Creamy, hoppy and very drinkable at home, it can be low on aroma, and harshly bitter with a nasty metallic flavour, or just plain bland and undistinguished-tasting when sampled away.

HALLS HARVEST BITTER (OG 1037, ABV 3.5%)

A sweet, caramel tasting bitter.

BASS

Head office: 30, Portland Place, LONDON, W1

The country's largest brewer with over 7,000 pubs. The original home of Bass is in Burton-on-Trent where Draught Bass is still brewed. Draught Bass is a common sight in Devon, appearing in many Heavitree Houses and in the free trade.

DRAUGHT BASS (OG 1044, ABV 4.4%)

Can be low on aroma, but has a discernably hoppy nose otherwise. Malty and fruity with a distinctive bitter finish; a beer which can vary tremendously in character depending on its age and distancetravelled since brewed. Can taste pronouncedly hoppy. Not an easy beer to keep, and often sold too green, but when it's good, it is a classic pint.

CHARRINGTON IPA (OG 1039, ABV 3.6%)

Not particularly hoppy or malty. Little aroma, though can be fruity; the flavour varies with cellar life, from very sweet to dry and bitter. In either condition, bland but not unpleasant; drinkable but not inspiring.

COURAGE

Courage Ltd., Bristol Brewery, Bath Street, Bristol, Avon, BS1 6EX. Tel (0272) 297222.

The former Georges Brewery, now Courage's only real ale brewery in the South, following the closure of traditional breweries in London, Reading and Plymouth, and the buyout of Ushers. Growing demand for cask beer has resulted in expansion at this plant in recent years, with Best and Directors well promoted nationally but Bitter Ale somewhat neglected, its sales confined mostly to the West Country and South-East Wales.

BITTER ALE (OG 1031, ABV 3.2%)

A pale, light-bodied bitter, with a delicately hoppy, bitter, malty taste. A dry bitter finish and a hoppy aroma.

BEST BITTER (OG 1039, ABV 4%

A pale brown bitter with a good balance of bitter hops, grainy malt (sometimes fruit) and a slight sweetness. The aroma is malty and hoppy; the finish is bitter and malty.

DIRECTORS (OG 1046, ABV 4.8%)

A fine well-balanced, red/brown malty ale, with ample malt, hops and fruit in the nose. The strong , malty, dry, hoppy taste has a faint fruitiness, and develops into a bitter, dry finish. All too often served below par.

COTLEIGH

Cotleigh Brewery, Ford Road, Wiveliscombe, Somerset, TA4 2RE. Tel (0984) 24086

Continued growth has taken this brewery a long way from its first home - a stable block at Cotleigh Farmhouse in 1979. 1985 saw the completion of a purpose-built brewhouse and there was further expansion in 1991 with the purchase of adjoining premises and the doubling of brewing capacity. Most of the beers are seasonal and brewed for special occasions only. Serves 100 outlets, mostly in Devon and Somerset, although the beers are also available across the country.

Harrier SPA (OG 1036, ABV 3.6%)

A straw-coloured beer with a very hoppy aroma and flavour, and a hoppy, bitter finish. Plenty of flavour for a light low gravity beer.

Nutcracker Mild (OG 1036, ABV 3.6%)

A dark mild, an occasional brew.

Tawny Bitter (OG 1040, ABV 4.2%)

A mid brown-coloured, very consistent beer. A hoppy aroma, a hoppy but quite well-balanced flavour, and a hoppy, bitter finish.

Aldercote Ale (OG 1042, ABV 4.2%)

An occasional brew for East-West Ales wholesalers

Barn Owl Bitter (OG 1048, ABV 4.5%)

Brewed only occasionally, in aid of the brewery's adopted charity, the Hawk and Owl Trust.

Old Buzzard (OG 1048, ABV 4.8%)

Dark ruby-red beer, tasting strongly of roast malt, balanced with hops. Roast malt again in the finish, with bitterness. Very drinkable once the taste is acquired.

Rebellion (OG 1050, ABV 5%)

An occasional brew.

Red Nose Reinbeer (OG 1060, ABV 5.6%)

A dark and warming christmas brew.

EXMOOR

Exmoor Ales Ltd., Golden Hill Brewery, Wiveliscombe, Somerset, TA4 2NY. Tel (0984) 23798.

When it first started production in 1980, this brewery won immediate national acclaim, with its Exmoor Ale winning the Best Bitter award at CAMRA's Great British Beer Festival. Operating from the former Hancock's Brewery at Wiveliscombe (closed 1959), it now supplies real ale to some 150 pubs in the region and a wholesale network covering virtually the whole country. No houses of its own. A new addition to the range is Exmoor Beast, a winter ale.

Exmoor Ale (OG 1039, ABV 3.8%)

Pale brown beer with a malty aroma and a malty, dry, taste. Bitter and malty finish. Very drinkable.

Exmoor Gold (OG 1045, ABV 4.5%)

Yellow/golden in colour, with a malty aroma and flavour, and a slight sweetness and hoppiness. Sweet, malty finish.

Exmoor Stag (OG 1050, ABV 5.2%)

Pale brown beer, with a malty taste and aroma, and a bitter finish. Slightly sweet. Very similar to Exmoor Ale and drinks as easily.

Exmoor Beast (OG 1066, ABV 6.6%)

A winter brew: October-March.

COTLEIGH BREWERY

BREWERS OF TRADITIONAL ALES

Cotleigh Brewery, Ford Road, Wiveliscombe, Somerset
Tel: (0984) 24086

FULLERS

Fuller, Smith and Turner PLC, Griffin Brewery, Chiswick Lane South, Chiswick, London, W4 2QB. Tel. (081) 994 3691

One of the two surviving London independent brewers after the 1960s take-over spree. Uses the CAMRA logo in advertisements for its cask beers; this is not surprising as they are regular CAMRA award-winners. All but three of its 200 tied houses serve real ale and an expanding free trade takes in about 500 outlets, with a brewery having a majority interest in Classic Real Ales. Brewery redevelopments are still progressing.

Chiswick Bitter (OG 1034, ABV 3.5%)

A distinctively hoppy beer when fresh, with strong maltiness and a fruity character. Finishes with a lasting, dry bitterness and a pleasing aftertaste. Champion Beer of Britain 1989.

London Pride (OG 1040, ABV 4.1%)

An excellent beer with a strong, malty base and a rich balance of well-developed hop flavours and powerful bitterness.

Mr Harry (OG 1048, ABV 4.3%)

An occasional brew.

ESB (OG 1054, ABV 5.5%)

A copper-red, strong, robust beer with great character. A full-bodied maltiness and a rich hoppiness are immediately evident and develop into a rich fruitiness with an underlying sweet fullness.

GIBBS MEW

Gibbs Mew PLC, Anchor Brewery, Milford Street, Salisbury, Wilts, SP1 2AR. Tel. (0722) 411911

Established in 1898 by the amalgamation of Salisbury brewers Bridger Gibbs and Sons and Herbert Mew and Co. It is still run by the Gibbs family, brewing with water from its own well, the deepest in the district. Its tied estate has grown considerably in the last 10 years and real ale is supplied to all its 123 pubs. Healthy free trade in southern and south-western England.

Chudley Local Line (OG 1036, ABV 3.5%)

A clean-tasting bitter to be savoured. Moderately-hopped and slightly fruity. An ideal lunchtime ale.

Wiltshire Traditional Bitter (OG 1036, ABV 3.5%)

A pleasant enough flavour of malt and hop, but frankly bland and uninspiring. Dry finish.

Premium Bitter (OG 1042, ABV 4%)

A truly bland and uninteresting beer. A small, corky taste and an overbearing sweetness are only tempered by bitterness in the aftertaste. Dwindling availability.

Salisbury Best Bitter (OG 1042, ABV 4.2%)

A rather chewy, sweet ale, decidedly lacking in bitterness. All the same a pleasant beer.

The Bishop's Tipple (OG 1066, ABV 6.5%)

Weaker than the average barley wine, but not lacking in flavour. The full-bodied taste is marvellously malty with a kick that leaves the brain rather less clear than the beer.

PALMERS

JC & RH Palmer Ltd., Old Brewery, Bridport, Dorset, DT1 4JA. Tel. (0308)

Thatched brewery in a delightful seaside setting. Brewing has taken place in these former mill buildings since at least 1794, and the Palmer family have been there since the late 1880s. The tied estate is growing slowly but steadily, with cask-conditioned beer in all 68 tied-houses, although top pressure and cask breathers are widely in use. About 40 direct free trade outlets, and increasing sales through wholesalers and agents across southern England.

Bridport Bitter or BB (OG 1032, ABV 3.2%)

A light beer with a hoppy aroma, clean, hoppy taste with some bitterness, and a bitter aftertaste.

Best Bitter or IPA (OG 1040, ABV 4.2%)

A good balance of fruit, bitterness and hop in the taste, with malty undertones, leads to a predominantly bitter finish. A fruity aroma, with some hop.

Tally Ho! (OG 1046, ABV 4.7%)

A dark and complex brew with malty aroma. The nutty taste is dominated by roast malt balanced with some bitterness. Malty and bitter aftertaste. Difficult to find especially in winter.

RUDDLES

Ruddles Brewery Ltd, Langham, Oakham, Leicestershire, LE15 7JD. Tel. (0572) 756911

Possibly the best-known brewer of real ale in Britain, founded in 1858, but which lost its independence when it was taken over by Grand Metropolitan in 1986. Ruddles beers subsequently became national brands. Acquired by Dutch lager giants Grolsch in 1992.

Best Bitter (OG1037, ABV 3.8%)

Thin, with a faint, fruity, malty nose leading into an astringent bitter palate, with little discernible malt or hop presence.

County (OG 1050, ABV 5%)

Copper-coloured, with a fruity, malty aroma and taste; sweetish on the tongue, but with a dry, malty aftertaste. Pleasant, but nothing like the County of old. Lacks hoppiness for a beer of this gravity.

ST AUSTELL

St Austell Brewery Co. Ltd., 63 Trevarthian Road, St Austell, Cornwall, PL25 4BY. Tel (0726) 74444.

Brewing company set up in 1851 by malster and wine merchant Walter Hicks. It moved to the present site in 1893 and remains a popular family business, with many of Hicks's descendents employed in all areas of the company. Its 140 tied houses are spread right across Cornwall, nearly all of them serving traditional ale, with some 200 free trade outlets are also supplied. A new visitors' centre has been added.

Bosun's Bitter (OG 1036, ABV 3.4%)

A refreshing session beer, sweetish in aroma and bittersweet in flavour. Lingering, hoppy finish.

XXXX Mild (OG 1039, ABV 3.6%)

Little aroma, but a strong, malty, caramel-sweetish flavour is followed by a good, lingering aftertaste, which is sweet but with a fruity dryness. Very drinkable.

Tinners Ale (OG 1039, ABV 3.7%)

A deservedly-popular, golden beer with an appetising malt aroma and a good balance of malt and hops in the flavour. Lasting finish.

Hicks Special Draught (HSD) (OG 1051, ABV 5%)

An aromatic, fruity, hoppy bitter which is initially sweet, has an aftertaste of pronounced bitterness, but whose flavour is fully-rounded.

Winter Warmer* (OG 1060, ABV 6%)

Available November-February.

USHERS

Ushers brewery Ltd., Parade House, Trowbridge, Wilts, BA14 8JF. Tel. (0225) 763171

Along with Ruddles, another recent escapee from the Grand Metropolitan/Courage net. This West Country brewery was founded in 1824, but lost its identity after being swallowed up by Watney in 1960. A successful management buy-out in 1992 has given Ushers back its independence and the once famous Founders Ale is now brewed again in Wiltshire. The old Pale Ale mat also be reintroduced. Supplies real ale to virtually all its 437 tied houses and to Courage/Grand Met Inntrepreneur pubs.

Best Bitter (OG 1037, ABV 3.8%)

Cleaner-tasting than its lacklustre Grand Met predecessor, with gentle malt and hops but a harsh bitter dryness. Drinks light for a best bitter but, at the time of sampling, the brewery was still working on the beer.

Founders Ale (OG 1044, ABV 4.5%)

WADWORTH

Wadworth & Co. Ltd., Northgate Brewery, Devizes, Wilts, SN10 1JW. Tel. (0380) 723361

Delightful market town tower brewery set up in 1885 by Henry Wadworth. Solidly traditional, the brewery still runs horse-drawn drays. The brewery has recently undergone some expansion with the installation of new fermenting vessels to cope with increased demand from the free-trade - some 500 outlets are now supplied directly by the brewery, and over 3,000 more via other brewers and wholesalers. Always keen to expand the tied estate (currently 182 houses, all of which offer real ale). 6X remains one of the south's most famous ales, whilst Henry Wadworth IPA is now called Henry's Original IPA.

Henry's Original IPA (OG 1034, ABV 3.8%)

A golden brown-coloured beer with a gentle, malty and slightly hoppy aroma, a good balance of flavours, with maltiness gradually dominating, and then a long-lasting aftertaste to match, eventually becoming biscuity. A good session beer, more pleasing than the popular 6X.

6X (OG 1040, ABV 4.3%)

Mid-brown in colour, with a malty and fruity nose and some balancing hop character. The flavour is similar, with some bitterness and a lingering malty but bitter finish. Full-bodied and distinctive.

Farmer's Glory (OG 1046, ABV 4.5%)

Can be delightfully hoppy and fruity, but is variable in flavour and conditioning. The aroma is of malt and it should have a dryish, hoppy aftertaste.

Old Timer (OG 1055, ABV 5.8%)

Available in winter only. A rich, copper-brown beer with a strong, fruity, malty aroma. The flavour is full-bodied and complete, with hints of butterscotch and peaches, beautifully balanced by a lasting, malty, dry finish. A classic beer.

WHITBREAD

Head Office: The Brewery, Chiswell Street, London EC1

Established in 1742, Whitbread now own 6,400 pubs across the country, with a heavy concentration in the Exeter area. As a result of a local trading agreement, Whitbread beers are also on sale in Heavitree houses, often alongside draught Bass, again in the Exeter area. The following beers are a few selected from the Whitbread portfolio.

Flowers IPA (OG 1036, ABV 3.6%)

Little aroma, but a fairly well balanced bitter flavour with malt slightly dominant. A dry but malty finish.

Flowers Original (OG 1044, ABV 4.5%)

Hoppy aroma and hops dominate the flavour, but there is some malty character and a slight tinge of fruit. A notably bitter finish.

Best Bitter (OG 1036, ABV 3.5%)

Until very recently this beer was only available in the keg version.

DEVON PUBS

ABBOTSKERSWELL

BUTCHERS ARMS (Map Ref E6)
11 - 3 ; 5 - 11. (M-S)
ABBOTSKERSWELL, NEWTON ABBOT
Tel: (0626) 60731

Draught Bass	(H)
Eldridge Pope Hardy Country	(H)
Flowers IPA	(H)

CD (EUCHRE) CP DB DF FA LM ME ML
OD PG RF
A large village local in a very nice setting.
Old farm tools provide the decor. The pub
has been pleasantly enlarged. Live music.

COURT FARM INN (Map Ref E6)
11 - 3 ; 6 - 11 (M-S)
WILTON WAY, ABBOTSKERSWELL,
NEWTON ABBOT
Tel: (0626) 61866

Draught Bass	(H)
Marston's Pedigree	(H)
Flowers IPA	(H)

CD (EUCHRE) CP DB DF FA LM ME ML
OD PB PG RF
Impressive c17 Grade 2 listed manor type
house with wood pews and a stone
flagged floor. Converted to a pub in 1972.
Accent on food. Free minibus service for
parties of 6 and over. (local only)

TWO MILE OAK (Map Ref E6)
11 - 2.30 ; 5 -11. (M-F (W), 11-11 Sat AND
M-F (S))
TWO MILE OAK CROSS, TOTNES ROAD,
ABBOTSKERSWELL
Tel: (0803) 812411

Draught Bass	(G)
Eldridge Pope Royal Oak	(H)
Flowers IPA	(G)

AC CP DB ME ML OD PB PG QP RF
15th century coaching house, mostly
original. Good food, folk on Tuesdays.

ALSWEAR

BUTCHERS ARMS (Map Ref D3)
ALSWEAR, Nr. SOUTH MOLTON,
Tel: (07697) 477

Flowers Original	(H)

APPLEDORE

BEAVER INN (Map Ref B2)
IRSHA STREET, APPLEDORE, Nr.
BIDEFORD
Tel: (0237) 474822

Morland Old Speckled Hen	(H)
Ruddles County	(H)

COACH & HORSES (Map Ref B2)
11.30 - 2.30 ; 6.30 - 11. (M-Th. 11-11 F, Sat)
5, MARKET STREET, APPLEDORE,
BIDEFORD
Tel: (0237) 474470

Fullers London Pride	(H)
Ushers Best Bitter	(H)

ROYAL GEORGE (Map Ref B2)
IRSHA STREET, APPLEDORE, BIDEFORD
Tel: (0237) 474335

Ind Coope Burton Ale	(H)
Guest Beer Occasional	(H)

ROYAL HOTEL (Map Ref B2)
BUDE STREET, APPLEDORE, Nr.
BIDEFORD
Tel: (0237) 474305

Draught Bass	(H)

SEAGATE HOTEL (Map Ref B2) 1
1 - 3 ; 6 - 11. (M-S (W) 11 - 11 M-S (S))
THE QUAY, APPLEDORE, Nr. BIDEFORD,
Tel: (0237) 472589

Ind Coope Burton Ale	(H)

PROTECT YOUR PLEASURE

JOIN CAMRA NOW

ASHBURTON

EXETER INN (Map Ref D6)
11 - 2.30 ; 6 - 11. (M-S)
WEST STREET, ASHBURTON
Tel: (0364) 52013

Draught Bass	(H)
Hall & Woodhouse Badger Best Bitter	(H)
Ruddles Best Bitter	(H)

CA CI GD ME ML OD PB QP
11th century former coaching house where
Sir Walter Raleigh was arrested. Parking is
available in the local car park at rear.
Courtyard at rear is a suntrap in summer.

FLEECE & FIRKIN (Map Ref D6)
11 - 11 (M-S, EXCEPT WED. 11 - 3, 7 - 11)
ST. LAWRENCE LANE, ASHBURTON
Tel: (0364) 52382

John Smith's Bitter	(H)
Ushers Best Bitter	(H)

CA FA PG
Pub near former railway station, which
was previously named 'Silent Whistle'.
Recently released from Courage.

GOLDEN LION HOTEL (Map Ref D6)
11.30 - 2.30 ; 7 - 11. (M-S)
EAST STREET, ASHBURTON
Tel: (0364) 52205

Draught Bass	(H)
Courage Best Bitter	(H)

AC CA CI CP FA GD LM MR OD PG RF
Large roadside pub that is the H.Q. of the
Monster Raving Looney Party, who hold
their annual conference there each autumn.
Many live groups at weekends. Coaches
welcome.

LONDON HOTEL (Map Ref D6)
11 - 3 ; 5:30 - 11 (M-S)
11, WEST STREET, ASHBURTON
Tel: (0364) 52478

Thompsons	
Black Velvet	(H)
Best Bitter	(H)
IPA	(H)
Botwrights Man-O-War	(H)
Figurehead	(H)

AC CI CP ME ML QP RF
Home of Thompsons Aysheburton
brewery. A coaching house, not actually a
hotel. Large bar, good food.

RED LION (Map Ref D6)
EAST STREET, ASHBURTON
Tel: (0364) 52378

Draught Bass	(H)
Boddingtons Bitter	(H)

ASHILL

ASHILL INN (Map Ref F3)
12 - 3 : 5:30 -11 (CLOSED MON A.M., SAT
12 - 11)
ASHILL, Nr. CULLOMPTON,
DEVONSHIRE.
Tel: (0884) 840506

Eldridge Pope	
Dorchester	(H)
Hardy Country	(H)

CP DF FA ME ML (NOT TUES.) OD PG QP
RF
Built as a pub in 1835 with an open
inglenook fire. A typical village local

ASHPRINGTON

DURANT ARMS (Map Ref D7)
11:30 - 2:30 ; 6 - 11 (M-S)
ASHPRINGTON, TOTNES
Tel: (0803) 732240

Draught Bass	(H)
Furgusons Dartmoor Best Bitter	(H)
Palmers IPA	(H)

DF FA ME ML OD PG QP RF
Refurbished pub in a pretty village. Two
bars plus dining room. Folk music on
Mondays. Unusual pink marbled urinal in
gents for bog-buffs. All beers are real - no
keg bitters.

AVETON GIFFORD

TAVERNERS (Map Ref D7)
12 - 2:30 ; 6 - 11 (M-S)
FORE STREET, AVETON GIFFORD
Tel: (0548) 550316

Courage Best Bitter	(H)
Ushers Best Bitter	(H)

CH FA ME ML OD (COURTYARD) PG
(BAR SKITTLES) RF ST
Large, L-shaped bar with horse brasses on
the walls. Separate games/family room,
and skittle alley at rear.

AVONWICK

AVON INN (Map Ref D7)
11:30 - 3 ; 5:30 - 11 (M-S)
AVONWICK, Nr. SOUTH BRENT
Tel: (0364) 73475

Draught Bass	**(H)**
Charrington IPA	**(H)**
Guest Beer Regular	**(H)**

CA CP GD ME ML OD PB PG QP RF
Friendly, two-bar, village pub with pasta
and seafood a-la-carte menu.

WOODPECKER INN (Map Ref D7)
11 - 2:30 ; 6 - 11 (M-S)
AVONWICK, Nr. SOUTH BRENT

Draught Bass	**(H)**
Tetley Bitter	**(H)**

CA ME ML OD

AXMINSTER

AXMINSTER INN (Map Ref G4)
11 - 11 (M-S)
SILVER STREET, AXMINSTER,
(BEHIND CHURCH)
Tel: (0297) 34947

Palmers		
	BB	**(H)**
	IPA	**(H)**
	Tally Ho!	**(H)**

AC BR (AXMINSTER) CI (TAUNTON
TRADITIONAL) DF FA ML OD PB PG RF
Part of the pub used to be the local
Prudential office and a fishmongers.
Originally a farmers local, the pub was
owned by the Stuart family for over a
hundred years up to 1985.

JOIN NOW

GEORGE HOTEL (Map Ref G4)
11 - 11 (M-S)
VICTORIA PLACE, AXMINSTER,
Tel: (0297) 32209

Draught Bass (H)	
Boddingtons Bitter (H)	
Castle Eden Ale (H)	
Flowers IPA (H)	
Flowers Original (H)	

AC BR (AXMINSTER) CI (TAUNTON
TRAD., ADDLESTONES) DF FA ML OD
PG
An historic hotel with ceilings dating back
to Anglo-Saxon times. The first Georgian
posting inn, handling sixteen coaches per
day when the fare was 5/- to Aldersgate.
Nelson and George III stayed here, as did
the Duke of Monmouth during the
pitchfork rebellion. Now a fully
refurbished large town pub.

HUNTERS LODGE (Map Ref G4)
11 - 3 ; 6 - 11 (M-S (W), 11 - 11 (S))
RAYMOND'S HILL, CHARMOUTH RD.,
AXMINSTER, DEVONSHIRE. (1 MILE
EAST OF AXMINSTER ON A35.),
OS: SY3196
Tel: (0297) 433286

Draught Bass	**(H)**
Worthington Best Bitter	**(H)**

AC CA CP DB DF FA GD ME ML OD PB
PL QP RF RM RS SN
Roadside eating house with large
comfortable lounge bar area adjoining
restaurant with good economic menu

LAMB INN (Map Ref G4)
11:30 - 2:30 ; 5 : - 11: (M-W. 11-3 T,F. 11-11
Sat.)
LYME ROAD, AXMINSTER,
Tel: (0297) 33922

Hall And Woodhouse		
	Badger Best Bitter	**(H)**
	Tanglefoot	**(H)**

AC CP DF FA ME ML OD PG QP
The Lamb has been a pub for over 100
years, although it burnt down and was
rebuilt in 1899. Friendly pub on main A35
east of town centre.

MILLWEY (Map Ref G4)
11 - 2:30 ; 7 - 11 (M-S)
CHARD ROAD, AXMINSTER,
(A358)
Tel: (0297) 32774

Palmers
    BB   (H)
    IPA   (H)

DF FA ML (NOT SUN, MON.) OD PB PG
1967 modern estate pub on the outskirts of
town.

NEW COMMERCIAL (Map Ref G4)
10:30 - 11 (M-S)
TRINITY SQUARE, AXMINSTER,
Tel: (0297) 33225

Palmers
    IPA   (G)
    Tally Ho!   (H)

BR (AXMINSTER) DF FA ME ML PB PG
QP
Yes, it really is a pub although it gives the
appearance of being anything but! The
enterprising licencees also run the bread
shop next door. Bridport IPA is only real if
you can see the barrels on the bar!

RED LION (Map Ref G4)
11 - 11 (M-S)
LYME STREET, AXMINSTER,
Tel: (0297) 32016

Tetley Bitter   (H)

FA ME ML OD PG
A 17th century inn which is now very
sports orientated, but still a basic town
centre local.

AXMOUTH

HARBOUR INN (Map Ref G5)
11 - 2:30 ; 6 - 11 (M-S, 12 - 2.30 ; 7 - 10.30
SUN)
AXMOUTH, SEATON.
(SOUTHERN END OF VILLAGE.)
Tel: (0297) 20371

Cornish Royal Wessex   (H)
Flowers IPA   (H)
Flowers Original   (H)

CA CC CI CP DB DF FA GD ME ML OD
PB PG PL QP RF SN ST
Friendly pub with a fine ambience and a
cheerful landlord.

SHIP INN (Map Ref G5)
11 - 2 ; 6 - 11 ((W), 11 - 2.30 ; 6 - 11 (S))
CHURCH ST, AXMOUTH.
(NORTHERN END OF VILLAGE),
Tel: (0297) 21838

Cornish Original   (H)
Flowers Original   (H)

CA CC CI CP DB DF FA GD ME ML OD
PB PG PL QP RF SH SN ST
Well known pub with excellent food in an
extended dining room. Convalescing owls
make unusual drinking companions One
of only 2 pubs in Devon in every edition of
GBG.

AYLESBEARE

HALFWAY HOUSE INN (Map Ref F5)
11 - 2:30 ; 5:30 - 11 (M-S (W), 11 - 11 (S))
AYLESBEARE, Nr. EXETER, (ON A3052
AT JUNCTION WITH B3180),
OS: SY047904
Tel: (0395) 32273

Draught Bass   (H)
Flowers Original   (H)

CA CC CP DB DF (ACCESS) FA (DINING
ROOM ONLY) GD ME ML OD PB PG QP
RM (BACKGROUND) RS (DINING
ROOM)
Two bar country pub & restaurant situated
at a busy crossroads. Good value food, and
friendly management and staff.

BAMPTON

EXETER INN (Map Ref E3)
11: -2:30; 6 : - 11: (M-S)
TIVERTON ROAD, BAMPTON,
Tel: (0398) 331345

Exmoor Ale   (H)

AC CH CP DF FA ME ML OD PB PG QP
RF SN
Pleasant roadside in popular for food.

SWAN HOTEL (Map Ref E3)
STATION ROAD, BAMPTON,
Tel: (0398) 331257

Cotleigh Tawny   (H)
Guest Beer Regular   (H)

TIVERTON INN (Map Ref E3)
11 - 11 (M-S)
BRITON STREET, BAMPTON.
Tel: (0398) 331480

Oakhill
Bitter	(H)
Black Magic Stout	(H)
Yeoman	(H)

AC FA ML OD
Currently being refurbished.

WHITE HORSE INN (Map Ref E3)
11 - 3 ; 7 - 11 (M-S)
FORE STREET, BAMPTON,
Tel: (0398) 331245

Cotleigh Tawny	(H)
John Smith's Bitter	(H)
Ushers Best Bitter	(H)

AC FA ME ML OD
Breakfasts available from 9.00 am. Horse stables at rear.

BANTHAM

SLOOP INN (Map Ref C7)
11 - 2:30 ; 6 - 11 (M-S)
BANTHAM, KINGSBRIDGE
Tel: (0548) 560481

Draught Bass	(H)
Courage Best Bitter	(H)
Ushers Best Bitter	(H)

AC CA CI CP FA ME ML OD PG QP RF
c16 village pub, once a smugglers refuge, with a collection of naval crests and quayside paintings.

BARNSTAPLE

BARNSTAPLE INN (Map Ref C2)
11 - 2:30 ; 5 - 11 (M-Th., 11 - 11 F., 11 - 4, 7 - 11 Sat)
12, TRINITY STREET, BARNSTAPLE
Tel: (0271) 43483

Courage Best Bitter	(H)
John Smith's Bitter	(H)

BR (BARNSTAPLE) ML PB PG QP
Traditional and friendly town local in a Victorian part of the town.

CHICHESTER ARMS (Map Ref C2)
12 - 11 (M-S (W), 11 - 11 (S))
28, PILTON STREET, PILTON,
BARNSTAPLE,
Tel: (0271) 75285

Courage Best Bitter	(H)
Ushers Best Bitter	(H)

FA PB RF
Grade 2 listed building with a lively atmosphere. A beer garden is awaiting the outcome of a planning application.

CORNER HOUSE (Map Ref C2)
11 - 2:30 ; 5:30 - 11 (M-S)
108, BOUTPORT STREET, BARNSTAPLE,
Tel: (0271) 43528

Draught Bass	(H)
Guest Beer Regular	(H)

BR (BARNSTAPLE) FA ML OD PB PG
Convivial wooden pannelled, walled pub with bare floor boards & a good drinking atmosphere.

COUNTRYMAN (Map Ref C2)
11 - 2:30 ; 6:30 - 11 (M-S)
CASTLE STREET, BARNSTAPLE.
Tel: (0271) 75964

Courage Best Bitter	(H)
Ushers Best Bitter	(H)

BR (BARNSTAPLE) ML PB PG
Pleasant two room pub with good whisky selection and a welcoming landlord.

MARSHALLS (Map Ref C2)
11 - 2:30 ; 6 - 11 (M-Th., 11 - 11 F, Sat)
95, BOUTPORT STREET, BARNSTAPLE,
Tel: (0271) 76633

Draught Bass	(H)
Boddingtons Bitter	(H)

BR (BARNSTAPLE) ML (NOT SUNDAY) PG
Comfortable one bar hostelry in centre of town.

NORTH COUNTRY INN (Map Ref C2)
BOUTPORT STREET, BARNSTAPLE,
Tel: (0271) 42568

John Smith's Bitter	(H)

REFORM INN (Map Ref C2)
REFORM STREET, PILTON,
BARNSTAPLE,
Tel: (0271) 71682

Draught Bass	(H)
Boddingtons Bitter	(H)

ML PB PG RF

ROLLE QUAY INN (Map Ref C2)
11 - 11 (M-S)
ROLLE QUAY, BARNSTAPLE,
Tel: (0271) 45182

Ruddle County	(H)
Ushers Best Bitter	(H)
Guest Beer Regular	(H)

AC BR (BARNSTAPLE) ME ML OD PB PG
Plush food orientated town centre pub.

BEER

ANCHOR HOTEL (Map Ref G5)
11 - 2:30 ; 5:30 - 11 ((W). 11 - 11 (S))
FORE STREET, BEER, (ALMOST ON
BEACH),
Tel: (0297) 20386

Furgusons
Dartmoor Best Bitter	(H)
Dartmoor Strong	(H)
(SUMMER ONLY)Wadworth 6X	(H)

AC CA CC CI DB FA GD (overlooks beach)
ME ML OD PB PG QP RF RS SN
Large hotel with 3 bars, overlooking the
sea. Large bar areas and a separate
restaurant (bookings advisable in summer)
Situated at the end of Fore Street, right
above the beach.

BARREL OF BEER (Map Ref G5)
11:30 - 2:30 ; 5 - 11: (M-Th. 11.30 - 11 F, Sat.
11.30 - 11 (S))
FORE STREET, BEER, (150 METRES
TOWARDS SEA FROM CHURCH.),
Tel: (0297) 20099

Cornish Royal Wessex	(H)
Castle Eden Ale	(H)
Whitbread WCPA	(H)
Guest Beer Regular	(H)
(SUMMER ONLY)	

CA CH CI DB FA ME ML QP
One bar locals pub.

DOLPHIN HOTEL (Map Ref G5)
11 - 3 ; 6 - 11 (M-S)
FORE STREET, BEER.(100 METRES
TOWARDS SEA FROM CHURCH.)
Tel: (0297) 20068

Draught Bass	(H)

AC CA FA ME ML
More an eating house than a pub.

BEESANDS

CRICKET INN (Map Ref D8)
11 - 2:30 ; 6:30 - 11: (M-S)
BEESANDS, KINGSBRIDGE
Tel: (0548) 580215

Marston's Pedigree	(H)
Flowers IPA	(H)
Guest Beer Regular	(H)

CC CD (EUCHRE) CH CI FA ME ML OD
PG
Locals pub in a remote village on the edge
of a large beach. Guest beers in summer.
Large family room with electronic games.

BELSTONE

TORS INN (Map Ref C4)
11 - 2:30 ; 6 - 11. (M-S)
BELSTONE, Nr. OKEHAMPTON.
Tel: (0837) 840689

Butcombe Bitter	(H)
Otter Ale	(H)

AC FA ME ML OD PG RF
Stone built 100 year old house in the
Dartmoor national park with good views.
Convenient for walkers.

BERE ALSTON

EDGCUMBE HOTEL (Map Ref B6)
11:30 - 2:30 ; 6:30 - 11.   (M-F. 11.30 - 3 SAT)
MAINE, BERE ALSTON
Tel: (0822) 840252

Courage Best Bitter	(H)
Marston's Pedigree	(H)

AC BR (BERE ALSTON) PB PG
Basic, busy, village pub.

BERE FERRERS

OLD PLOUGH INN (Map Ref B6)
12 - 3 ; 7 - 11. (M-F. 12 - 4 Sat - SUPPER
LICENSE)
BERE FERRERS.
Tel: (0822) 840358

Draught Bass	(H)
Boddingtons Bitter	(H)
Courage Best Bitter	(H)
Summerskills Best Bitter	(H)
Guest Beer Regular	(H)

BR (BERE FERRERS) CI DF ME ML OD PG
QP RF
Small c16 village inn, beside River Tavy,
with its own moorings for visitors and a
separate room for pool.

BERRYNARBOR

OLDE GLOBE (Map Ref C1)
11:30 - 2:30 ; 7 - 11: (M-S)
BERRYNARBOR, ILFRACOMBE,
OS: SS559467
Tel: (0271) 882465

Courage Directors	(H)
Ushers Best Bitter	(H)

CP ME ML OD PG
A pretty village pub, dating back to 1675,
with uneven stone floors and genuine low
beams.

BICKINGTON

OLD BARN INN (Map Ref C2)
11:30 - 2:30; 6:30 - 11: (M-Th., 5 - 11 Sat.,
12 - 2 Sun)
TEWS LANE, BICKINGTON,
BARNSTAPLE.
Tel: (0271) 72195

Draught Bass	(H)
Guest Beer Regular	(H)

CP ME ML
Converted barn with variable beer quality.

PLOUGH INN (Map Ref C2)
BIDEFORD ROAD, BICKINGTON,
BARNSTAPLE.
Tel: (0271) 43176

Flowers IPA	(H)
Flowers Original	(H)

BICKINGTON (SD)

**DARTMOOR HALFWAY INN (Map Ref
D6)**
BICKINGTON, NEWTON ABBOT
Tel: (0626) 821270

Draught Bass (H)
Boddingtons Bitter (H)
Flowers Original (H)

TOBY JUG INN (Map Ref D6)
11: - 2:30 ; 6: - 11: (M-S)
BICKINGTON, NEWTON ABBOT
Tel: (0626) 821278

Draught Bass	(H)
Flowers IPA	(H)

CP FA ME ML OD PB PG QP RF
A neat lounge and a newer bar with a
stone flagged floor, hung with curios.
Magnificent collection of Toby Jugs in a
good, traditional pub. A very welcoming
atmosphere, and excellent value
home-cooked food.

BICKLEIGH

FISHERMANS COT (Map Ref E3)
11 - 11. (M-S)
BICKLEIGH, Nr. TIVERTON.
Tel: (0884) 855237 & 855239

Draught Bass	(H)
Best Bitter	(H)

AC CA CP DF FA ME ML OD
Splendid inn, beautifully situated on the
banks of the River Exe adjacent to
Bickleigh Bridge. It is said that Paul Simon
wrote his hit song "Bridge over troubled
waters", whilst staying at inn.

BIDEFORD

JOINERS ARMS (Map Ref B2)
12: - 3: ; 7: - 11: (M-F, 11-11 Sat.)
MARKET SQUARE, BIDEFORD.
Tel: (0237) 472675

Draught Bass	(H)
Fullers London Pride	(H)
Tetley Bitter	(H)

AC FA ME ML OD PG
Attractive town pub with a display of
carpenter's tools on walls surrounding a
partitioned single room bar. Once issued
its own coinage as change or prize money
on quiz/games nights.

KINGS ARMS (Map Ref B2)
11 - 11. (M-S)
THE QUAY, BIDEFORD.
Tel: (0237) 475196

Draught Bass	(H)
Wadworth 6X	(H)
Flowers IPA	(H)

AC FA ME ML PG QP RF
Old seafarers pub with river views. Locals
haunt. Beer range sometimes varies.

PORTOBELLO INN (Map Ref B2)
11:30 - 3 ; 5:30 - 11. (M-F, 11.30 - 11 Sat.)
SILVER STREET, MARKET PLACE,
BIDEFORD.
Tel: (0237)

Ushers		
	Founders	(H)
	1824 Particular	(G)
	Best Bitter	(H)

DF (LIMITED) FA PB PG (CHESS) SH
Named after a battle in Panama in 1739,
this small unspoilt inn has two bars and a
good local atmosphere.

BIGBURY

ROYAL OAK (Map Ref C7)
11:30 - 3 ; 5:30 - 11. (M-S)
BIGBURY, KINGSBRIDGE
Tel: (0548) 810313

Draught Bass	(H)
Furgusons Dartmoor Best Bitter	(H)

AC CC CD (EUCHRE) CP DB FA ME ML
OD PG RF
Village local, foody lounge, always good
quality beer.

BISHOP'S TAWTON

THREE PIGEONS (Map Ref C2)
11: - 3 : ; 6 : -11: (M-S)
BISHOPS TAWTON, BARNSTAPLE.
Tel: (0271) 72269

Flowers IPA	(H)

CP FA OD PB PG QP
Good, basic, friendly local

BISHOPSTEIGNTON

BISHOP JOHN DE GRANDISSON (Map Ref E6)
11 - 3 ; 5 - 11. (M-S)
CLANAGE STREET, BISHOPTEIGN-
TON, NEWTON ABBOT
Tel: (0626) 775285

Flowers IPA	(G)

AC CA CD (EUCHRE) CI CP FA OD PB
PG QP RF SH SN
Quiant, olde worlde, village local, with a
landlady there for 33 years, and couches
and wooden settles with cushions in
lounge.

COCKHAVEN MANOR INN (Map Ref E6)
COCKHAVEN ROAD, BISHOPS-
TEIGNTON
Tel: (0626) 775252

Furgusons Dartmoor Best Bitter	(H)

RING OF BELLS (Map Ref E6)
11 - 11. (M-S)
FORE STREET, BISHOPSTEIGNTON
Tel: (0626) 775468

John Smith's Bitter	(H)
Castle Eden Ale	(H)
Whitbread Best Bitter	(H)

CH FA GD ME ML PG
Recently refurbished pub, bright and clean,
but with several cosy corners.

BITTAFORD

HORSE & GROOM (Map Ref C7)
11 - 3 ; 5:30 - 11. (M-S)
BITTAFORD, IVYBRIDGE
Tel: (0752) 892358

Courage Best Bitter	(H)
Founders	(H)
Best Bitter	(H)

AC CP ME ML OD RF
Large friendly pub.

BLACK DOG

BLACK DOG INN (Map Ref D3)
12 - 2:30 ; 6:30 - 11. CLOSED M-W LUNCH
(W) M LUNCH (S)
BLACK DOG, NEAR TIVERTON
Tel: (0884) 860336

Boddingtons Bitter	(H)
Marston's Pedigree	(H)
Whitbread WCPA	(H)

CA CC CP DF FA ME ML MR OD PG QP
RF RS
Rural inn located at a crossroads with
good, value for money food. There is a
separate restaurant. Camping at the rear of
the pub.

BLACK TORRINGTON

TORRIDGE INN (Map Ref B4)
12 - 3 ; 6:30 - 11. (M-F, 11 - 11 Sat)
BROAD STREET, BLACK TORRINGTON .
Tel: (0409) 23243

Boddingtons Bitter	(H)
Courage Directors	(H)
Eldridge Pope	
Hardy Country	(H)
Blackdown Porter	(H)
Guest Beer Regular	(H)

AC CA CI (BULMERS) CP DM FA ME ML
MR OD PG RF RS ST
Large L-shaped comfortable bar, with
function room and small restaurant.
Display of large collection of CAMRA
glasses.

BLACKAWTON

FORCES TAVERN (Map Ref D7)
BLACKAWTON, TOTNES, OS: SX808528
Tel: (080421)

Flowers IPA	(H)
Guest Beer Regular	(H)

GEORGE INN (Map Ref D7)
12: - 2:30 ; 7: - 11: (M-S (W), 12 - 3, 6 - 11 (S))
MAIN STREET, BLACKAWTON,
OS: SX805509
Tel: (0803) 821342

Furgusons Dartmoor Strong	(H)
Flowers IPA	(H)
Guest Beer Regular	(H)

AC CH CI CP DB DM FA GD ME (NOT
MONDAYS) ML MR OD PB PG RF
Two bar village local with large function
room, family room, and a garden
overlooking a vineyard.

NORMANDY ARMS (Map Ref D7)
12 - 2:30 ; 7 - 11. (M-S)
CHAPEL STREET, BLACKAWTON,
OS: SX806510
Tel: (0803) 821316

Draught Bass	(H)
Blackawton Bitter	(H)
Devon Gold	(H)
(SUMMER ONLY)	
44 Special	(H)
(AUTUMN ONLY)	
Headstrong	(H)
(WINTER ONLY)	
Ruddle Best Bitter	(H)

AC CC CH CP DB DF FA GD ME ML OD
PG QP RF RS SH
Engaging 15th century village pub with a
reputation for good food. The lounge is
bedecked with D-Day paraphernalia in
memory of the extensive preparations that
so deeply affected the South Hams. A
quietly impressive pub. The pub was one
requisitioned by the allies when the most
part of the South Hams was used as a
training ground for the Normandy
landings.

SPORTSMANS ARMS (Map Ref D7)
11 - 2:30 ; 5:30 - 11. (M-S (W), 11 - 11 (S))
HEMBOROUGH POST, BLACKAWTON
(ON A3122 MIDWAY BETWEEN
HALWELL AND DARTMOUTH),
OS: SX831523
Tel: (080421) 231

Draught Bass	(H)
Boddingtons Bitter	(H)

CH CP FA GD ME ML OD PG RF RS ST
(BAR SKITTLES)
Large roadside pub with separate
restaurant area. well equipped family
room with toys and wall blackboard. Large
garden with children's playb equipment.

BLACKMOOR GATE

OLD STATION HOUSE INN (Map Ref C1)
11 - 2:30 ; 6 - 11. (M-F, 11-11 Sat.)
BLACKMOOR GATE, BARNSTAPLE.
(JUNCTION OF A39 & A399)
Tel: (05983) 274

John Smith's Bitter	(H)
Ushers Best Bitter	(H)

CP FA ME ML OD PG RS
Large pub, set partly in station on old
Barnstaple & Lynton railway. Large new
restaurant attatched. Pub contains a small
collection of railway relics.

BOVEY TRACEY

BELL INN (Map Ref D5)
11:30 - 3 ; 5 - 11. (M-S)
TOWN HALL PLACE, BOVEY TRACEY
Tel: (0626) 833495

Boddingtons Bitter	(H)
Castle Eden Ale	(H)
Flowers IPA	(H)

AC ML OD PG SN
Lively pub at the top end of Bovey Tracey,
large bar area with pool table darts and
the obligatory juke box. Friendly
atmosphere.

OLD THATCHED INN (Map Ref D5)
11 - 3 ; 7 - 11. (M-S)
STATION ROAD, BOVEY TRACEY
Tel: (0626) 833421

Cornish Royal Wessex	(H)
Marston's Pedigree	(H)
Wadworth 6X	(H)

DF FA ME ML OD PG
c13 thatched inn - like all of the pubs in
Bovey Tracey it has none of the country
atmosphere, but there are some redeeming
features such as a stone floor and open
fire. Large bar area with pool table, darts,
machines and a CD juke box.

RIVERSIDE INN (Map Ref D5)
11 - 11 (M-S)
FORE STREET, BOVEY TRACEY
Tel: (0626) 832293

Draught Bass	(H)
Whitbread Best Bitter	(H)
Flowers Original	(H)

AC CA CD (CRIB) DB DF FA ME ML MR
OD PG QP RF
Large spacious bar, with function room at
rear. Mill leat runs under pub entrance,
whilst the 'DETRACEY BAR' is watched
over by a suit of armour.

The Normandy Arms
15 th. Century Inn
A Fully Licensed Freehouse

Blackawton.

BOW

KINGS ARMS (Map Ref D4)
11 - 11. (M-S)
BOW, Nr. CREDITON.
Tel: (0363) 82284

Beer Engine Piston Bitter	(H)
Exmoor Ale	(H)

CA CH DB DF FA GD ME ML OD PG PL
RF (AGA & WOODBURNER)
Pleasant village pub, frequented by young
people. Separate pool room, children's
room and an outside play area.

WHITE HART (Map Ref D4)
12 - 3 ; 7 - 11. (M-S)
BOW, Nr. CREDITON.
Tel: (0363) 82240

Draught Bass	(H)
Butcombe Bitter	(H)

AC CA DB FA GD ME ML OD PG PL QP
RF RS ST
Pleasant, timbered village pub with large
log fire, and a superb collection of framed
Guiness Calender cartoons.

BRADNINCH

CASTLE INN (Map Ref E4)
12: - 2:30; 6: - 11: (M-S)
1, FORE STREET, BRADNINCH, Nr.
EXETER.
Tel: (0392) 881378

Furgusons Dartmoor Best Bitter	(H)
Ind Coope Burton Ale	(H)

CP DF FA ME ML OD PG
An old coaching inn which has recently
been renovated. Offers a warm and
friendly atmosphere in comfortable
surroundings. Good value home-cooked
meals.

OLDE WHITE LION INN (Map Ref E4)
11 - 3 ; 6:30 - 11. (M-S)
26, HIGH STREET, BRADNINCH, Nr.
EXETER.
Tel: (0392) 881263

Boddingtons Bitter	(H)

CP DB DF FA ME ML OD PG RF
Busy, friendly country local.

BRADWORTHY

BRADWORTHY INN (Map Ref A3)
11:30 - 2 ; 6:30 - 11. (M-S)
THE SQUARE, BRADWORTHY.
OS: SS323140
Tel: (0409) 241222

Draught Bass	**(H)**

AC CP DF FA OD PG RF
Remote and unpretentious. Has a WC
available for the disabled.

BRAMPFORD SPEKE

AGRICULTURAL INN (Map Ref E4)
11 - 3 ; 7 - 11
BRAMPFORD SPEKE, EXETER. (IN
VILLAGE CENTRE), OS: SX925986
Tel: (0392) 841868

Draught Bass	**(H)**
Worthington Best Bitter	**(H)**
John Smith's Bitter	**(H)**
Wadworth 6X	**(H)**

BB DB DF FA GD ME ML OD PB PG QP
RM
Country pub with a difference! Traditional
style with large upstairs dining area -
extensive menu.

BRANDIS CORNER

BICKFORD ARMS (Map Ref B4)
BRANDIS CORNER, HOLSWORTHY.
Tel: (0409) 221318

Draught Bass	**(H)**
Guest Beer Regular	**(H)**

BRANSCOMBE

FOUNTAIN HEAD (Map Ref G5)
11 - 2:30 ; 6:30 - 11. (M-S (S),1100 - 0200,
0630 - 1030 (W))
BRANSCOMBE, NEAR SEATON. (ON
MAIN LANE AT TOP END OF VILLAGE),
OS: SY1888
Tel: (029780) 359

Branscombe Vale	
Branoc	**(H)**
Old Stoker	**(H)**
Hall & Woodhouse Badger Best Bitter	**(H)**

AC CA CP DB DM ME ML OD PB QP RF
SH SN
c14 pub with a huge log fire in lounge
during winter months. Lounge bar
formerly the village blacksmith's shop - the
forge now forms the fireplace in the centre
of the room. Main outlet for the local
(Branscombe Vale) brewery. Good simple
food.

MASONS ARMS (Map Ref G5)
11 - 2:30 ; 5:30 - 11. (M-S)
BRANSCOMBE. (LOWER END OF
VILLAGE, APPROX 3/4 MILE FROM
BEACH.), OS: SY2088
Tel: (029780) 300

Draught Bass	**(H)**
Furgusons Dartmoor Best Bitter	**(H)**
Wadworth 6X	**(H)**

AC CA CP DB DF FA GD ME ML OD QP
RF SH
Creeper clad c14 inn once famous for
smugglers. Accommodation in pub and in
thatched cottages opposite. Wide range of
home cooked food with spit roasts on
Thursdays. Good but expensive.

**THREE HORSESHOES INN, (Map
Ref G5)**
11 - 11 ;   - .(M-S)
BRANSCOMBE, SEATON.
(ON A3052, 1 ml WEST OF TURN TO
BEER.), OS: SY1891
Tel: (029780) 251

Draught Bass	**(H)**
Guest Beer Occasional	**(H)**

AC CA CP DB FA GD ME ML OD PL QP
RF
Large roadside inn with a predominance
towards food.

BRATTON CLOVELLY

CLOVELLY INN (Map Ref B5)
11 - 2:30 ; 6 - 11. (M-S)
BRATTON CLOVELLY, OKEHAMPTON.
OS: SS464918
Tel: (083787) 348

Courage Best Bitter	**(H)**

ME ML OD PB QP RF
Isolated village local with reputation for
good steaks. Occasional guest beer.

BRATTON FLEMING

WHITE HART (Map Ref C2)
11 - 3 ; 5 - 11. (M-S)
BRATTON FLEMING, BARNSTAPLE.
OS: SS644377
Tel: (0598) 710344

John Smith's Bitter	**(H)**
Ushers Best Bitter	**(H)**

CP ME ML PG

BRAUNTON

AGRICULTURAL INN (Map Ref B2)
25, EAST STREET, BRAUNTON.
Tel: (0271) 812169

Draught Bass (H)

BLACK HORSE INN (Map Ref B2)
11 - 2:30 ; 5 - 11. (M-F, 11 - 11 SAT)
CHURCH STREET, BRAUNTON,
BARNSTAPLE.
Tel: (0271) 812386

Marston's Pedigree	(H)
Flowers Original	(H)

ML PG
comfortable local in old part of village.

LONDON INN (Map Ref B2)
11 - 2:30 ; 6 - 11. (M-Th, 11 - 11 F. Sat (W),
11 - 11 M-S (S))
CAEN STREET, BRAUNTON,
BARNSTAPLE.
Tel: (0271) 812603

Courage Best Bitter	(H)
Ushers Founders	(H)
Ushers Best Bitter	(H)

CP DB DF FA ME ML OD PG SH ST
Open plan bar with old fireplace
(bricked-up at present).

MARINERS ARMS (Map Ref B2)
11: - 3. ; 6: - 11: (M-S)
SOUTH STREET, BRAUNTON,
BARNSTAPLE.
Tel: (0271) 813160

Eldridge Pope Hardy Country	(H)
Exmoor Ale	(H)
Fullers London Pride	(H)
Morland Old Speckled Hen	(H)
Wadworth 6X	(H)

Above beer range varies with availability.

DB DF FA ME ML OD PB PG RS SH ST
Pleasant back street local with good food.
L-shaped bar with a solid oak, rough-cut,
bar top.

NEW INN (Map Ref B2)
SILVER STREET, BRAUNTON,
BARNSTAPLE.
Tel: (0271) 812254

Ind Coope Burton Ale	(H)
Ushers Best Bitter	(H)

BRENDON

STAGHUNTERS INN (Map Ref D1)
11 - 3 ; 5 - 11. (M-S (W), 11 - 11 (S))
BRENDON, Nr. LYNTON.
OS: SS767481
Tel: (05987) 222

Butcombe Bitter	(H)
Ind Coope Burton Ale	(H)
(SUMMER ONLY) Tetley Bitter	(H)

AC CP DF ME ML OD PB PG QP RF RS
Situated in the Exmoor national park east
of Countisbury this riverside hotel is well
situated for a wide range of activities. Bar
snacks only at lunch but there is a separate
restaurant for evening meals.

BRENTOR

BRENTOR INN (Map Ref B5)
BRENTOR, Nr. TAVISTOCK

Draught Bass	(H)
Courage Best Bitter	(H)
Courage Directors	(H)

BRIDESTOWE

FOX & HOUNDS (Map Ref B5)
11 - 11. (M-S)
BRIDESTOWE, Nr. OKEHAMPTON.
(ON A386 AT JUNCTION WITH B3278),
OS: SX525866
Tel: (082282) 206

Boddingtons Bitter	(H)
Flowers IPA	(H)
Flowers Original	(H)

AC CA CC CP FA ME ML QP RF ST
Large pub on Dartmoor near Lydford
Gorge. The skittle alley is available for hire.

BRIDFORD

BRIDFORD INN (Map Ref D5)
12 - 2:30 ; 6 - 11. (M-S)
BRIDFORD, Nr. MORETONHAMPSTEAD
Tel: (0697) 52436

Draught Bass	(H)
Furgusons Dartmoor Strong	(H)
Guest Beer Regular	(H)

CP DF FA ME ML OD PG RF
c17 pub in hillside village. The interior is
one huge room with an oak bar as large as
a cricket square - well almost!

BRIDGERULE

BRIDGE INN (Map Ref A4)
BRIDGERULE, Nr. HOLSWORTHY.
Tel: (028881) 316

Wadworth 6X	(H)
Flowers Original	(H)
Guest Beer Regular	(H)

BRIXHAM

BELL INN (Map Ref E7)
108, DREW STREET, BRIXHAM
Tel: (0803) 851815

Courage Best Bitter (H)
Ushers Best Bitter (H)

BLUE ANCHOR (Map Ref E7)
11 - 11. (M-S)
83, FORE STREET, BRIXHAM
Tel: (0803) 859373

Blackawton Headstrong	(H)
Furgusons Dartmoor Strong	(H)

LM ME ML PG RF
Cheery harbourside lounge bar with
ancient parts of a former c16 chapel.

BULLER'S ARMS (Map Ref E7)
11 - 11. (M-S) 4,
THE STRAND, BRIXHAM
Tel: (0803) 853329

Courage Best Bitter	(H)
Smiles Best Bitter	(H)

LM ML PG RF
Lively quayside pub, popular with
tourists, with live music, sports
connections, and a friendly landlord.

HOLE-IN-THE-WALL (Map Ref E7)
11 - 11. (M-S)
8, KING STREET, BRIXHAM
Tel: (0803) 858589

Ushers		
	Founders	(H)
	Best Bitter	(H)

ME ML PG RF RS
c14 pub with a friendly atmosphere and
upstairs restaurant.

BRIXTON

FOXHOUND INN (Map Ref C7)
11:30 - 2:30; 6 - 11. (M -Th. 11.30 - 3, 6 - 11 F,
Sat)
BRIXTON, Nr. PLYMOUTH
Tel: (0752) 880271

Courage Best Bitter	(H)
Marston's Pedigree	(H)

CA CP DF ME ML PG
Large village local with a collection of
fox-hunting pictures on the walls. Good
value food.

BROADCLYST

HUNGRY FOX (Map Ref E4)
11:30 - 3 ; 7 - 11. (M-S)
STATION ROAD, BROADCLYST, Nr.
EXETER (1/2 ML OFF A30, ON ROAD TO
BROADCLYST), OS: SX992950
Tel: (0392) 61231

Furgusons		
	Dartmoor Best Bitter	(H)
	Dartmoor Strong	(H)

CP ME ML OD
Large and spacious, food orientated pub.

NEW INN (Map Ref E4)
11 - 3 ; 5 - 11. (M-S (W), 11 - 11 (S))
WHIMPLE ROAD, BROADCLYST, Nr.
EXETER, OS: SX992972
Tel: (0392) 61312

Draught Bass	(H)
Flowers IPA	(H)
Flowers Original	(H)

CP DF GD ME ML OD PG RF
Busy country pub with excellent home
cooked food.

RED LION INN (Map Ref E4)
11 - 3 ; 5:30 - 11. (M-S)
BROADCLYST, Nr. EXETER.
Tel: (0392) 61271

Draught Bass	(H)
Eldridge Pope Royal Oak	(H)
Furgusons Dartmoor Best Bitter	(H)

DF FA ME ML OD PB QP RF

BROADHEMBURY

DREWE ARMS (Map Ref F4)
11 - 2 ; 6 - 11. (M-S)
BROADHEMBURY, Nr. HONITON.
Tel: (040484) 267

Draught Bass	(G)
Cotleigh Tawny	(H)
Otter Bitter	(H)

CA CI (BOLLHAYES DRY) DB DM FA (WELL BEHAVED CHILDREN) ME (NOT Sun.) ML OD PB PG QP RF SH ST
A picturesque exterior and an old fashioned interior in an inn which is full of character. Check the blackboard for the latest beer menu. Guest beers. Largely unspoilt village pub in a picture-book setting amongst thatched, whitewashed cottages and adjacent to church.

BROADHEMPSTON

COPPA DOLLA (Map Ref D6)
Tel: (0803) 812455

Draught Bass	(H)
Palmers IPA	(H)
Wadworth 6X	(H)

MONKS RETREAT (Map Ref D6)
11 - 2:30 ; 7 - 11. (M-S)
THE SQUARE, BROADHEMPSTON
Tel: (0803) 812203

Draught Bass	(H)
Mill Janner's Old Original	(H)

CI CP DF ME ML
Dating from 1456 the monks retreat was formerly called the Church House Inn. It is a listed building of architectural interest and is said to have a monastic ghost. An excellent range of home-cooked bar food includes vegetarian dishes. The cider is made from the village's apples.

BUCKFASTLEIGH

ABBEY INN (Map Ref D6)
11 - 3 ; 6 - 11. (M-S)
BUCKFAST ROAD, BUCKFASTLEIGH
Tel: (0364) 42343

Draught Bass	(H)
Guest Beer Regular	(H)

AC CI FA ME ML OD QP RF
Formerly 'Black Rock Hotel', it has its own fishing rights to the stretch of the River Dart flowing through the grounds. All food is freshly made on the premises, and there are occasional 'speciality evenings'.

DART BRIDGE INN (Map Ref D6)
11 - 2:30 ; 5 - 11. (M-S)
TOTNES ROAD, BUCKFASTLEIGH
Tel: (0364) 42214

Furgusons Dartmoor Best Bitter	(H)
Wadworth 6X	(H)

AC CA CP GD ME ML MR OD QP RF RS
Attractive exterior hides a hotel style bar and elongated restaurant. A picturesque roadside pub, beside the River Dart, with recently extended accommodation. Food range encompasses basic through to up-market fare, including vegetarian. A function room caters for up to 100 people.

GLOBE INN (Map Ref D6)
123, PLYMOUTH ROAD, BUCKFAST-LEIGH
Tel: (0364) 42223

Marston's Pedigree	(H)
Flowers IPA	(H)

AC CA CI FA ME ML OD PG QP RS
Large pub in centre of town, with a FREE public car prk at rear.

KINGS ARMS (Map Ref D6)
FORE STREET, BUCKFASTLEIGH
Tel: (0364) 42341

Ushers		
	Founders	(H)
	Best Bitter	(H)

SUN INN (Map Ref D6)
11:30 - 3 ; 6 - 11. (M-Th, 11 - 11 F,Sat)
1, CHURCH STREET, BUCKFASTLEIGH
Tel: (0364) 42397

Draught Bass	(H)

CA CI FA GD OD PB PG PL QP RF
Basic, traditional pub at the back end of town, with a separate pool room. Pub has a small collection of stuffed animals.

WATERMANS ARMS (Map Ref D6)
22, CHAPEL STREET, BUCKFASTLEIGH
Tel: (0626) 43200

Courage Best Bitter	(H)
John Smith's Bitter	(H)
Wadworth 6X	(H)

BUCKLAND BREWER

COACH AND HORSES (Map Ref B3)
11:30 - 2:30 ; 5 - 11. (M-S)
HIGH STREET, BUCKLAND BREWER,
BIDEFORD. OS: SS419208
Tel: (0237) 451395

Wadworth 6X	(H)
Flowers IPA	(H)
Flowers Original	(H)

AC CP FA ME ML OD PB QP RF
Old coaching inn in the middle of the
village with low beams. Quiet bar with a
sloping floor that levels out during
consumption of beer! Friendly and
welcoming atmosphere.

BUCKLAND MONACHORUM

DRAKE MANOR INN (Map Ref B6)
11 - 3:30 ; 6:30 - 11. (M-S)
BUCKLAND MONACHORUM, Nr.
YELVERTON, OS: SX490681
Tel: (0822) 853892

Courage Best Bitter	(H)
John Smith's Bitter	(H)
Ushers Founders	(H)
Ushers Best Bitter	(H)

CD (EUCHRE) CI CP DB FA GD ME ML
OD PB PG QP RF SH
Low ceilinged practical pub near church,
with a small car park.

BUDLEIGH SALTERTON

FEATHERS HOTEL (Map Ref F5)
11 - 3 ; 5 - 11. (M-S (W)). 11-11 (S))
35, HIGH STREET, BUDLEIGH
SALTERTON, DEVONSHIRE. (MIDWAY
DOWN MAIN STREET).
Tel: (0395) 442042

Theakston Best Bitter	(H)
Wadworth 6X	(H)
Flowers IPA	(H)
Guest Beer Occasional	(H)

DB FA ME ML OD PB PG QP ST
Large town pub with a friendly
atmosphere, making it the community
pub. Basic, economic, but sustaining menu.

KING WILLIAM IV (Map Ref F5)
7, HIGH STREET, BUDLEIGH
SALTERTON, DEVONSHIRE. (MIDWAY
ALONG MAIN STREET.)
Tel: (0395) 442075

Flowers IPA	(H)
Guest Beer Regular	(H)

SALTERTON ARMS (Map Ref F5)
11 - 3 ; 5:30 - 11. (M-S)
CHAPEL STREET, BUDLEIGH
SALTERTON. (100METRES OFF MIDDLE
OF MAIN STREET)
Tel: (0395) 445048

Draught Bass	(H)
Worthington Best Bitter	(H)
John Smith's Bitter	(H)

DB FA ME ML QP RS
Split level pub, with good menu. Pleasant
atmosphere in a well modernised
surrounding.

BURGH ISLAND

PILCHARD INN (Map Ref C8)
11 - 3 ; 7 - 11. (M-S (W)). 11 - 11 (S))
BURGH ISLAND, BIGBURY,
KINGSBRIDGE
Tel: (0548) 810344

Ushers Founders	(H)
Ushers Best Bitter	(H)
Wadworth 6X	(G)

CA CI FA ME (SUMMER ONLY) ML
(SUMMER ONLY) PB PG QP RF SH
Marvellous c14 smugglers inn, consisting
of two old bars, a downstairs eatery and a
seaside terrace. Candle-lit in winter when
the log fire blazes.

BURLESCOMBE

HAYWAIN (Map Ref F3)
11 - 11. (M-S)
BURLESCOMBE, Nr. TIVERTON.
Tel: (0823) 672071

Gibbs Mew Salisbury	(H)

AC CP DF ME ML OD PB PG QP RF
Popular roadside inn with extensive menu
and a friendly atmosphere.

POACHERS POCKET (Map Ref F3)
11 - 3 ; 7 - 11. (M-S)
BURLESCOMBE, Nr. TIVERTON.
Tel: (0823) 672286

Exe Valley Bitter	(H)
Theakston Best Bitter	(H)

AC CC CP FA
Large roadside 17th century hotel, built in
1644 as a coaching inn, but still retains
much of the olde worlde charm.

The George Inn, Chardstock

BURRINGTON

BARNSTAPLE INN (Map Ref C3)
11 - 11. (M-S)
BURRINGTON, Nr. WINKLEIGH.
OS: SS638167
Tel: (07693) 277

Butcombe Bitter	(H)

ME ML PB QP RF
Friendly local's pub in centre of village.

BURSDON MOOR

WESTCOUNTRY INN (Map Ref A3)
11:30 - 3 ; 6:30 - 11. (12 - 2.30, 7 - 11 IN
WINTER)
BURSDON MOOR, Nr. HARTLAND.
(A39, 4 MILES SOUTH OF HARTLAND),
OS: SS270193
Tel: (0237) 441724

Marston's Pedigree	(H)
Flowers IPA	(H)

AC CA CP DF FA ME ML OD PB PG PL RF
RM
Large roadside pub in desolate terrain,
serving a scattered community. There is a
conservatory and pool room for families.
B & B available.

BUTTERLEIGH

BUTTERLEIGH INN (Map Ref E4)
12 - 3 ; 6 - 11. (FRIDAYS 5 - 11)
BUTTERLEIGH, Nr. TIVERTON.
Tel: (0884) 855407

Cotleigh	
Harrier	(H)
Tawny	(H)
Old Buzzard	(H)

AC CA CD CP DB DF DM FA GD ME ML
OD PB PG QP RF SH ST
Friendly village inn with stained glass
porch, popular for food and top rate ales.

CADELEIGH

CADELEIGH ARMS (Map Ref E4)
11 - 11. (M-S)
CADELEIGH, Nr. TIVERTON.
Tel: (0884) 855238

Draught Bass	(H)
Butcombe Bitter	(H)
Cotleigh	
Harrier	(H)
Tawny	(H)
Old Buzzard	(H)

CA DF FA ME ML OD PG
Warm, friendly atmosphere, with fantastic
views across the Exe and Creedy valleys.

CALIFORNIA CROSS

CALIFORNIA INN (Map Ref D7)
11 - 3 ; 6:30 - 11. (M-S (W), 10.30 - 11 (S))
CALIFORNIA CROSS, DIPTFORD, Nr.
SOUTH BRENT (ON B3207, BETWEEN
MODBURY AND SOUTH BRENT)
OS: SX704530
Tel: (0748) 82449

Furgusons Dartmoor Best Bitter	(H)
Wadworth 6X	(H)

BB CA CD (EUCHRE) CI CP DB FA LM
ME ML OD PB PG RF
A local's country pub, with a large bottle
collection in an ante-room dominated by a
stuffed peacock. Western bar at rear with
live music on Saturday nights. Indoor
adventure playground for children.

CHAGFORD

GLOBE HOTEL (Map Ref D5)
11 - 3 ; 6 - 11. (M-S)
HIGH STREET, CHAGFORD
Tel: (0473) 433485

Draught Bass	**(H)**
Smiles Exhibition	**(H)**
Guest Beer Regular	**(H)**

AC DF FA ME ML PB PG RF
16th century 2 bar coaching inn within the
Dartmoor national park. Separate
restaurant. Up to 4 guest beers throughout
year and cider in summer.

RING O'BELLS (Map Ref D5)
11 - 3 ; 6 - 11. (M-S)
44, THE SQUARE, CHAGFORD
Tel: (0647) 423466

Draught Bass	**(H)**
Furgusons Dartmoor Best Bitter	**(H)**
Ind Coope Burton Ale	**(H)**
Palmers IPA	
or	
Wadworth 6X	**(H)**

CA CI DF FA GD ME ML OD PG QP RS
(DINING AREA)
c12, one-bar village pub, with a dining area
and large garden. A finest suit of armour in
Chagford resides in a corner of the pub,
which over the years has been used as a
holding prison and a mortuary.

The Exchange, Crediton

CHALLACOMBE

BLACK VENUS INN (Map Ref D1)
11 - 2:30 ; 6 - 11. (M-S)
CHALLACOMBE. (ON B3358)
Tel: (05983)

251 John Smith's Bitter	**(H)**
Ushers Best Bitter	**(H)**

CP FA (RESTAURANT ONLY) ME ML OD
PG
Small pub on edge of Exmoor, well known
for its good food.

CHARDSTOCK

GEORGE INN (Map Ref G4)
11:30 - 3 ; 6 - 11. (M-S)
CHARDSTOCK, Nr. AXMINSTER,
Tel: (0460) 20241

Boddingtons Bitter	**(H)**
Wadworth 6X	**(H)**
Flowers Original	**(H)**

AC CP DF FA LM ME ML (NOT MON.
(W)) OD PG QP RF ST
A very comfortable one bar pub cum
restaurant with much original old
woodwork.

CHERITON BISHOP

GOOD KNIGHT INN (Map Ref D4)
11 - 3 ; 6 - 11. (M-S)
CHERITON BISHOP, Nr. EXETER.
Tel: (0647) 24227

Exe Valley Bitter	**(H)**
Whitbread Best Bitter	**(H)**

CA CH CP DF FA ME ML OD PB PG RF
SN
Modern, pub on main road. Family room
and games room. Bar snacks every day.

OLD THATCH INN (Map Ref D4)
12 - 23:0 ; 6 - 11. (M-S)
CHERITON BISHOP, Nr. EXETER.
Tel: (0647) 24204

Furgusons Dartmoor Best Bitter	**(H)**
Wadworth 6X	**(H)**

AC CA CI (GRAYS) FA (NO CHILDREN
UNDER 14) ME ML RF
Olde worlde thatched village pub.

CHERITON FITZPAINE

HALF MOON (Map Ref E4)
11 - 2:30 ; 7 - 11. (M-S)
CHERITON FITZPAINE, Nr. TIVERTON.
Tel: (0363) 866219

Wadworth 6X	(H)
Flowers IPA	(H)

CP OD PB PG RF
Friendly village inn.

RING O' BELLS (Map Ref E4)
12: - 2:30; 7: - 11: (M-F. 12-3 Sat.)
WELLS TERRACE, CHERITON
FITZPAINE.
Tel: (0363) 866374

Flowers IPA	(H)

AC CP FA ME ML OD PB RF
14th century country inn.

CHILLATON

CHICHESTER ARMS (Map Ref B5)
CHILLINGTON, TAVISTOCK
Tel: (082286) 283

Courage Best Bitter	(H)
Courage Directors	(H)
John Smith's Bitter	(H)

CP ME ML PG PL RF RS
A very pleasant one bar village local, with
a 'front lounge' feel. Restaurant offers
English and Chinese food.

CHILLINGTON

UNION INN (Map Ref D8)
11 - 3 ; 6 - 11. (M-S)
CHILLINGTON, Nr. KINGSBRIDGE, OS:
SX794427
Tel: (0548) 580241

Marston's Pedigree	(H)
Flowers Original	(H)
Guest Beer Regular	(H)

CC CH CI DB FA GD ME ML OD PB PG
RF
Small roadside, low-ceilinged village inn
with a separate dining room, garden and
'sun terrace'. Live music Wed.& Sat
evenings in summer and Folk on 3rd Thurs
of each month. 'Take-away' fish & chips,
and summer BBQs.

CHIPSHOP

CHIPSHOP INN (Map Ref B6)
12 - 3 ; 7 - 11. (M-S)
CHIPSHOP, Nr. TAVISTOCK (OFFA386, 3
MILES SOUTH WEST OF LAMERTON),
OS: SX436751
Tel: (0822) 832322

Draught Bass	(H)
Exmoor Ale	(H)
Smiles Best Bitter	(H)
Guest Beer Regular	(H)

CC CP FA ME ML OD PG RF
One bar pub on remote crossroads, skittle
alley available for hire.

CHITTLEHAMHOLT

EXETER INN (Map Ref C3)
11:30 - 2:30 ; 6 - 11. (M-S)
CHITTLEHAMHOLT, UMBERLEIGH.
Tel: (0769) 540281

Ushers Best Bitter	(H)

CP FA PG QP RF
Thatched pub in centre of village.

CHITTLEHAMPTON

BELL (Map Ref C2)
11: - 11: (M-S)
EAST STREET, CHITTLEHAMPTON,
UMBERLEIGH.
Tel: (0769) 540368

Draught Bass	(H)

FA ME ML OD PB PG PL RF
Grade 2 listed, victorian pub, opposite
impressive village square and church.
Tiled entrance and separate pool room
help retain pub's character.

CHUDLEIGH

BISHOP LACEY (Map Ref E5)
11 - 2:30 ; 5 - 11. (M-Th, 11-11 F, Sat)
FORE STREET, CHUDLEIGH
Tel: (0626) 852196

Wadworth 6X	(H)
Flowers IPA	(H)

AC CA CI CP GD OD PB PG RF
Historic building, as the name implies,
dates from 1309, when it was a monastery.
It is reputed to have an active ghost of a
monk. Comfortable lounge with an open
fire.

COACHING HOUSE (Map Ref E5)
11 - 11. (M-S)
FORE STREET, CHUDLEIGH
Tel: (0626) 853270

Furgusons	
Dartmoor Best Bitter	(H)
Dartmoor Strong	(H)
Guest Beer Regular	(H)

GLOBE INN (Map Ref E5)
11 - 2:30 ; 5 - 11. (M-S)
FORE STREET, CHUDLEIGH
Tel: (0626) 853219

Draught Bass	(H)
Eldridge Pope Royal Oak	(H)

AC CA CI CP ME ML MR OD PB PG QP
City style pub with a lively public bar
Function room available.

SHIP INN (Map Ref E5)
FORE STREET, CHUDLEIGH
Tel: (0626) 853268

Draught Bass	(H)
Flowers IPA	(H)

CHUDLEIGH KNIGHTON

CLAYCUTTERS ARMS (Map Ref E5)
CHUDLEIGH KNIGHTON
Tel: (0626) 853345

Draught Bass	(H)
Eldridge Pope Royal Oak	(H)

CHULMLEIGH

BARNSTAPLE INN (Map Ref D3)
12 - 2:30 ; 6:30 - 11. (M-S. VARIABLE IN
SUMMER)
SOUTH MOLTON STREET,
CHULMLEIGH, DEVONSHIRE.
Tel: (0769) 80388

Draught Bass (H)
Butcombe Bitter (H)
Marston's Pedigree (H)

AC CC CI DF FA ME ML OD PB PG RF
An old court house where Charles I once
stayed, and a former coaching inn. Basic
village pub with a friendly welcome.

CHURCHSTOW

CHURCH HOUSE INN (Map Ref D7)
11 - 2:30 ; 6 - 11. (M-S)
CHURCHSTOW, KINGSBRIDGE
Tel: (0548) 852237

Draught Bass	(H)
Marston's Pedigree	(H)
Ruddles County	(H)

CA CC CP DB DF FA ME ML QP RF
Formerly a 13th century monks rest home,
original wood beams and stone walls,
make it a splendid country pub. BEWARE!
the very low beams.

CLAYHIDON

HALF MOON INN (Map Ref F3)
12: - 2:30; 7: - 11: (M-S)
CLAYHIDON, Nr. HONITON,
Tel: (0823) 680291

Draught Bass	(H)
Cotleigh	
Tawny	(H)
Old Buzzard	(H)

CA CC CI CP DF FA ME ML OD PG QP RF
Old but well cared for village local with
nice views across the Culm valley.

CLEARBROOK

SKYLARK (Map Ref B6)
11 - 2:30 ; 6 - 11 (M-S (W). 11 - 3, 6 - 11 (S))
CLEARBRROK, YELVERTON.
OS: SX520655
Tel: (0822) 853258

Draught Bass	(H)
Courage Best Bitter	(H)

CP FA ME ML OD QP RF
Popular two bar pub on Dartmoor, with an
old baker's oven in bar area.

JOIN NOW

CLYST HONITON

BLACK HORSE (Map Ref E4)
11 - 11. (M-S)
LONDON ROAD, CLYST HONITON
Tel: (0395) 366649

Boddingtons Bitter	(H)
Marston's Pedigree	(H)
Flowers IPA	(H)
Flowers Original	(H)

One beer available from above list.

CP DF (ACCESS)
A good value 'Bernie Classic' inn.

DUKE OF YORK (Map Ref E4)
11 - 11:30. (M-S)
LONDON ROAD, CLYST HONITON
Tel: (0392) 367855

Boddingtons Bitter	(H)

AC CD (EUCHRE) CP DB DF (ACCESS)
DM FA ME ML OD PG PL QP
Basic but pleasant roadside pub, with an
'L'- shaped bar area. Near to airport.

EXETER INN (Map Ref E4)
11 - 3 ; 5:30 - 11. (M-F; 11-11 Sat & BANK
HOLIDAYS)
LONDON ROAD, CLYST HONITON
Tel: (0392) 367907

Marston's Pedigree	(H)
Castle Eden Ale	(H)
Guest Beer Regular	(H)

AC CD (EUCHRE) CP DB DF (ACCESS)
GD ME ML OD PG PL RF
Pleasant roadside pub near to airport.

CLYST HYDON

FIVE BELLS INN (Map Ref F4)
CLYST HYDON, CULLOMPTON,
Tel: (08847) 288

Furgusons Dartmoor Best Bitter (H)
Tetley Bitter (H)
Wadworth 6X (H)

CA CC CP FA GD ME ML OD QP RF RS
16th century thatched inn with a
reputation for good home cooked food.
There is a large beer garden and childrens
play area, the pub is near the village open
air swimming pool.

CLYST ST. GEORGE

GEORGE AND DRAGON (Map Ref E5)
11 - 2:30 ; 5:30 - 11 (M-F; 11 - 11 Sat)
CLYST ST. GEORGE, Nr. EXETER, (ON
A376 AT JUNCT WITH ROAD TO
TOPSHAM.), OS: SX9888 Tel: (0392)
876121

Draught Bass	(H)

AC BR (TOPSHAM. APPROX 3/4 ml.) CP
DB DF FA GD ME ML OD QP RS
Country Hotel with conference and
banqueting facilities. Bar food all week +
restruaurnt. Easy access from J30 M5
approx. 2miles.

CLYST ST. MARY

BLUE BALL INN (Map Ref E5)
11 - 11. (M-S)
OLD RYDON LANE, SANDYGATE,
EXETER, (NEAR J30 OF M5
MOTORWAY.), OS: SX967909
Tel: (0392) 873401

Draught Bass (H)
Boddingtons Bitter (H)
Wadworth 6X (H)
Flowers Original (H)
Wethered Winter Royal (H)

CP FA GD ME ML OD PB QP
Comfortable pub near M5 GRANADA
services. Well known for food. BEWARE!
Some beers dispensed from cellar via gas
pumps and FAKE CASKS.

CAT AND FIDDLE INN, (Map Ref E5)
11 - 3 ; 6 - 11. (M-S)
SIDMOUTH ROAD, CLYST ST. MARY,
EXETER, (ON A3052, 1ML. FROM
VILLAGE.), OS: SX9990
Tel: (0392) 873317

Courage Best Bitter	(H)
Ushers Best Bitter	(H)

CA CH CP DB DF FA GD ME ML OD PB
PG PL QP RM SN ST
Large pub, best known as an eating house,
with a very good menu. Original part of
pub dates from c16. New skittle alley /
dance floor recently installed.

HALF MOON (Map Ref E5)
11 - 3 ; 5 - 11. (M-F, 1100 - 1100 SAT.)
CLYST ST. MARY, Nr. EXETER, (CENTRE
OF VILLAGE),
Tel: (0392) 873515

Draught Bass	(G)
Boddingtons Bitter	(G)
Flowers IPA	(G)
Wethered Winter Royal	(G)

CI DB FA GD ME ML OD PB PG QP RF
Very friendly village pub with superb
economical meals. Close to J30, M5.
Approx 1/2 mile.

MALTSTERS ARMS (Map Ref E5)
11 - 3 ; 5 - 11. (M-F, 1100 - 1100 SAT.)
CLYST ST MARY, EXETER, (CENTRE OF
VILLAGE, OPPOSITE GENERAL STORE.)
Tel: (0392) 873445

Draught Bass	(E)
Flowers IPA	(H)

AC DB FA GD LM ME (NOT THURS, FRI,
SAT) ML OD PB PG PL QP RF (LOUNGE
ONLY) SN ST
Friendly village pub.

COCKINGTON

DRUM INN (Map Ref E6)
11 - 2:30 ; 6 - 11. (M-S (W), 11 - 11 (S))
COCKINGTON, TORQUAY
Tel: (0803) 605143

Furgusons
Dartmoor Best Bitter	(H)
Dartmoor Strong	(H)

CA FA ME ML OD
Delightful inn, set in a picturesque village.
Very busy with tourists in summer.

**PROTECT
YOUR
PLEASURE**

COCKWOOD

ANCHOR (Map Ref E5)
11: 11 - 2:30 ; 6 - 11. (11 - 11 SATURDAY)
COCKWOOD, STARCROSS, EXETER
(OFF A 379, BY HARBOUR.)
Tel: (0626) 890203

Draught Bass	(H)
Boddingtons Bitter	(H)
Eldridge Pope Hardy Country	(H)
Marston's Pedigree	(H)

CC CI (INCH'S) CP DB ME ML OD QP RF
Old harbourside pub with atmospheric bar
divided into three areas. Local shellfish are
on the menu. Children are allowed in the
dining area only. There is a patio area
outside. Can be crowded in summer, not
suitable for families with toddlers.

SHIP INN (Map Ref E5)
11 - 23:0 ; 6 - 11. (M-S)
COCKWOOD, STARCROSS, EXETER,
(OFF A379)
Tel: (0626) 890373

Ushers
Best Bitter	(H)
Founders	(H)

CI (BULMERS WESTCOUNTRY) ME ML
RF RS
Comfortable pub with small bar and large
restaurant areas.

COFFINSWELL

LINNEY (Map Ref E6)
11:30 - 2:30; 6:30 - 11: (M-S)
COFFINSWELL, NEWTON ABBOT
Tel: (0803) 873192

Draught Bass	(H)
Furgusons Dartmoor Strong	(H)
Tetley Bitter	(H)

CC CP DF FA ME ML OD PG QP RF RS
Well furnished, low ceilinged, thatched,
14th century pub with cosy alcoves and a
restaurant upstairs.

COLATON RALEIGH

OTTER INN (Map Ref F5)
11 - 2:30 ; 6 - 11 (M-S)
EXMOUTH ROAD, COLATON
RALEIGH,, OS: SY078874
Tel: (0395) 68434

Ruddles
Best Bitter	(H)
County	(H)
Ushers Best Bitter	(H)
Wadworth 6X	(H)

CA CH CP DB DF FA GD ME ML OD PB
PG PL QP SN ST
Friendly village pub well known for its
food. Large separate games room. Very
popular in winter.

COLEFORD

NEW INN (Map Ref D4)
11:30 - 2:30 ; 6 - 11 (M-S)
COLEFORD, Nr. CREDITON,
Tel: (0363) 84242

Wadworth 6X	(H)
Flowers IPA	(H)
Flowers Original	(H)
Guest Beer Occasional	(H)

AC CP DF FA ME ML OD QP RF
13th century thatched and cob pub. Once a
monks retreat, now specialises in good
home cooked food. Outside, ducks feed in
the mill stream, but inside watch out for
the parrot.

COLYFORD

WHEELWRIGHT INN (Map Ref G4)
11 - 3 ; 6 - 11 (M-S)
SWAN HILL ROAD, COLYFORD,
SEATON. OS: SY251926
Tel: (0297) 552585

Draught Bass	(H)
Flowers Original	(H)

CA DB DF DM FA ME ML OD PG (CRIB)
QP RF RS SN ST
Picturesque c16 Grade2-listed thatched
village pub and restaurant providing a
good local trade with home cooked food
and a changing beer menu.

WHITE HART (Map Ref G4)
SWAN HILL ROAD, COLYFORD, OS:
SY254926
Tel: (0297) 552358

Draught Bass	(E)

COLYTON

COLCOMBE CASTLE (Map Ref G4)
11 - 2:30 ; 7 - 11 (M-F, 11 - 4 Sat)
MARKET PLACE, COLYTON
Tel: (0297) 552257

John Smith's Bitter	(H)
Ruddles County	(H)

BR (SEATON TRAMWAY) CA CH
(SKITTLE ALLEY IN SUMMER) DB DF
(ACCESS ONLY) FA ME ML MR OD
(COURTYARD) PB PG PL RF ST
Old pub, rebuilt in 1877 after great Colyton
village fire. Cellar bar has a stone slabbed
floor, integral well, wooden settles, and
tractor seats on pedestals. Pub is home to 4
darts teams and 10 skittles teams.

GERRARD ARMS (Map Ref G4)
11:30 - 3 ; 6 - 11 (M-S)
ST. ANDREWS SQUARE, COLYTON, Nr.
SEATON. OS: SY245941
Tel: (0297) 52588

Draught Bass	(H)
Furgusons Dartmoor Best Bitter	(H)
Guest Beer Occasional	(H)

CA CH (SUMMER ONLY) DF (ACCESS
ONLY) ME ML OD (PATIO AT REAR) PG
ST
Victorian one bar local, strong on food.
Situated on north side of the church.
Skittles.

KINGFISHER (Map Ref G4)
11 - 2:30 ; 6 - 11 (M-S)
DOLPHIN STREET, COLYTON, Nr.
SEATON, OS: SY248942
Tel: (0297) 552476

Hall And Woodhouse Badger Best Bitter	(H)
Hook Norton Old Hooky	(H)
Wadworth 6X	(H)
Flowers Original	(H)

CA CH DB DF (ACCESS ONLY) FA ME
ML OD (PATIO AT REAR) PG (QUIZ) QP
SN ST
Stone walled, c17, former brewhouse on
edge of village. Timber beams to ceiling
(not original) but tastefully decorated.

WHITE COTTAGE HOTEL
(Map Ref G4)
11 - 2:30 ; 5:30 - 11
DOLPHIN STREET, COLYTON, Nr.
SEATON, OS: SY248942
Tel: (0297) 552401

Changing Beer Menu

AC CA CH CP DF (ACCESS ONLY) FA GD
ME ML OD QP RF RS
Newly opened hotel in a c15 thatched
cottage. Originally a farmhouse and
believed to be the oldest building in the
village.

COMBE MARTIN

CASTLE INN (Map Ref C1)
12 - 2 ; 7 - 11 (NOT M,T,F LUNCH,
LONGER IN SUMMER)
HIGH STREET, COMBE MARTIN,
Tel: (0271) 883706

Draught Bass	**(H)**
Worthington Best Bitter	**(H)**

CP FA ME ML MR (FUNCTION ROOM)
OD PG
Friendly pub in centre of village, with a
varying guest beer.

DOLPHIN INN (Map Ref C1)
11 - 11. (SUMMER ONLY - WINTER
VARIABLE) SEASIDE, COMBE MARTIN,
Tel: (0271) 883424

Draught Bass	**(H)**
Courage Directors	**(H)**

DF FA ME ML OD (PATIO)
Comfortable lounge bar on seafront.

FOCSLE INN (Map Ref C1)
12 - 3 ; 7 - 11. (M-S (W), 11-11 (S))
SEASIDE, COMBE MARTIN,
Tel: (0271) 883354

Ruddles County	**(H)**
Ushers Best Bitter	**(H)**

AC FA ME ML OD PG
Large pub overlooking the beach.

LION INN (Map Ref C1)
VICTORIA STREET, COMBE MARTIN,
Tel: (0271) 882485

Draught Bass	**(H)**

LONDON INN (Map Ref C1)
11 - 4 ; 6 - 11 (M-S)
LEIGH ROAD, COMBE MARTIN,
Tel: (0271) 883409

Draught Bass	**(H)**
Courage Directors	**(H)**

AC CP FA ME ML OD PG
Large pub at top end of village, with a
friendly atmosphere and interesting range
of guest ales.

OLDE GEORGE AND DRAGON
(Map Ref C1)
CASTLE STREET, COMBE MARTIN,
Tel: (0271) 882282

Draught Bass	**(H)**

PACK O' CARDS (Map Ref C1)
12 - 2 ; 7 - 11. (M-S (W), 11 - 11 (S))
HIGH STREET, COMBE MARTIN,
Tel: (0271) 882300

Draught Bass	**(H)**
Courage Directors	**(H)**

AC CP FA GD ME ML OD PG QP
Large, imposing pub with an interesting
history, and unusual architecture. Guest
ales in the summer.

ROYAL MARINE INN (Map Ref C1)
SEASIDE, COMBE MARTIN,
Tel: (0271) 882470

Boddingtons Bitter	**(H)**
Marston's Pedigree	**(H)**

TOP GEORGE INN (Map Ref C1)
VICTORIA STREET, COMBE MARTIN,
Tel: (0271) 883564

Draught Bass (H)

COOMBEINTEIGNHEAD

COOMBE CELLARS (Map Ref E6)
11 - 3 ; 5 - 11. (M-S)
COOMBINTEIGNHEAD, NEWTON
ABBOT
Tel: (0626) 872423

Draught Bass	(H)
Boddingtons Bitter	(H)
Mill Janner's Ale	(H)
Flowers Original	(H)

CA FA GD ME ML OD QP RF RS
Large open-plan pub, next to River Teign.
A large galleon in the garden, and a
restaurant.

WILD GOOSE (Map Ref E6)
11:30 - 2:30 ; 6:30 - 11. (M-S)
COOMBEINTEIGNHEAD, NEWTON
ABBOT
Tel: (0626) 872241

Cotleigh Old Buzzard	(H)
Exe Valley Dob's Best Bitter	(H)
Exeter Old	(H)
Mill Janner's Ale	(H)
Wadworth 6X	(H)
Guest Beer Regular	(H)

CI (WESTCOUNTRY) CA CP FA ME ML
OD QP
17th century farmhouse in a super position
overlooking the River Teign. Plenty of
character in this happy and some would
say mildly eccentric pub. Jazz club on
Mondays. Good food available from an
excellent menu, including vegegtarian fare.

COPPLESTONE

CROSS HOTEL (Map Ref D4)
11 - 2:30 ; 5:30 - 11 (M-S)
COPPLESTONE, Nr. CREDITON, (ON
A377, SOUTHBOUND SECTION OF
ONE-WAY SYSTEM.)
Tel: (0363) 84273

Draught Bass	(H)
Hall And Woodhouse Tanglefoot	(H)
Morland Old Speckled Hen	(H)

AC BR (COPPLESTONE) CA CC CI
(INCH'S) CP DB DF FA PG RF
Genuine village local, clean polite and
friendly. Licensee has been in this pub for
56 years. Must be the cheapest pint of Bass
in Devon. Not all beers on at same time.

CORNWOOD

CORNWOOD INN (Map Ref C7)
CORNWOOD, IVYBRIDGE
Tel: (0752) 837225

Courage Best Bitter	(H)
Courage Directors	(H)
John Smith's Bitter	(H)

CORNWORTHY

HUNTERS LODGE INN (Map Ref D7)
11:30 - 3 ; 6:30 - 11. (M-S)
CORNWORTHY, TOTNES, OS: SX827557
Tel: (0803) 732204

Blackawton 44 Special	(H)
Ushers Best Bitter	(H)

CD (EUCHRE) CP FA (FOR MEALS) GD
ME ML OD RS
Agreeable village pub in River Dart creek
country. One bar and a dining room
serviced by a mouth watering menu.

COUNTISBURY

EXMOOR SANDPIPER INN (Map Ref D1)
COUNTISBURY, Nr. LYNTON,
Tel: (05987) 263

Marston's Pedigree	(H)
Guest Beer Regular	(H)

CREDITON

CREDITON INN (Map Ref D4)
11 - 11. (M-S)
28a, MILL STREET, CREDITON.
Tel: (0363) 772882

Draught Bass	(H)
Guest Beer Regular	(H)

BR (CREDITON) CP FA ME ML MR PG ST
Lively town centre local built in 1852. The
inn sign depicts St. Boniface. Function
room and skittle alley at rear.

DARTMOOR RAILWAY (Map Ref D4)
11 -2:30 ; 5:30 - 11. (ALL DAY SATURDAY)
STATION ROAD, CREDITON
Tel: (0363) 772489

Draught Bass	(H)
Boddingtons Bitter	(H)

AC BR (CREDITON) CI (BULMERS) CP
ME ML OD PG RF RS
Large open plan bar close to the station, at
the edge of town. There is a restaurant to
the rear.

DUKE OF YORK (Map Ref D4)
12 - 3 ; 5:30 - 11. (M-S)
HIGH STREET, CREDITON
Tel: (0363) 772655

Draught Bass	**(H)**
Boddingtons Bitter	**(H)**
Guest Beer Occasional	**(H)**

ML OD
Popular local with real mahogany bar top.

EXCHANGE (Map Ref D4)
11 - 11. (M-S)
113, HIGH STREET, CREDITON,
Tel: (0363) 775853

Courage Best Bitter	**(H)**
Courage Directors	**(H)**
Webster's Yorkshire Bitter	**(H)**

BR (CREDITON) FA GD ME ML MR OD
QP RS (STEAK & WINE BAR IN CELLAR)
Comfortable open plan lounge area with
separate steak and wine bar. Award
winning garden and TOILETS. Function
room upstairs.

PLYMOUTH INN (Map Ref D4)
DEAN STREET, CREDITON
Tel: (0363) 772057

Boddingtons Bitter	**(H)**

SHIP (Map Ref D4)
HIGH STREET, CREDITON
Tel: (0363) 772963

Draught Bass	**(E)**
Cotleigh Tawny	**(E)**

THREE LITTLE PIGS (Map Ref D4)
11 - 3 ; 5 - 11. (M-S)
PARLIAMENT STREET, CREDITON
Tel: (0363) 774587

Draught Bass	**(E)**
Boddingtons Bitter	**(E)**

BR (CREDITON) DF ML OD
Large open plan pub with animals heads
protruding through walls. An adjoining
wine bar provides regular live music.
Motorists use the public car park at the
side. BEWARE! FAKE HANDPUMPS.

CROCKERNWELL

CROW'S NEST (Map Ref D5)
11 - 11. (M-W. 11 - 1am Th,F,Sat.)
CROCKERNWELL, EXETER, (BETWEEN
CROCKERNWELL AND WHIDDON
DOWN VILLAGES.), OS: SX742924
Tel: (0647) 21267

Thompsons	
Black Velvet Porter	**(H)**
Best Bitter	**(H)**
Botwrights Man-O-War	**(H)**

AC CA CP DB DF FA GD LM ME ML OD
PB PG PL QP RF
Pleasant motel on OLD A30, with a good
food menu, and an interest in local cask
ales.

CROYDE

CARPENTERS ARMS (Map Ref B2)
12, HOBBS HILL, CROYDE, BRAUNTON,
Tel: (0271) 890356

Flowers Original (H)

MANOR HOUSE INN (Map Ref B2)
11 - 2 ; 7 - 11 (M-S (W), VARIES IN
SUMMER)
ST. MARY'S ROAD, CROYDE,
BRAUNTON,
Tel: (0271) 890241

Tetley Bitter	**(H)**
Flowers IPA	**(H)**

CP FA ME ML OD
Large, comfortable pub in popular tourist
area.

**THATCHED BARN INN (Map Ref
B2)**
11 - 2:30 ; 6 - 11 (M-S (W), 11 - 11 (S))
14, HOBBS HILL, CROYDE, BRAUNTON,
Tel: (0271) 890349

Ind Coope Burton Ale	**(H)**
Tetley Bitter	**(H)**

AC CA CP FA ME ML OD Thatched inn,
near popular sandy beach, with a
reputation for good food. Guest ales in
summer.

CULLOMPTON

BELL INN (Map Ref F9)
11 - 11.
EXETER ROAD, CULLOMPTON,
Tel: (0884) 34432

Draught Bass	(H)
Boddingtons Bitter	(H)

AC DB FA GD ME ML OD PB PG
Busy pub, popular for darts.

KINGS HEAD (Map Ref F4)
11 - 3 ; 5:30 - 11. (M-Th, 11 - 11 F,Sat.)
HIGH STREET, CULLOMPTON,
Tel: (0884) 32418

Draught Bass	(H)
John Smith's Bitter	(H)
Ushers Best Bitter	(H)
Wadworth 6X	(H)
Webster's Yorkshire Bitter	(H)

FA ME ML OD PB
Large public bar and small lounge in a
popular town centre local. Occasional
guest beers.

MANOR HOUSE HOTEL (Map Ref F4)
11 - 11. (M-S)
2/4, FORE STREET, CULLOMPTON,
Tel: (0884) 32281

Draught Bass	(H)
Eldridge Pope Hardy Country	(H)

AC DF FA ME ML OD PG RF
16th century town centre hotel. Good value
food.

MARKET HOUSE INN, (Map Ref F4)
11 - 3 ; 6 - 11. (M-S (W), 11 - 11 F,Sat (S))
HIGH STREET, CULLOMPTON,
Tel: (0884) 32339

Boddingtons Bitter	(H)
Flowers Original	(H)
Guest Beer Occasional	(H)

CP DB DF FA GD ME ML OD PB PG
Town centre pub recently enlarged interior.
Pleasant garden backing onto car park.

PONY AND TRAP (Map Ref F4)
11 - 2:30 ; 6 - 11. (M-F. 11 - 11 Sat)
EXETER HILL, CULLOMPTON,
Tel: (0884) 33254

Boddingtons Bitter	(H)

DF OD PG
Town pub popular with local darts players.

WEARY TRAVELLER, (Map Ref F4)
11 - 2:30 ; 5 - 11. (M-F, 11 - 11 Sat.)
STATION ROAD, CULLOMPTON,
(NEAR JUNCTION 27 ON M5
MOTORWAY.)
Tel: (0884) 32317

Eldridge Pope Hardy Country	(H)
Flowers Original	(H)

CP FA GD ME ML OD PB
Next to M5 junction 28, formerly the
'SHOWMAN'. Busy pub on outskirts of
town next to industrial estates.

WHITE HART (Map Ref F4)
11 - 11 (M-S)
19, FORE STREET, CULLOMPTON,
Tel: (0884) 33260

Courage Best Bitter	(H)
Courage Directors	(H)
John Smith's Bitter	(H)

AC DB DF FA ME ML PB PG RF RS
Recently modernised town centre pub with
upstairs bar and restaurant.

CULMSTOCK

CULM VALLEY INN (Map Ref F3)
11 - 3 ; 6 - 11. (M-S (W), 11 - 11 (S))
CULMSTOCK, Nr. CULLOMPTON
Tel: (0884) 840354

Butcombe Bitter	(H)
Cotleigh Tawny	(H)
Wadworth 6X	(H)

AC CP DF FA ME (NOT MONDAYS - BAR
FOOD ONLY) ML (NOT MONDAYS -
BAR FOOD ONLY) OD PB PG RF
Wide range of guest beers in a friendly
town pub, containing a collection of
railway memorabilia.

ILMINSTER STAGE (Map Ref F3)
11 - 2 ; 5 - 11. (M-S)
FORE STREET, CULMSTOCK, Nr.
CULLOMPTON
Tel: (0884) 840872

Draught Bass	(H)
Boddingtons Bitter	(H)

PG QP RF SN (VERY SUBSTANTIAL)
Town type pub in a village, with a good
local trade.

DALWOOD

TUCKERS ARMS (Map Ref G4)
11:30 - 3 ; 6 - 11 (M-S)
DALWOOD, Nr. AXMINSTER
Tel: (0404) 88342

Boddingtons Bitter	(H)
Otter Ale	(H)
Wadworth 6X	(H)
Flowers Original	(H)

AC CA DF FA ME ML OD PB PG QP RF
Large, carefully extended, ancient village
inn, with a proudly displayed collection of
miniture bottles. Generally guest ales
available.

DARTINGTON

COTT INN (Map Ref D6)
11 - 2:30 ; 6 - 11. (M-S (W), 11 - 3, 5.30 - 11
(S))
DARTINGTON, TOTNES
Tel: (0803) 863777

Blackawton 44 Special	(H)
Furgusons Dartmoor Best Bitter	(H)
Palmers IPA	(H)

AC CA CI CP DF FA (RESTAURANT
ONLY) ME ML OD QP RF RS
C14 (1320), thatched, picturesque pub
rebuilt after a fire in 1989. Large open bar
area with lovely log fire and low oak
beams (original). Good food.

WHITE HART BAR (Map Ref D6)
12 - 2:30 ; 6 - 11 (M-S)
DARTINGTON CENTRE, DARTINGTON
(IN CORNER OF COURTYARD IN OLD
DARTINGTON HALL COMPLEX)
Tel: (0803) 862022

Blackawton Bitter	(H)
Furgusons Dartmoor Best Bitter	(H)

CI DF OD QP RF SN
Converted storehouse in magnificent
setting of Dartington Hall & gardens.

DARTMOUTH

CHERUB INN (Map Ref E7)
11 - 3 ; 5 - 11 (M-S)
13 HIGHER STREET, DARTMOUTH
Tel: (0803) 832571

Blackawton Bitter	(H)
Ind Coope Burton Ale	(H)
Wadworth 6X	(H)
Flowers Original	(H)

CI FA ME ML
Ornate and fragile looking, grade 1
preservation listed, pub in the back streets
of Dartmouth. One very small bar with
wood panels and a restaurant upstairs.
Famous for its food.

THE QUAY, DARTMOUTH

Draught Bass (H)
Flowers IPA (H)
Pompey Royal (H)

AC ME ML PB
Smart and busy hotel in front of the
Dartmouth boat float. Caters for casual
drinkers in the public bar and diners in the
lounge. Separate restaurant upstairs.

DAWLISH

EXETER INN (Map Ref E5)
11 - 3 ; 5 - 11 (M-S)
BEACH STREET, DAWLISH, (ON
NARROW ROAD NEAR STATION)
Tel: (0626) 865677

Draught Bass	(H)
Boddingtons Bitter	(H)
Eldridge Pope Hardy Country	(H)
Flowers IPA	(H)
Wethered Winter Royal	(H)
(WINTER ONLY)	

BR (DAWLISH) CH CI (TAUNTON) DF
FA ME (SUMMER ONLY) ML PG (TABLE
SKITTLES)
Interesting old pub, with family room,
toilets, and cellar, on opposite side of street.

LANSDOWNE HOTEL (Map Ref E5)
8, PARK ROAD, DAWLISH.
Tel: (0626) 863201

Boddingtons Bitter (H)

MARINE HOTEL (Map Ref E5)
11 - 11. (M-S)
MARINE PARADE, DAWLISH,
Tel: (0626) 865245

Furgusons Dartmoor Best Bitter	(H)
Ind Coope Burton Ale	(H)

AC BR (DAWLISH) FA ME ML OD

PRINCE ALBERT (Map Ref E5)
28, THE STRAND, DAWLISH,
Tel: (0626) 862132

Draught Bass	(H)
Flowers IPA	(H)

Small one bar quiet pub, also known as the
hole in the wall.

PRINCE OF WALES INN (Map Ref E5)
13,OLD TOWN STREET, DAWLISH,
Tel: (0626) 862145

Eldridge Pope Hardy Country	(H)
Flowers IPA	(H)

RAILWAY (Map Ref E5)
BEACH STREET, DAWLISH,
Tel: (0626) 863226

Flowers IPA	(H)

SOUTH DEVON INN (Map Ref E5)
12 - 2:30 ; 5 - 11. (M-F. 11.30 - 3, 6 - 11 Sat)
STRAND HILL, DAWLISH,
Tel: (0626) 862198

Boddingtons Bitter	(H)

BR (DAWLISH) FA PB
Small, friendly, corner pub on edge of
town.

SWAN INN (Map Ref E5)
OLD TOWN STREET, DAWLISH,
Tel: (0626) 863677

Boddingtons Bitter	(H)
Marston's Pedigree	(H)
Flowers IPA	(H)

AC BR (DAWLISH) DB PB RF
Comfortable local.

TEIGNMOUTH INN (Map Ref E5)

WHITE HART (Map Ref E5)
6, ALBERT STREET, DAWLISH,
Tel: (0626) 863063

Courage Best Bitter	(H)
John Smith's Bitter	(H)

DAWLISH WARREN

MOUNT PLEASANT (Map Ref E5)
MOUNT PLEASANT ROAD, DAWLISH
WARREN,
Tel: (0626) 863151

Boddingtons Bitter	(H)
Flowers Original	(H)

DENBURY

UNION INN (Map Ref D6)
11 - 2:30 ; 6 - 11 (M-S)
THE GREEN, DENBURY, NEWTON
ABBOT
Tel: (0803) 812595

Draught Bass	(H)
Marston's Pedigree	(H)
Flowers IPA	(H)
Flowers Original	(H)

CI LM ME ML OD QP RF
Typical village local which caters for all,
several separate areas around one bar.
Live entertainment and good food.

DITTISHAM

FERRY BOAT INN (Map Ref E7)
11 - 3 ; 6 - 11 (M-S)
MANOR STREET, DITTISHAM, OS:
SX866548
Tel: (0804) 22368

Ushers		
	Founders	(H)
	Best Bitter	(H)

CC ME ML OD PG QP
Riverside pub beside Greenham ferry (foot
passengers only). Use the car park
halfway up the village and walk the rest
(200 yards).

DODDISCOMBSLEIGH

NOBODY INN (Map Ref E5)
12 - 2:30 ; 7 - 11. (12 - 3 Sat. (W), 6 - 11 (S))
DODDISCOMBELEIGH, Nr. EXETER,
Tel: (0647) 52394

Draught Bass	**(G)**
Exe Valley Devon Glory	**(H)**
Flowers IPA	**(H)**
Guest Beer Regular	**(H)**

AC CC CP DF ME ML OD (PATIO) QP RF
c16 inn with many original features,
including beams and fireplace. Well known
for its superb food and immense range of
wines and whiskeys.

DOLTON

ROYAL OAK (Map Ref C3)
11 - 2:30 ; 6 - 11. (M-Th. 11 - 11 F, Sat)
THE SQUARE, DOLTON, Nr.
TORRINGTON.
Tel: (08054) 288

Butcombe Bitter	**(H)**
Fullers London Pride	**(H)**

AC CA CC CP FA ME ML PB PG RF RS
Convivial village free house off the tourist
beat. Carved chairs in the public, bus seats
in the lounge. Regular guest beers in
summer. Separate restaurant.

DOWN THOMAS

LANGDON COURT HOTEL (Map Ref B7)
12 - 2:30 ; 6:30 - 11. (M-S)
DOWN THOMAS, Nr. PLYMOUTH
Tel: (0752) 862358

Flowers IPA	**(E)**
Flowers Original	**(E)**
Guest Beer Regular	**(E)**

AC CA CP ME ML
Elizabethan manor house surrounded by
fields and woodland. Only 1.5 miles from
Wembury beach. The beers are kept in
Saxon cellars where the temparature is 55C
all year round. Follow HMS. Cambridge
signs from Elburton on the A379 to find the
pub. Guest beers.

MUSSEL INN (Map Ref B7)
11:30 - 2:30 ; 6 - 11. (M-S (W). 11 - 11 (S))
DOWN THOMAS, Nr. PLYMOUTH
Tel: (0752) 863328

Courage Best Bitter	**(H)**
Courage Directors	**(H)**

CA CP FA (DINING AREA) GD ME ML
OD RF
Meandering lounge bar. Large garden, safe
for children. Formerly cottages converted
into a pub. Popular for food.

DOWSLAND

BURRATOR INN (Map Ref C6)
11 - 11. (M-S)
DOUSLAND, YELVERTON, Nr.
PLYMOUTH
Tel: (0752)

Draught Bass	**(H)**
Worthington Best Bitter	**(H)**
St Austell HSD	**(H)**
Wadworth 6X	**(H)**

AC CA CP DF FA ME ML OD PB PG RF
Large, family run, hotel on Dartmoor.

DREWSTEIGNTON

DREWE ARMS (Map Ref D5)
10:30 - 2:30 ; 6 - 11. (M-S)
THE SQUARE, DREWSTEIGNTON,
EXETER. OS: SX736908 Tel: (0647) 21224

Flowers IPA	**(G)**

CA CD CI (BULMER WEST COUNTRY
DRY) DB FA PG QP RF
Old and original unspoilt pub. Home to
Britains oldest and longest serving
licensee.

DUNCHIDEOCK

LORD HALDON (Map Ref E5)
DUNCHIDEOCK, Nr. EXETER. (LEAVE
M5 @ J31, 1st. LEFT TO IDE, FOLLOW
DUNCHIDEOCK SIGNS.)
Tel: (0392) 832483

Draught Bass (H)
Tetley Bitter (H)

DUNKESWELL

ROYAL OAK (Map Ref F4)
11 - 2:30 ; 6 - 11. (M-S)
DUNKESWELL, Nr. HONITON
Tel: (0404) 891280

Draught Bass	**(H)**
Wadworth 6X	**(H)**
Flowers Original	**(H)**

CP DF FA ME ML OD PB PG QP ST
Handy for sky divers. 16th century inn.
Wassailing started here, the practice of
knocking apples out of trees to scare
witches. Skittle alley.

DUNSFORD

ROYAL OAK (Map Ref D5)
11:30 - 2:30 ; 6:30 - 11. (M-Th. 11 - 3, 6 - 11 F
& Sat.)
DUNSFORD, EXETER.
Tel: (0647) 52256

Draught Bass	**(H)**
Boddingtons Bitter	**(H)**
Brains Bitter	**(H)**
Greene King Abbot	**(H)**
Guest Beer Regular	**(H)**

AC CC CP FA ME ML MR OD PG
(VARIOUS) QP RF SN
Lively well appointed village local, well
worth a visit. Victorian building in mostly
original condition.

EAST ALLINGTON

FORTESCUE ARMS (Map Ref D7)
12: - 2: ; 6:30 - 11: (M-S)
EAST ALLINGTON, KINGSBRIDGE
Tel: (0548) 52215

Courage Best Bitter	**(H)**
Ruddles County	**(H)**

AC CA CP DF FA ME ML OD PB PG QP
RF RS
Village local, bar and food area separated.
Friendly atmosphere.

EAST BUDLEIGH

ROLLE ARMS (Map Ref F5)
11 - 3 ; 6 - 11. (M-S)
EAST BUDLEIGH, DEVONSHIRE. (ON
CORNER OF A376 & MAIN STREET
THROUGH VILLAGE.), OS: SY0684
Tel: (0395) 442012

Oakhill Bitter	**(H)**
Flowers IPA	**(H)**
Flowers Original	**(H)**

AC CA CP DB FA ME ML OD QP RS SN
ST
Main village pub - very popular.

SIR WALTER RALEIGH (Map Ref F5)
11 - 3 ; 6 - 11. (M-S)
22, HIGH STREET, EAST BUDLEIGH.
(OPPOSITE CHURCH), OS: SY0684
Tel: (0395) 442510

Boddingtons Bitter	**(H)**
Marston's Pedigree	**(H)**
Flowers Original	**(H)**
(SUMMER ONLY)	

AC CA DM FA GD ME ML OD QP
Cosy village pub close to Sir Walter
Raleigh's birthplace.

EAST DOWN

PYNE ARMS (Map Ref C1)
11 - 2:30 ; 6 - 11. (M-S)
EAST DOWN. (HALF MILE OFF A39),
OS: SS600415
Tel: (0271) 850207

Courage Directors	**(H)**
John Smith's Bitter	**(H)**

CP ME ML OD PG
Pleasant, food orientated pub, close to
Arlington Court (National Trust).

EAST PRAWLE

PIGS NOSE INN (Map Ref D8)
EAST PRAWLE, SALCOMBE
Tel: (05485) 209

Boddingtons Bitter (H)
(SUMMER ONLY)
Wadworth 6X (H)
Flowers IPA (H)

PROVIDENCE INN (Map Ref D8)
11 - 3 ; 5 - 11. (M-S (W), 11 - 11 (S))
EAST PRAWLE, SALCOMBE
Tel: (05485) 208

Furgusons Dartmoor Best Bitter	**(H)**
Wadworth 6X	**(H)**

CA CC CP DF FA ME ML PG QP RF
Pleasant single bar pub in the Grade 2
listed building dating from 1430. It is the
village pub for the southernmost village in
Devon, and has one large bar and a
homely lounge/TV room. Two regular
guest beers in summer, often Butcombe or
Nethergate.

EGGESFORD

**FOX AND HOUNDS HOTEL (Map
Ref D3)**
11: - 2:30; 5:30 - 11: (M-S)
EGGESFORD, Nr. CHULMLEIGH.
Tel: (0769) 80345

Draught Bass	**(H)**
Charrington IPA	**(H)**

AC BR CI CP DF FA ME ML OD QP RF
A country house frequented by the country
fraternity and providing conference
facilities. There is good salmon and trout
fishing close by.

ERMINGTON

CROOKED SPIRE (Map Ref C7)
11:30 - 2:30 ; 6:30 - 11. (M-S)
ERMINGTON, Nr. IVYBRIDGE
Tel: (0548) 830202

Marston's Pedigree	**(H)**
Flowers Original	**(H)**

AC DF FA (RESTAURANT ONLY) ME ML
OD PB PG QP RF RS
A Heavitree pub with a separate A La
Carte restaurant.

FIRST & LAST INN (Map Ref C7)
11:30 - 3 ; 6:30 - 11. (M-S)
CHURCH STREET, ERMINGTON, Nr.
IVYBRIDGE
Tel: (0548) 830671

Draught Bass	**(H)**
Wadworth 6X	**(H)**

CA CD (EUCHRE) CI (SUMMER ONLY)
CP ME ML OD PG RF
Cheery village pub, near the trout farm,
with good local trade.

EXEBRIDGE

ANCHOR INN (Map Ref E2)
11 - 2:30 ; 6:30 - 11. (M-S (W) 6 - 11 (S))
EXEBRIDGE, DULVERTON,
DEVONSHIRE.
Tel: (0398) 23433

Ruddles County	**(H)**
Ushers Best Bitter	**(H)**
Webster's Yorkshire Bitter	**(H)**

AC CC CH CP DF FA ME ML OD PG QP
RF
Small, country pub, over 300 years old,
with a cosy bar, restaurant, function rooms,
and family room, overlooking River Exe
just outside the Exmoor National Park.

EXETER

ADMIRAL VERNON (Map Ref E5)
11 - 11. (M-S)
44, CHUDLEIGH ROAD, ALPHINGTON
EXETER. (THROUGH VILLAGE
TOWARDS A38.)
Tel: (0392) 76990

Draught Bass	(H)
Whitbread WCPA	(H)

CD DB PB PG ST
Typical local pub.

ARTFUL DODGER (Map Ref E5)
11 - 11. (M-S) RED COW VILLAGE,
EXETER.
Tel: (0392) 74754

Cornish Original	(H)
Wadworth 6X	(H)

BR (EXETER ST. DAVIDS) CI (BULMERS
WEST COUNTRY DRY) DB ME ML
Large renovated pub, popular with
students.

BARTS TAVERN (Map Ref E5)
11:30 - 11: (M-S)
53, BARTHOLOMEW STREET WEST,
EXETER. OS: SX916923 Tel: (0392) 75623

Furgusons Dartmoor Strong	(H)
Morland Old Speckled Hen	(H)
Wadworth 6X	(H)
Branscombe Olde Stoker	(H)

BR (EXETER CENTRAL) FA (NOT IN BAR
AREA) LM ME ML (12-1030) PG SN
Energetic town pub with frequent live
music in an upstairs function room.

BELLONA (Map Ref E5)
QUEEN STREET ARCADE, EXETER
Tel: (0392)

Boddingtons Bitter	(H)
Guest Beer Regular	(H)

BISHOP BLAIZE, (Map Ref E5)
12 - 2 ; 7 - 11. (M-Th, 11 - 11 F,Sat.)
COMMERCIAL ROAD, EXETER. (CROSS
OVER ROAD BRIDGE AT END OF QUAY,
ON RIGHT HAND SIDE.)
Tel: (0392) 54884

Greene King Abbot	(H)
Wadworth 6X	(H)
Guest Beer Regular	(H)

GD LM ML (BBQs in summer ONLY) OD
Possibly the oldest pub outside the old city
walls. Once used by fullers and other wool
trade apprentices.

BLACK HORSE (Map Ref E5)
11 - 11. (M-S)
LONGBROOK ST, EXETER.
Tel: (0392) 57974

Boddingtons Bitter	(H)
Wadworth 6X	(H)
Flowers IPA	(H)
Flowers Original	(H)
Guest Beer Regular	(H)

BR (EXETER CENTRAL & ST. JAMES) CI
(GREEN VALLEY) GD LM ML OD
Recently refurbished city centre pub just
off the High St, with up to 11 real ales
available. Whitbread's 1st. 'Cask Ale
House' in S. W. England, and probably the
best. Beers are well kept and guests served
from a gravity stillage behind bar.
Excellent food at lunchtimes, especially the
recently introduced Sausage range, at
sensible prices. Beer prices are VERY
HIGH.

BOWLING GREEN (Map Ref E5)
11: - 23:0 ; 5: - 11: (M-F. 11 - 3, 7 - 11 Sat.)
BLACKBOY ROAD, EXETER.
Tel: (0392) 422527

Draught Bass	(H)
Boddingtons Bitter	(H)
Wadworth 6X	(H)

BR (EXETER ST. JAME'S PARK) CI
(TAUNTON TRADITIONAL) LM ML
Friendly pub, popular with students and
locals alike. Landlord was a former
licensee of GREAT BRITISH BEER
FESTIVAL. Regular live music.

BUTLERS (Map Ref E5)
11 - 11. (M-S)
MARY ARCHES STREET, EXETER.
Tel: (0392) 71586

Draught Bass	**(E)**
Flowers Original	**(E)**

BR (EXETER CENTRAL)
Typical, over-smart, Devenish refurbished
pub. Overpriced beer, served too cold
through FAKE HANDPUMPS.

BYSTOCK HOTEL - STOCKS BAR.
(Map Ref E5)
11 - 11. (M-S)
BYSTOCK TERRACE, EXETER.
(NEAR CLOCK TOWER.),
Tel: (0392) 214437 (BAR)

Draught Bass	**(H)**
Wadworth 6X	**(H)**

AC BR (EXETER CENTRAL) DB FA GD
ME ML OD PB (COCKTAIL BAR) PG PL
Typical hotel bar.

CHAUCERS INN (Map Ref E5)
11 - 3 ; 5 - 11. (M-S. CLOSED SUNDAYS IN
WINTER.) 226, HIGH STREET, EXETER.
Tel: (0392) 422365

Draught Bass	**(H)**
Worthington Best Bitter	**(H)**
Exe Valley Dob's Best Bitter	**(H)**

BR (EXETER CENTRAL) FA LM ME ML
Busy city centre pub underneath C&A.
Above average food and good beer. Smart
dress required in evenings.

CLIFTON INN (Map Ref E5)
1, CLIFTON ROAD, EXETER.
Tel: (0392) 73527

Draught Bass	**(H)**
Boddingtons Bitter	**(H)**
Marston's Pedigree	**(H)**

COOLINGS WINE BAR (Map Ref E5)
11, GANDY STREET, EXETER.
Tel: (0392) 434184

Boddingtons Bitter	**(H)**

COUNTESS WEAR LODGE (Map Ref E5)
11 - 2:30 ; 5 - 11. (M-S. CLOSED SUNDAY
EVENING)
398, TOPSHAM ROAD, COUNTESS
WEAR, EXETER.
Tel: (0392) 875441

Draught Bass	**(H)**
Ruddles Best Bitter	**(H)**

AC CP DF FA ME ML MR (CONFERENCE
/ FUNCTION SUITES) OD RM RS
Food orientated bar for motel and
conference/function centre. Situated at
junction of Exeter bypass and Topsham
road. Easy access to and from J30 of M5
motorway.

COUNTRY HOUSE INN (Map Ref E5)
305, TOPSHAM ROAD, EXETER.
Tel: (0392) 55826

Draught Bass	**(H)**

COWICK BARTON INN (Map Ref E8)
11 - 2:30 ; 6:30 - 11. (M-S)
COWICK LANE, ST. THOMAS, EXETER.
Tel: (0392) 70411

Draught Bass	**(H)**
Courage Best Bitter	**(H)**
Ruddles County	**(H)**

CP DF (PRIORY BAR ONLY) FA GD
(CHILDREN'S PLAY AREA) ME ML OD
PB QP RF
This converted Elizabethan house is a
country pub within the city boundary. It
consists of an interesting old lounge, a
newish public bar and a large garden and
comes complete with its own ghost.

COWLEY BRIDGE INN (Map Ref E8)
11 - 2:30 ; 6 - 11. (M-S)
COWLEY BRIDGE ROAD, EXETER.
Tel: (0392) 74268

Boddingtons Bitter	**(H)**
Eldridge Pope Royal Oak	**(H)**
Flowers IPA	**(H)**
Flowers Original	**(H)**

ME ML PB PG RF
Comfortable, friendly non-glitter pub
popular with students and train spotters.
By the junction of the A377 & A396, and
the Barnstaple branch & main lines of BR.
Good food, but note the Addlestones cider
is top pressure.

CRAWFORD (Map Ref E5)
107, ALPHINGTON ROAD, EXETER. OS:
SX916912
Tel: (0392) 72093

Boddingtons Bitter	(H)

CROWN AND SCEPTRE (Map Ref E5)
: - : 7 - 11. (M-S)
IRONBRIDGE, LOWER NORTH STREET
EXETER, DEVONSHIRE. (OPPOSITE
GUILDHALL SHOPPING CENTRE.).
Tel: (0392) 56397

Exe Valley	
Dob's Best Bitter	(H)
Exeter Old	(H)
Theakston Old Peculier	(H)
Younger Scotch	(H)

BR (EXETER CENTRAL) CP GD LM
(CELLER BAR) OD PG PL RF RM
Large former coaching house by the iron
bridge on North Street. One large
U-shaped bar, downstairs there is a cellar
bar for live music. Only open in evenings,
and a favourite with students.

DEVON YEOMAN (Map Ref E5)
11 - 3 ; 6 - 11. (M-Th, 11 - 11 F, Sat)
BEACON LANE, BEACON HEATH,
EXETER.
Tel: (0392) 59528

Worthington Best Bitter	(H)
Courage Best Bitter	(H)
John Smith's Bitter	(H)

CP DB DF (ACCESS) OD PB PG (QUIZ) PL
RF
Typical two-bar estate pub with a friendly
atmosphere.

DEVONPORT INN, (Map Ref E5)
FORE ST, EXETER.
Tel: (0392) 56319

Draught Bass	(H)
Boddingtons Bitter	(H)
Flowers Original	(H)

DOUBLE LOCKS (Map Ref E5)
11: - 11: (M-S)
CANAL BANKS, MARSH BARTON,
EXETER. (FOLLOW LANE NEXT TO
INCINERATOR, OVER CANAL, TURN
RIGHT), OS: SX932900 Tel: (0392) 56947

Blackawton Headstrong	(G)
Boddingtons Bitter	(G)
Eldridge Pope Royal Oak	(G)
Everards Old Original	(H)
Exe Valley Devon Glory	(G)
Greene King Abbot	(G)
Oakhill Stout	(G)
Wadworth 6X	(G)

CA CC CD CH CI CP DB DF (ACCESS)
DM FA GD LM ME (ALL DAY) ML
(ALLDAY) OD PB (OUTSIDE IN
SUMMER) PG RF RM
Highly successfull, slightly eccentric
canalside pub with a huge outdoor area
and two rooms suitable for families plus an
atmospheric old bar. Good value food,
barbecues in summer, frequent live music,
volleyball, always something going on.
Guest beers, 4 ciders and the possibility of
mild on the beer menu.

DUKE OF YORK (Map Ref E5)
SIDWELL STREET, EXETER.
Tel: (0392) 56515

Draught Bass	(H)
Boddingtons Bitter	(H)
Flowers IPA	(H)

EAGLE TAVERN (Map Ref E5)
11: - 11: (M-S)
HOWELL ROAD, EXETER.
Tel: (0392) 214659

Boddingtons Bitter	(H)
Flowers Original	(H)

AC BR (CENTRAL & ST. DAVIDS) DF FA
ML PB PG
Local's pub with friendly staff.

EWE (Map Ref E5)
11 - 2:30 ; 7 - 11. (M-S VARIABLE)
CORNWALL HOUSE, EXETER
UNIVERSITY CAMPUS.

Draught Bass	(H)
Worthington Best Bitter	(H)

DF
Busy university bar with a PUBLIC license.
"LEMON GROVE" in the same building
hosts concerts on Fri. & Sat nights.
Admission charged.

EXETER ARMS MOTEL (Map Ref E5)
RYDON LANE, MIDDLEMOOR, EXETER .
Tel: (0392) 435353

Draught Bass	**(H)**

FLYING HORSE (Map Ref E5)
8, DRYDEN ROAD, WONFORD, EXETER,
DEVONSHIRE.
Tel: (0392) 73872

Ushers	
Founders	**(H)**
Best Bitter	**(H)**

GLOBE (Map Ref E5)
CLIFTON STREET, EXETER.
Tel: (0392) 56491

Boddingtons Bitter	**(H)**
Marston's Pedigree	**(H)**
Flowers IPA	**(H)**

GREAT WESTERN HOTEL
(Map Ref E5)
11 - 3 ; 5 - 11. (M-F. 11 - 11 Sat)
RED COW VILLAGE, EXETER, (AT EXIT
TO EXETER ST. DAVID'S STATION.)
Tel: (0392) 74039

Draught Bass	**(H)**
Worthington Best Bitter	**(H)**
Guest Beer Regular	**(H)**

AC BR (EXETER ST. DAVIDS) CP DF FA
ME ML PB
Busy railway hotel with two comfortable
lounge bars. Popular with thirsty
travellers. Good value food.

Historically a railway inn, the Great
Western Hotel has been tastfully
modernised, retaining much of the old
railway charm.
The loco and Brunel bars offer a wide
selection of homemade bar meals to
compliment our excellent Bass,
(Rumoured to be the best in the West!)
and other Guest Ales. Whilst our
elegant Brunel's Restaurant offers both
English and French Cuisine.

GREEN GABLES (Map Ref E5)
BUDDLE LANE, ST. THOMAS, EXETER,
OS: SX908918
Tel: (0392) 58404

Boddingtons Bitter	**(H)**

HALF MOON INN (Map Ref E5)
68, WHIPTON VILLAGE ROAD, EXETER,
Tel: (0392) 67395

Ushers Founders	**(H)**
Ushers Best Bitter	**(H)**

HEART OF OAK (Map Ref E5)
34, MAIN ROAD, PINHOE, EXETER,
Tel: (0392) 67329

Boddingtons Bitter	**(H)**
Castle Eden Ale	**(H)**

HOLE IN THE WALL (Map Ref E5)
11 - 2:30 ; 5:30 - 11. (M-S. CLOSED
SUNDAYS)
LITTLE CASTLE ST, EXETER,
Tel: (0392) 73341

Eldridge Pope Hardy Country	**(H)**
Royal Oak	**(H)**

BR (EXETER CENTRAL) ML PB
Busy pub, warm and friendly, popular
with students. Good value lunchtime
food.

HONITON INN (Map Ref E5)
11 - 11. (M-S)
74,PARIS STREET, EXETER,
Tel: (0392) 72775

Draught Bass	**(H)**
Boddingtons Bitter	**(H)**

CP ML OD QP
One bar pub opposite the coach station.
Luggage and rucksacks are not welcome
in the pub. A place for a leisurely meal
rather than a quick snack.

HORSE AND DRAY (Map Ref E5)
10, BLACKBOY ROAD, EXETER,
Tel: (0392)

Flowers IPA	**(H)**

HORSE AND GROOM (Map Ref E5)
11 - 11. (M-S. SUNDAY 12 - 2)
52, FORE STREET, HEAVITREE, EXETER,
Tel: (0392) 437322

Draught Bass	(H)
Eldridge Pope Hardy Country	(H)
Flowers IPA	(H)

LM (OCCASIONALLY) ML OD PL
Two bar pub, formerly the 'TAP' for
Heavitree Brewery next door.

IMPERIAL HOTEL (Map Ref E5)
NEW NORTH ROAD, EXETER,
Tel: (0392) 211811

Flowers IPA	(H)

JOLLY PORTER (Map Ref E5)
11 - 11. (M-S)
ST. DAVID'S HILL, EXETER,
Tel: (0392) 54848

Courage Best Bitter	(H)
Courage Directors	(H)
John Smith's Bitter	(H)
Wadworth 6X	(H)
Guest Beer Regular	(H)

BR (EXETER ST. DAVIDS) LM (JAZZ ON
Wed. NIGHTS) ME ML PG PL
Long narrow pub on several levels,
popular with students. Good value food,
and well kept guest beers. Jazz club on
Wed. nights.

KINGS ARMS (Map Ref E5)
11 - 3 ; 4:30 - 11. (M-S)
COWICK STREET, ST. THOMAS, EXETER,
(OPPOSITE ST. THOMAS RAILWAY
STATION.),
Tel: (0392) 74423

Draught Bass	(H)

AC BR (EXETER ST. THOMAS) ML PB ST
Unpretentious local.

JOIN NOW

MILL ON THE EXE (Map Ref E5)
11 - 11
BONHAY ROAD, EXETER,
Tel: (0392) 214464 & 426413

Beer Engine Piston	(H)
Exe Valley Bitter	(H)
Furgusons Dartmoor Strong	(H)
Ind Coope Burton Ale	(H)
Tetley Bitter	(H)

BR (EXETER. ST. THOMAS & DAVIDS) CP
DF FA (RESTAURANT AREA ONLY) GD
LM ME ML OD PB (CELLAR BAR)
A busy riverside pub with food in a
converted mill. Meeting place of Exeter
folk club. (Just purchased by St Austell
Brewery.)

MOUNT PLEASANT INN (Map Ref E5)
MOUNT PLEASANT ROAD, EXETER,
Tel: (0392) 51624

Flowers IPA	(H)
Flowers Original	(H)

MOUNT RADFORD INN (Map Ref E5)
11 - 11 (M-S)
MAGDALEN ROAD, WONFORD,
EXETER,
Tel: (0392) 58221

Draught Bass	(H)
Flowers IPA	(H)
Flowers Original	(H)

ML PB
Two bar, friendly corner pub, with good
food at lunchtimes. Quiet lounge and
games oriented bar, popular with students
from the nearby St. Lukes College. 6 cask
gravity stillage recently installed behind
bar.

NEW INN (Map Ref E5)
11 - 11 (M-S)
76, CHURCH ROAD, ALPHINGTON,
EXETER. (CENTRE OF VILLAGE
OPPOSITE CHURCH.)
Tel: (0392) 72584

Draught Bass	(H)
Eldridge Pope Royal Oak	(H)
Flowers IPA	(H)

DF GD ME ML OD
Friendly local pub with homemade food.

NEW VICTORIA INN, (Map Ref E5)
11 - 11 (M-S)
32, QUEEN STREET, EXETER,
Tel: (0392) 422455

Draught Bass	**(H)**
Wadworth 6X	**(H)**

BR (EXETER CENTRAL (opposite)) DF ME
ML
Formerly 'GARBO'S', has now reverted to
its origional name. Typical town pub.

ODDFELLOWS (Map Ref E5)
11 - 11 (M-S)
60, NEW NORTH ROAD, EXETER.
Tel: (0392) 437336

Boddingtons Bitter	**(H)**
Flowers IPA	**(H)**
Flowers Original	**(H)**

BR (EXETER CENTRAL) CI (VARIOUS)
DF (ACCESS ONLY) FA LM ME ML
Recently re-vamped, city centre pub, with
one long bar. Low priced, wholesome food,
and a range of ciders at prices aimed at the
businessmans market.

OLD FIREHOUSE (Map Ref E5)
12 - 3 ; 5 - 11 (M-F, 7 - 11 Sat. 12 - 3 Sun
ONLY)
NEW NORTH ROAD, EXETER,
Tel: (0392) 77279

Boddingtons Bitter	**(H)**
Morland Old Speckled Hen	**(H)**
Wadworth 6X	**(H)**

BR (CENTRAL) FA ME (5-8pm) ML OD
Friendly pub converted from an old fire
station.

ON THE WATERFRONT (Map Ref E5)
11 - 2:30 ; 5 - 11 (M-S)
THE QUAY, EXETER,
Tel: (0392) 210590

Courage Best Bitter	**(H)**
Courage Directors	**(H)**
John Smith's Bitter	**(H)**

Excellent pub in former wharehouse set
into cliff face. Renouned for its 'Dustbin
Lid' sized pizzas and take-away offers

PACK HORSE INN (Map Ref E5)
56, ST. DAVID'S HILL, EXETER,
Tel: (0392) 54757

Flowers IPA	**(H)**

PAPERMAKERS ARMS (Map Ref E5)
14, EXE STREET, EXETER,
Tel: (0392) 78980

Draught Bass	**(H)**

PIG AND TRUFFLE (Map Ref E5)
8, GANDY STREET, EXETER,
Tel: (0392) 426416

Furgusons Dartmoor Best Bitter	**(H)**
Tetley Bitter	**(H)**

POLTIMORE ARMS (Map Ref E5)
11 - 3 ; 53:0 - 11. (M-S. 630 - 11 Wed.)
MAIN ROAD, PINHOE, EXETER,
Tel: (0392) 67517

Flowers IPA	**(H)**
Flowers Original	**(H)**

BR (PINHOE) DB RF
Comfortable pub on edge of Exeter with a
'villagey' feel.

PORT ROYAL INN, (Map Ref E5)
11 - 11
WEIRFIELD ROAD, EXETER, (APPROX
400m DOWNSREAM OF QUAY - EAST
BANK.), OS: SX924918
Tel: (0392) 72360

Draught Bass	**(H)**
Wadworth 6X	**(H)**
Flowers Original	**(H)**

DF GD ME (SUMMER & XMAS ONLY)
ML OD PB PG PL (2 TABLES) QP
Pleasant riverside pub with a good local's
trade.

PRINCE ALBERT (Map Ref E5)
54, COWICK STREET, EXETER,
Tel: (0392) 54196

Flowers Original	**(H)**

PRINTERS PIE (Map Ref E5)
SIDWELL STREET, EXETER,
Tel: (0392) 76049

Boddingtons Bitter	(H)
Flowers IPA	(H)
Flowers Original	(H)

PROSPECT INN (Map Ref E5)
11:30 - 2:30 ; 6 - 11. (M-S)
THE QUAY, EXETER,
Tel: (0392) 422303

Draught Bass	(H)
Eldridge Pope Royal Oak	(H)
Guest Beers Regular	(H)

BB BR (EXETER ST. THOMAS) DB DF
(WELCOMED) ME ML OD
Popular pub down in the quay area near to
the maritime museum.

QUEEN VICTORIA (Map Ref E5)
TUDOR STREET, EXETER, (OFF
WESTERN WAY AT EXEBRIDGE
(NORTH)),
Tel: (0392) 71376

Boddingtons Bitter	(H)
Brains Bitter	(H)
Flowers Original	(H)
Guest Beer Regular	(H)

QUEENS HEAD HOTEL (Map Ref E5)
270, PINHOE ROAD, EXETER,
Tel: (0392) 74473

Flowers Original	(H)

RED COW (Map Ref E5)
11 - 11. (M-S)
RED COW VILLAGE, ST. DAVIDS,
EXETER,
Tel: (0392) 72318

Draught Bass	(G)
Eldridge Pope Royal Oak	(G)

BR (EXETER ST. DAVIDS) CI
(LUSCOMBE, TAUNTON
TRADITIONAL) DB OD PB RF
Unspoilt traditional town pub near St.
David's station. Popular with students,
postal workers and railway workers alike.

RED HOUSE HOTEL (Map Ref E5)
WHIPTON VILLAGE ROAD, WHIPTON,
EXETER,
Tel: (0392) 56104

Boddingtons Bitter	(H)
Wadworth 6X	(H)

**ROUGEMENT HOTEL - DRAKE'S BAR
(Map Ref E5)**
QUEEN STREET, EXETER,
Tel: (0392) 54982

Courage Directors	(H)

**ROYAL CLARENCE HOTEL (Map
Ref E5)**
CATHEDRAL YARD, EXETER,
Tel: (0392) 58464

Courage Directors	(H)

ROYAL OAK (Map Ref E5)
FORE ST, HEAVITREE, EXETER,
Tel: (0392) 54121

Draught Bass	(H)
Marston's Pedigree	(H)
Flowers IPA	(H)

SAWYERS ARMS (Map Ref E5)
121, COWICK STREET, EXETER,
Tel: (0392) 79296

Whitbread Best Bitter	(H)
Flowers IPA	(H)

SEVEN STARS (Map Ref E5)
ALPHINGTON ROAD, EXETER,
Tel: (0392) 59567, 59482

Draught Bass	(H)
Worthington Best Bitter	(H)

SHIP AND PELICAN (Map Ref E5)
54, FORE STREET, HEAVITREE, EXETER,
Tel: (0392) 55174

Draught Bass	(H)
Wadworth 6X	(H)
Guest Beer Regular	(H)

SHIP INN (Map Ref E5)
11 - 2:30 ; 5:30 - 11 (M-S)
MARTINS LANE (OFF HIGH STREET)
EXETER,
Tel: (0392) 472040

Draught Bass	(H)
Boddingtons Bitter	(H)
Flowers IPA	(H)
Flowers Original	(H)

BR (EXETER CENTRAL) CI (GREEN VALLEY) ME ML
Sir Francis Drake's favourite port of call when not bowling at Plymouth. Pub full of armada paintings etc. Good food in the upstairs restaurant, handy for shoppers and visitors to the cathedral.

ST. ANNS WELL BREWERY (Map Ref E5)
11 - 11 (M-S; CLOSED SUNDAY LUNCH)
18a, LOWER NORTH STREET, EXETER
Tel: (0392) 53284

Draught Bass	(H)
Fuller London Pride	(H)
Botwrights Man-O-War	(H)
Wadworth 6X	(H)

BR (CENTRAL & ST. DAVIDS) CP DF (ACCESS) LM ME (EARLY ONLY) ML OD SN
Large, single bar pub, in part of a former brewery. Live bands several nights a week.

STEAMERS (Map Ref E5)
11 - 2:30 ; 5 - 11. (M-S)
St. THOMAS STATION, COWICK St. EXETER. (UNDERNEATH STATION IN VIADUCT),
Tel: (0392) 494474

Boddingtons Bitter	(H)
Flowers IPA	(H)

BR (EXETER St. THOMAS ABOVE) CP (SAINSBURY'S NEXT DOOR) DF FA ME ML PL
Recently opened pub, formerly 'The Station' and closed for many years.

STOKE ARMS (Map Ref E5)
STOKE HILL, EXETER,
Tel: (0392) 77702

Boddingtons Bitter	(H)
Flowers IPA	(H)

TALLY HO! (Map Ref E5)
COUNTESS WEAR ROAD, HIGHER WEAR, EXETER, (TURN OFF TOPSHAM ROAD BY COUNTESS WEAR SUB POST OFFICE)
Tel: (0392) 71460

Draught Bass	(H)
Boddingtons Bitter	(H)
Flowers IPA	(H)

TAP AND BARREL (Map Ref E5)
BURNTHOUSE LANE, EXETER,

Worthington Best Bitter	(H)
John Smith's Bitter	(H)

THATCHED HOUSE INN (Map Ref E5)
11 - 2:30 ; 5 - 11. (M-F. 11 - 11 Sat.)
EXWICK ROAD, EXWICK, EXETER.
Tel: (0392) 72920

Ruddles		
	Best Bitter	(H)
	County	(H)

CD CP DB ME ML OD PB PL
Pleasant thatched pub serving modern housing estate.

THE EXCHANGE (Map Ref E5)
11 - 11. (M-S)
ST. MARY ARCHES STREET, EXETER,
Tel: (0392) 56086

Draught Bass	(H)
Boddingtons Bitter	(H)
Wethered Winter Royal	(H)

BR (EXETER CENTRAL) DF (ACCESS ONLY) ME ML PL RM
Pleasant city centre pub, recently refurbished after changing from 'The Mitre'. U-shaped bar with good food and well kept beer. Guess the brewer of the house beer 'OLD BODGER'?

TURKS HEAD (Map Ref E5)
202, HIGH STREET, EXETER,
Tel: (0392) 56680

Boddingtons Bitter	(H)
Flowers IPA	(H)

VALLIANT SOLDIER (Map Ref E5)
St. THOMAS CENTRE, COWICK St.,
EXETER,
Tel: (0392) 57036

Flowers Original	(H)
Guest Beer Occasional	(H)

VICTORIA INN (Map Ref E5)
11 - 11. (M-S)
UNION ROAD, EXETER,
Tel: (0392) 54176

Marston's Pedigree	(H)
Wadworth 6X	(H)
Flowers Original	(H)

BR (ST. JAMES PARK) DF ML
Renovated city pub with original green
tiled exterior and a standard Inn Leisure
interior - the angling version. Has
nevertheless retained some atmosphere.
Popular with students, but don't let this
put you off. Guest beer.

VILLAGE INN (Map Ref E5)
11 - 3 ; 5 - 11. (M-S)
1, St. ANDREW'S ROAD, EXWICK,
EXETER,
Tel: (0392) 72665

Draught Bass	(H)
Boddingtons Bitter	(H)

DB DM ML OD PG (QUIZ, EUCHRE)
Formerly the 'Lamb Inn'.

VINES (Map Ref E5)
11 - 11 (M-S)
23, GANDY STREET, EXETER,
Tel: (0392) 213924

Courage Best Bitter	(H)
Courage Directors	(H)
Guest Beer Occasional	(H)

BR (EXETER CENTRAL) LM ML OD
Busy, popular city centre pub, tucked away
from main shopping area. Can get very
hectic on weekend evenings.

WELCOME INN (Map Ref E5)
11 - 2:30 ; 5:30 - 11. (M-S)
CANAL BANKS, OFF HAVEN ROAD,
EXETER, (NEAR MARITIME MUSEUM),
Tel: (0392) 54760

Cornish Royal Wessex	(H)

BR (EXETER St. THOMAS) DB OD PL
Unspoilt, one-bar pub with friendly
landlady.

WELL HOUSE (Map Ref E5)
11 - 2:30 ; 5 - 11 (OPENS 6 ON Sat.
CLOSED SUN LUNCH)
CATHEDRAL YARD, EXETER, (NEXT TO
ROYAL CLARENCE HOTEL)
Tel: (0392) 58464

Draught Bass	(H)
Courage Directors	(H)
Guest Beer Regular	(H)

(USUALLY 6 GUEST ALES ON) AC
(ROYAL CLARENCE, NEXT DOOR) BR
(EXETER CENTRAL) ML
An oasis of independent beer next to the
cathedral green. An ancient cellar is
inhabited by a victim of the Black death.
Interesting guest beers.

**WHIPTON VILLAGE INN (Map Ref
E5)**
54, WHIPTON VILLAGE ROAD, EXETER,
Tel: (0392) 67615

Draught Bass	(H)

WHITE HART HOTEL (Map Ref E5)
66, SOUTH STREET, EXETER,
Tel: (0392) 79897

Draught Bass	(H)
House Named Beer	(H)

WINDSOR CASTLE (Map Ref E5)
4, NORTH STREET, HEAVITREE,
EXETER,
Tel: (0392) 213693

Draught Bass (H)

WINSTONS (Map Ref E5)
81/2, FORE STREET, EXETER,
Tel: (0392) 73891

Flowers Original	(H)

EXMINSTER

ROYAL OAK (Map Ref E5)
12 - 2:30 ; 6:30 - 11. (6pm on SATURDAYS,
12-2.30 Sun.)
MAIN ROAD, EXMINSTER, EXETER,
Tel: (0392) 832332

Boddingtons Bitter	(H)
Wethered Winter Royal	(H)

CI CP DF FA GD OD PG QP RF ST
Recently renovated village pub with a
large beer garden.

STOWEY ARMS (Map Ref E5)
11 - 2:30 ; 6 - 11. (M-F. 11 - 3, 5.30 - 11 Sat.)
MAIN ROAD, EXMINSTER, EXETER,
Tel: (0392) 832216

Wadworth 6X	(H)
Flowers Original	(H)

CP DF FA LM (FORTNIGHTLY) ME ML
MR OD PG RF ST
Large village pub with friendly
atmosphere and good a-la-carte menu.

SWANS NEST (Map Ref E5)
STATION ROAD, EXMINSTER, EXETER,
(TURN LEFT AT ROUNDABOUT SOUTH
END SANNERVILLE WAY - A379)
Tel: (0392) 832371

Draught Bass	(H)
Furgusons Dartmoor Best Bitter	(H)

TURF HOTEL (Map Ref E5)
SOUTHERN END OF EXETER CANAL
(PAST SWANS NEST TO CANAL. WALK
ONLY SOUTH TO PUB - 1ml APPRO), OS:
SX964861
Tel: (0392) 833128

Boddingtons Bitter	(H)
Marston's Pedigree	(H)
Guest Beer Occasional	(H)

EXMOUTH

ALBION INN (Map Ref F5)
38, ALBION STREET, EXMOUTH,
(CLOSE TO TOWN CENTRE.),
Tel: (0395) 272960

Draught Bass	(H)

AMAZON (Map Ref F5)
11 - 3 ; 5:30 - 11. (M-F, 11 - 11 Sat.)
DINAN WAY, EXMOUTH, DEVON. (300m
ALONG DINAN WAY FROM JUNCT
WITH SALTERTON ROAD.),
Tel: (0395) 279533

Marston's Pedigree	(H)
Wadworth 6X	(H)

CP DB DF FA GD ME (BAR SNACKS
ONLY) ML (BAR SNACKS ONLY) OD PG
PL SN ST
Modern, purpose-built pub serving out of
town housing estates. Better than might be
expected. Good value snacks.

BEACH HOTEL (Map Ref F5)
11 - 2:30 ; 5 - 11. (M-S (W) 1100 - 1100 (S))
VICTORIA ROAD, EXMOUTH, (FOLLOW
SIGNS TO DOCKS, PUB AT JUNCTION
WITH SEA FRONT.)
Tel: (0395) 272090

Draught Bass	(H)
Eldridge Pope Royal Oak	(H)
Guest Beer Regular	(H)

BR (EXMOUTH) DB FA ME ML OD PB PG
PL QP RM SH SN
Modernised Victorian pub on harbour side,
with a nautical theme, especially the local
lifeboats. Wholesome home-cooked food at
reasonable prices.

BEACON VAULTS, (Map Ref F5)
THE BEACON, EXMOUTH, (ADJACENT
TO ROUDABOUT BY TOWN HALL.),
Tel: (0395) 272138

Draught Bass	(H)
Courage Directors	(H)
Webster's Yorkshire Bitter	(H)

BICTON INN (Map Ref F5)
11:30 - 3 ; 6 - 11. (M-S)
5, BICTON STREET, EXMOUTH,
(FOLLOW SOUTH ST. FROM POST
OFFICE & JOB CENTRE.),
Tel: (0395) 272589

Boddingtons Bitter	(H)
Marston's Pedigree	(H)
Flowers IPA	(H)
Flowers Original	(H)

BR (EXMOUTH) DB FA LM ML PG PL
Basic town pub much frequented by
students.

CLINTON ARMS (Map Ref F5)
MAER LANE, LITTLEHAM VILLAGE,
EXMOUTH,
Tel: (0395) 264054

Ushers Best Bitter	(H)
Webster's Yorkshire Bitter	(H)
Guest Beer Occasional	(H)

42

COUNTRY HOUSE INN, (Map Ref F5)
11 - 2:30; 5:11 - 11 (M-F, 1100 - 0345 & 500 - 1100 SAT.)
WITHYCOMBE VILLAGE ROAD, EXMOUTH, (BETWEEN 'HOLLY TREE' PUB AND FORD GARAGE)
Tel: (0395) 263444

Cornish Royal Wessex	(H)
Marston's Pedigree	(H)
Wadworth 6X	(H)

CD CH CI DB DM FA GD ME (SATURDAY ONLY - RESERVATIONS) ML (MON-FRI ONLY) OD PB PG PL QP SN
Village style local with an aviary in the large garden. Bar-B-Q's beside the stream during summer. Formerly a blacksmith's shop. Excellent food, especially Sat. evening.

DEER LEAP (Map Ref F5)
THE ESPLANADE, EXMOUTH, (MIDWAY ALONG ESPLANADE)
Tel: (0395) 265030

Draught Bass	(B)
Boddingtons Bitter	(B)
Flowers IPA	(B)
Flowers Original	(B)
Guest Beer Regular	(B)

EXMOUTH ARMS (Map Ref F5)
21, EXETER ROAD, EXMOUTH. (ALMOST OPPOSITE LIBRARY.),
Tel: (0395) 265292

Marston's Pedigree	(H)

FAMOUS OLDE BARREL (Map Ref F5)
11 - 2:30 ; 6 - 11. (M-F; 11 - 11 Sat)
PRINCES STREET, EXMOUTH (NEXT TO MAGNOLIA SHOPPING CENTRE CAR PARK)
Tel: (0395) 268226

Draught Bass	(H)
Boddingtons Bitter	(H)
Courage Directors	(H)
John Smith's Bitter	(H)
Flowers Original	(H)
Guest Beer Regular	(H)

BR (EXMOUTH) DB DF FA ME ML OD PG PL QP
Typical Devenish re-vamp of the former notorious 'Builder's Arms', which until recently has been youth orientated, but now aiming for a broader range of clientele. The recently installed 'False Barrel' dispense system has now been abandonded in favour of traditional hand pumps, much to the delight of the manager. (and CAMRA!)

FAMOUS SHIP (Map Ref F5)
18, HIGH STREET, EXMOUTH, (TOWN CENTRE BETWEEN ROLLE ST. & ORNAMENTAL FOUNTAIN.),
Tel: (0395) 264440

Castle Eden Ale	(H)
Flowers Original	(H)
Wethered Winter Royal	(H)
Guest Beer Occasional	(H)

FARMHOUSE INN (Map Ref F5)
11 - 11. (M-S)
CHURCHILL ROAD, BRIXINGTON, EXMOUTH,
Tel: (0395) 278000

Flowers IPA	(H)
Flowers Original	(H)

CA CD (EUCHRE) CH CP DB DF (ACCESS ONLY) FA GD LM ME ML MR (FUNCTION ROOM) OD PB PG (QUIZ, FOOTBALL) PL SN ST
Large 3 bar estate pub, soon to have a much needed refurbishment. Present landlord won a CAMRA award in 1988 in Preston, and is uprating and increasing the real ale facilities to include non - Whitbread guests.

GROVE (Map Ref F5)
11 - 3 ; 5:30 - 11. (M-S OCT-APR, 11 - 11 M-S
MAY-SEPT)
THE ESPLANADE, EXMOUTH, (ON SEA
FRONT NEAR DOCKS.)
Tel: (0395) 272101

Exe Valley Devon Glory	**(H)**
Fullers Chiswick	**(H)**
Greene King Abbot	**(H)**
Thompson's IPA	**(H)**
Wadworth 6X	**(H)**

BR (EXMOUTH) CP DF FA GD LM ME
ML OD QP RM SN
Newish sea front pub. Very warm and
friendly. Traditional bar and timber
decor/furniture. Good home cooked food
including locally caught sea food. A
constantly changing range of five beers
from all over the country are permanent,
in addition there is an occasional mini-beer
festival. Well worth a visit.

HEAVITREE ARMS (Map Ref F5)
HIGH ST, EXMOUTH, (TOWN CENTRE,
NEAR ORNAMENTAL FOUNTAIN.),
Tel: (0395) 263640

Marston's Pedigree	**(H)**
Castle Eden Ale	**(H)**
Whitbread Best Bitter	**(H)**
Flowers Original	**(H)**

HOLLY TREE (Map Ref F5)
11 - 2:30; 5:30 - 11 (M-F, 1100 - 1100 SAT.)
161, WITHYCOMBE VILLAGE ROAD,
EXMOUTH, (MIDDLE OF VILLAGE,
APPROX. 400m FROM CHURCH.)
Tel: (0395) 273440

Batemans Victory Ale	**(H)**
Brakspears Special	**(H)**
Everards Tiger	**(H)**
Exe Valley Devon Glory	**(H)**
Wadworth 6X	**(H)**

CP DB DF FA GD LM ME ML OD PB PL
QP RM SH SN
Tastefully modernised village pub with
large, comfortable lounge/dining area.
Economic, good food. Varying range of
real ales.

IMPERIAL HOTEL (Map Ref F5)
11 - 11 ; : - : (ALL YEAR)
THE ESPLANADE, EXMOUTH, (SET
BACK FROM SEA FRONT & CLOSE TO
TOWN CENTRE) Tel: (0395) 274761

Courage Directors	**(E)**

AC BR (EXMOUTH) CP FA GD ME ML
(BAR TYPE ONLY) MR OD QP RM RS SN
Comfortable lounge bar to a 3* hotel. views
across lyme bay to torbay. open to
non-residents. large garden.

LENNARDS BAR (Map Ref F5)
34, THE STRAND, EXMOUTH, (ON
ONE-WAY SYSTEM OPPOSITE TOWN
CENTRE GARDENS.),
Tel: (0395) 263031

Draught Bass	**(H)**

PARK (Map Ref F5)
11 - 3 ; 5:30 - 11. (M-Th., 11 - 11 F, Sat.)
114, EXETER ROAD, EXMOUTH,
Tel: (0395) 279667

Draught Bass	**(H)**

BR (EXMOUTH) CD (CRIB) CP DB DF
(ACCESS ONLY) GD ML OD PG PL
Large modernised victorian hotel.

**ROYAL BEACON HOTEL (Map Ref
F5)**
11 - 2:30 ; 5:45 - 11. (M-S)
THE BEACON, EXMOUTH, DEVON.
(FOLLOW ROAD UPHILL FROM
BEACON VAULTS PUB.),
Tel: (0395) 264886

Draught Bass	**(H)**
Guest Beer Occasional	**(H)**

AC BR (EXMOUTH) CP FA ME ML MR
QP RM RS
Bar in plush hotel overlooking Lyme Bay,
with views along coast to Torquay.

THE BANK, (Map Ref F5)
ST. ANDREW'S ROAD, EXMOUTH,
(150m FROM TOWN HALL TOWARDS
SEA FRONT / HARBOUR.),
Tel: (0395) 266782

John Smith's Bitter	**(H)**

TOWN CRIER (Map Ref F5)
31, EXETER ROAD, EXMOUTH
Tel: (0395) 272932

Cornish Steam Bitter	**(H)**
Royal Wessex	**(H)**
Marston's Pedigree	**(H)**

BR DF ML RF
Friendly local, formerly the Royal Oak.

VICTORIA, (Map Ref F5)
VICTORIA ROAD, EXMOUTH, (JUST OFF
ONE-WAY SYSTEM OPPOSITE LLOYDS
BANK.),
Tel: (0395) 272091

Boddingtons Bitter	**(H)**
Flowers Original	**(H)**

EXTON

PUFFING BILLY (Map Ref E5)
12 - 3 ; 6 - 11. (M-F; 12-11 Sat)
STATION ROAD, EXTON Tel: (0392)
873152

Draught Bass	**(H)**
Wadworth	
6X	**(H)**
Old Timer	**(H)**

(WINTER ONLY) BR (EXTON) CA CP DB
GD ME ML OD PB PG (CRIB) QP RF RM
c16, cob built, traditional pub, with good
food - especially the fish.

FAIRMILE

FAIRMILE INN (Map Ref F4)
11:30 - 2:30 ; 6:30 - 11. (M-S)
FAIRMILE, OTTERY ST. MARY, OS:
SY087971
Tel: (0404) 812827

Draught Bass	**(H)**

CP DF LM ME (NOT SUN) ML OD PG RF
Long and narrow one bar roadside pub.

FENITON

NOG INN (Map Ref F4)
11 - 2:30 ; 6:30 - 11. (M-S)
OTTERY ROAD, FENITON, Nr.
HONITON,
Tel: (0404) 850210

Cotleigh Tawny	**(H)**
Otter Ale	**(H)**

AC BR (FENITON) CI CP DF FA OD PB
PG QP RF
Genuine village local with a friendly, keen
landlord and a possesive cat with a
preference for real ale. Usually has a guest
draught mild. A squash court adjoins the
function room for you to work up a thirst.

FENNY BRIDGES

FENNY BRIDGES INN (Map Ref F4)
11 - 11. (M-S)
FENNY BRIDGES, Nr. HONITON, OS:
SY112985
Tel: (0404) 850218

John Smith's Bitter	**(H)**
Ruddles County	**(H)**
Guest Beer Regular	**(H)**

AC CP DF FA ME ML OD PB PG PL
Plush roadside pub with games in old
public bar. Landlord keen to try different
guest ales.

GREYHOUND INN (Map Ref F4)
11 - 11. (M-S)
FENNY BRIDGES, HONITON,
Tel: (0404) 850380

Ruddles Best Bitter	**(H)**
Ushers Best Bitter	**(H)**

AC CH CP FA ME ML OD QP
Named after the Greyhound post stop. A
very striking exterior and an upmarket
interior. Very food orientated. Almost
totally rebuilt after a disasterous fire in
early '70s. The thatched roof is a fine
example of local craftsmanship.

FILLEIGH

STAGS HEAD (Map Ref C2)
FILLEIGH, Nr. SOUTH MOLTON, OS:
SS679276
Tel: (0598) 760250

Draught Bass	**(H)**

FOLLY GATE

CROSSWAYS INN (Map Ref C4)
FOLLY GATE, Nr. OKEHAMPTON,
Tel: (0837) 52088

Draught Bass (H)
Ind Coope Burton Ale (H)

FREMINGTON

NEW INN (Map Ref B2)
12 - 3 ; 6 - 11. (M-S)
BIDEFORD ROAD, FREMINGTON,
BARNSTAPLE.
Tel: (0271) 73859

Ushers Best Bitter (H)

CP FA PB
Grade 2 listed building in a designated
conservation area - Excellent food.

FRITHELSTOCK

CLINTON ARMS (Map Ref B3)
12 - 2:30 ; 7 - 11. (M-S (W), 12 - 3, 6 - 11 (S))
FRITHLESTOCK, TORRINGTON.
OS: SS464195
Tel: (0805) 23279

Draught Bass (G)

AC CP DF ME ML OD PG RS
Comfortable family pub with two separate
restaurants and a conservatory with recent
royal patronage.

FROGMORE

GLOBE INN (Map Ref D8)
11 - 2:30 ; 5 - 11. (M-S (W), 11 - 11 (S))
FROGMORE, KINGSBRIDGE
Tel: (0548) 531351

Draught Bass (H)
Boddingtons Bitter (H)
Marston's Pedigree (H)
Guest Beer Occasional (H)

(WHITBREAD GUEST - SUMMER) AC CA
CI CP FA ME ML OD PB RF
Large wood-panelled lounge with nautical
paintings on walls. Good family facilities.

GEORGEHAM

KINGS ARMS (Map Ref B2)
GEORGEHAM, Nr. BARNSTAPLE,
Tel: (0271) 890240

Draught Bass (H)

ROCK INN (Map Ref B2)
11 - 3 ; 5 - 11. (M-Th. 11 - 11 F, Sat. (W),
11-11 M-S (S))
ROCK HILL, GEORGEHAM, Nr.
BARNSTAPLE.
Tel: (0271) 890322

Fullers ESB (H)
Marston's Pedigree (H)
Ruddles Best Bitter (H)
Ruddles County (H)
Tetley Bitter (H)
Ushers Best Bitter (H)

AC CP FA GD ME ML OD PG RF
Traditional unspoilt village pub offering
good food and a range of games. Pleasant
garden for drinkers. Believed to be the
only pub in North Devon offering 6 real
ales all year round.

GRENOFEN

HALFWAY HOUSE INN (Map Ref B6)
GRENOFEN, Nr. TAVISTOCK (ON A386
BETWEEN TAVISTOCK &
HORRABRIDGE), OS: SX493716
Tel: (0822) 612960

Boddingtons Bitter (H)
Flowers IPA (H)
Flowers Original (H)

HALBERTON

WELCOME INN (Map Ref F3)
93, HIGH STREET, HALBERTON, NR
TIVERTON
Tel: (0884) 820316

Boddingtons Bitter (H)
Marston's Pedigree (H)

HALLSANDS

HALLSANDS HOTEL (Map Ref D8)
11 - 11. (M-S)
HALLSANDS, KINGSBRIDGE.
OS: SX818387
Tel: (054851) 264

Draught Bass (H)
Guest Beer Regular (H)

AC CI CP DB FA OD PG RF SN (ALL DAY)
Isolated, old coaching inn, with
character(s), on South Devon Coastal
Footpath. Built in 1906, to replace original
London Inn washed into sea during the
Great Storm of 1903. The hotel has a
resident diver/auxilliary coastguard, and
hires boats and air. Impressive sea views
from patio on low cliff edge.

HALWELL

OLD INN (Map Ref D7)
11 - 2:30 ; 6 - 11. (M-S)
HALWELL, TOTNES
Tel: (080421) 329

Draught Bass	(H)
Greene King Abbot	(H)
Flowers IPA	(H)
Guest Beer Regular	(H)

AC CC CI CP DF FA ME ML OD PG QP
Welcoming roadside pub, extensively
modernised in recent years. Pub games
include "ring the bull". Original building
burnt down in c17, and was eventually
replaced in c19. Excellent visitors pub with
good valuefood, and a possessive cat!

HALWILL JUNCTION

JUNCTION INN (Map Ref B4)
HALWILL JUNCTION, Nr.
HOLSWORTHY, (JUST OFF B3218)
Tel: (0409) 221239

Boddingtons Bitter	(H)
Wadworth 6X	(H)

HARBERTON

CHURCH HOUSE INN (Map Ref D7)
12 - 3 ; 6 - 11. (M-S)
HARBERTON, TOTNES (2 MILES SOUTH
OF TOTNES, NEXT TO CHURCH), OS:
SX783563
Tel: (0803) 863707

Draught Bass	(H)
Courage Best Bitter	(H)
Guest Beer Regular	(H)

CI CP FA ME ML OD PG QP RF
Magnificent village inn, formerly a monks
charity house, once housed masons
building the church (hence its name). A
must for medieval architecture buffs, the
huge open plan interior features tudor
windows, a massive fireplace and an
impressive oak screen, which is feature of
the Grade 2 listing. The village's only pub
with good food from an extensive menu.
Family room equipped with high chair.

HARTLAND

ANCHOR INN (Map Ref A3)
FORE STREET, HARTLAND,
Tel: (0237) 441414

Draught Bass	(H)
Marston's Pedigree	(H)

HART INN (Map Ref A3)
THE SQUARE, HARTLAND.
Tel: (0237) 441474

Flowers Original	(H)

KINGS ARMS (Map Ref A3)
11 - 3 ; 7 - 11. (M-S)
THE SQUARE, HARTLAND.
Tel: (0237) 441222

Wadworth 6X	(H)
Guest Beer Regular	(H)
(SUMMER ONLY)	

AC CP DF FA ME ML MR OD PG
Recently renovated, busy roadside inn
with a large function room cum skittle
alley.

HATHERLEIGH

GEORGE HOTEL (Map Ref C4)
11 - 3:30 ; 6 - 11. (M-S)
MARKET STREET, HATHERLEIGH,
Tel: (0837) 810454

Draught Bass	(H)
Boddingtons Bitter	(H)
Pompey Royal	(H)
Flowers Original	(H)

AC FA ME ML OD PB RF
Large, old coaching hotel, with two small
bars at the front, and a large lounge bar to
the rear. Beer range sometimes varies.

MARKET INN (Map Ref C4)
11 - 11. (M-S)
MARKET STREET, HATHERLEIGH,
Tel: (0837)

Draught Bass	(H)

OD RF SN (ALL DAY)

TALLY HO! INN (Map Ref C4)
11 - 3 ; 6 - 11 (M-S)
14, MARKET STREET, HATHERLEIGH
Tel: (0837) 810306

Tally Ho
Dark Mild	(H)
Potboiler's Brew	(H)
Tarka's Tipple	(H)
Nutters	(H)
Thurgia	(H)
Jianni Jollop Winter Warmer	(H)

AC CP ME ML OD PG QP RF
Ancient market town pub with the accent on Italian home cooking. A brewery is situated at the rear of the pub for in-house use and can be visited on request. North Devon branch of CAMRA's 'Pub of the Year' 1992.

HAYTOR VALE

ROCK INN (Map Ref D5)
11 - 2:30 ; 6:30 - 11. (M-S)
HAYTOR VALE, NEWTON ABBOT
Tel: (03646) 305

Draught Bass	(H)
Eldridge Pope	
Dorchester	(H)
Hardy Country	(H)
Royal Oak	(H)

AC CA DF FA ME ML OD PB QP RF
Superb, 200 year old Dartmoor village inn with a large lounge and a tiny public bar. Formerly a coaching house, it is set just inside the Dartmoor National Park, and offers excellent food and accommodation.

HELE

CROSSWAYS TAVERN (Map Ref E4)
12 - 2 ; 7:30 - 11. (M-S)
STATION ROAD, HELE, EXETER, (1/2ml WEST, OFF B3181 AT BEARE.),
OS: SS996023
Tel: (0392) 881752

Furgusons Dartmoor Best Bitter	(H)

CP DB DF ME ML OD PG (INDOOR SHORT MAT BOWLS) PL RF ST
Pleasant pub near M5 motorway (no access).

HEMERDON

MINERS ARMS (Map Ref C7)
11 - 2:30 ; 5:30 - 11. (M-F. 11 - 3 Sat)
HEMERDON, Nr. PLYMPTON
Tel: (0752) 343252

Draught Bass	(H)
Furgusons Dartmoor Best Bitter	(H)
Ruddles County	(H)
Ushers Best Bitter	(H)

CA CI CP FA GD ME ML OD PB QP RF
Split level former tin miners pub set on the edge of Plympton suburbia. Many exposed beams support a low ceiling. There is a large granite fire place. BEER GARDEN AND CHILDREN'S PLAY AREA.

HEMYOCK

CATHERINE WHEEL (Map Ref F3)
12 - 11. (M-S (sometimes closes in pm if quiet))
HEMYOCK, Nr. CULLOMPTON
Tel: (0823) 680224

Courage Best Bitter	(H)
Eldridge Pope Hardy Country	(H)
Marston's Pedigree	(H)

CP DF FA ME ML OD PB PG RF
Lively pub in a quiet village.

HENNOCK

PALK ARMS (Map Ref D5)
HENNOCK, CHUDLEIGH
Tel: (0626) 833027

Furgusons Dartmoor Strong	(H)

HEYBROOK BAY

EDDYSTONE INN (Map Ref B7)
11:30 - 2:30 ; 6:30 - 11. (M-S)
HEYBROOK DRIVE, HEYBROOK BAY, WEMBURY
Tel: (0752) 862356

Draught Bass	(H)
Flowers IPA	(H)

CA CP FA ME ML OD
Pleasant pub with a patio where there are spectacular views of Wembury Bay and cliffs.

HIGH BICKINGTON

OLD GEORGE INN (Map Ref C3)
11 - 3 ; 6 - 11. (M-S)
POPULAR TERRACE, HIGH
BICKINGTON, OS: SS600205
Tel: (0769) 60513

Ind Coope Burton Ale	(G)
Guest Beer Regular	(G)

CP FA ME ML OD PG QP RF
c16 inn, recently changed ownership.

HOCKWORTHY

STAPLECROSS INN (Map Ref F3)
12 - 3 ; 6:30 - 11 (M-S, CLOSED MON-WED
LUNCHTIMES) HOCKWORTHY, Nr.
WELLINGTON
Tel: (0396) 374

Flowers Original	(G)

CP DF OD PB PG QP RF SN
Peacefull 400 year old pub in a quiet corner
of the county. Two traditional stone bars
with large fireplaces and an interesting
wooden clock in the lounge.

HOLBETON

**DARTMOOR UNION INN (Map Ref
C7)**
11:30 - 3 ; 6 - 11. (M-S)
FORE STREET, HOLBETON, Nr.
MODBURY
Tel: (075530) 288

Draught Bass	(H)
Summerskills Best Bitter	(H)

CA CI CP FA ME ML OD QP RF
Old pub, formerly the village workhouse,
is noted for its food.

MILDMAY COLOURS (Map Ref C7)
11 - 3 ; 6 - 11 (M-S)
HOLBETON, Nr. MODBURY
Tel: (075530) 248

Draught Bass	(H)
Boddingtons Bitter	(H)
Flowers IPA	(H)
House Beer	(H)

AC CD (EUCHRE) CI CP FA ME ML OD
PB PG PL RF
Friendly country pub where the house ale
is Castle Eden Ale.

HOLCOMBE

CASTLE INN (Map Ref E5)
12 - 2:30 ; 6 - 11 (M-S)
FORDAM ROAD, HOLCOMBE,
DAWLISH,
Tel: (0626) 862306

Draught Bass	(H)
Castle Eden Ale	(H)
Whitbread Best Bitter	(H)

DB ME ML OD
Friendly pub in centre of village.

SMUGGLERS INN (Map Ref E5)
TEIGNMOUTH ROAD, HOLCOMBE,
DAWLISH,
Tel: (0626) 862301

Courage Best Bitter	(H)
John Smith's Bitter	(H)
Wadworth 6X	(H)

HOLCOMBE ROGUS

PRINCE OF WALES (Map Ref F3)
12 - 3 ; 7 - 11. (M-S)
HOLCOMBE ROGUS, Nr. WELLINGTON
(CENTRE OF VILLAGE) Tel: (0823) 672070

Draught Bass	(H)
Cotleigh	
Harrier	(H)
Tawny	(H)
Old Buzzard	(H)

CP FA GD ME ML OD PG QP RF
Pleasant country pub with interesting
handpumps which resemble a cash
register. Guest beers.

HOLNE

CHURCH HOUSE INN (Map Ref D6)
12 - 3 ; 6:30 - 10:30 (M-Th,6.30 - 11 F,
Sat.(W) 12 - 3, 6.30 - 11 (S))
HOLNE, ASHBURTON
Tel: (03643) 208

Blackawton	
Bitter	(H)
44 Special	(H)
Furgusons Dartmoor Strong	(H)
Palmers IPA	(H)

AC CI DB FA ME ML OD PG (BAR
SKITTLES) QP RF RS
c14 inn on the edge of Dartmoor with good
value home-cooked food - no chips or
sarnies! Separate restaurant. Bright public
bar, and wood-panelled lounge, both with
open fires.

HOLSWORTHY

GOLDEN FLEECE (Map Ref A4)
11 - 11. (M-S)
BODMIN STREET, HOLSWORTHY,
Tel: (0409) 253263

St Austell Tinners	**(H)**

DF ME ML PB QP
Tastefully renovated pub with a
welcoming atmosphere. Exposed timber
beams, wood panelling, and a slate floor,
offer a relaxing environment.

KINGS ARMS (Map Ref A4)
11 - 11. (M-S)
THE SQUARE, HOLSWORTHY,
Tel: (0409) 253517

Draught Bass	**(H)**
Furgusons Dartmoor Best Bitter	**(H)**

ME ML PB PG QP RF
A magnificent example of a Devon market
town local. Two bars plus a snug! Huge
brewery mirrors, oak bars, lead glass
screen. Always good for a chinwag.

HONITON

CARLTON (Map Ref F4)
HIGH ST, HONITON,
Tel: (0404) 42903

Draught Bass	**(H)**

HEATHFIELD (Map Ref F4)
11:30 - 23:0 ; 6 - 11. (M-S)
WALNUT ROAD, HEATHFIELD EST.,
HONITON,
Tel: (0404) 45321/2

Furgusons Dartmoor Best Bitter	**(H)**
Ind Coope Burton Ale	**(H)**

AC CP FA (ONLY IF EATING) ME (NOT
SUN EVENINGS) ML OD PG RF ST
A former 16th century farmhouse, now an
upmarket estate local, with a good
reputation for food.

The Three Tuns, Honiton

RAILWAY (Map Ref F4)
11:30 - 2:30 ; 5:30 - 11. (M-S)
QUEEN STREET, HONITON,
Tel: (0404) 43686

Boddingtons Bitter	**(H)**
Otter Ale	**(H)**
Flowers IPA	**(H)**

BR (HONITON) CA CD CP DB DF FA ME
ML OD PB PG RF
Opened in 1860 shortly before the railway
was completed. In fact the first landlord
was instrumental in ensuring that the
railway did reach Honiton. A very
pleasant two bar local with a recent
extension.

RED COW (Map Ref F4)
11 - 3 ; 6 - 11 (M-S)
43, HIGH STREET, HONITON,
Tel: (0404) 47497

Worthington Best Bitter	**(H)**
John Smith's Bitter	**(H)**
Otter Ale	**(H)**
Ruddles County	**(H)**

AC BR (HONITON) CA DB ME ML OD
PG RF ST
Two bar comfortable town local.

STAR (Map Ref F4)
11 - 11. (M-S)
NEW STREET, HONITON,
Tel: (0404) 42045

John Smith's Bitter	**(H)**
Wadworth 6X	**(H)**
Flowers Original	**(H)**

AC BR (HONITON) CA DB ML (SUMMER
ONLY) MR OD PB PG PL ST
Basic two bar town local.

THREE TUNS (Map Ref F4)
11 - 3 ; 5:30 - 11. (11 - 11 Tues, Fri, Sat.)
HIGH ST, HONITON,
Tel: (0404) 42902

Draught Bass	**(H)**
Theakston Best Bitter	**(H)**

BR (HONITON) CA CD (EUCHRE, CRIB)
DB ML MR (FUNCTION ROOM) OD PB
ST
Very basic and lively public bar and a
quiet, comfortable lounge in a traditional
coaching inn, with a function room /
skittle alley.

VINE INN (Map Ref F4)
11 - 2:30 ; 6 - 11. (M-S)
VINE PASSAGES, HIGH ST, HONITON,
Tel: (0404) 42889

Otter Ale   (H)

BR (HONITON) CD DB OD PG (CRIB) QP
RF SH ST
Town local, with keen skittles, darts, and
crib teams.

VOLUNTEER (Map Ref F4)
11 - 11 (M-S)
HIGH ST, HONITON,
Tel: (0404) 42145

Brains Bitter   (H)
Cotleigh Tawny   (H)
Otter Ale   (H)

CI (LANE'S DRY) DB FA (IN POOL
ROOM) OD PB (SNUG) PG PL ST
A 400 year old town local which was once
a recruiting house for the militia hence the
name. Friendly town local with an
affectionate dog.

WHITE LION (Map Ref F4)
12 - 3 ; 6 - 11. (M-S)
194, HIGH STREET, HONITON,
Tel: (0404) 47062

Boddingtons Bitter   (H)
Marston's Pedigree   (H)
Castle Eden Ale   (H)
Flowers IPA   (H)

AC CH DB FA ME ML OD PG
The original White Lion was across the
road. The pub moved to its present
location when the original burnt down for
the second time. A comfortable one bar
town local with friendly staff.

HOPE COVE

**HOPE & ANCHOR INN (Map Ref
C8)**
HOPE COVE, KINGSBRIDGE
Tel: (0548) 561294

Draught Bass   (H)
Furgusons Dartmoor Best Bitter   (H)

LOBSTER POT INN (Map Ref C8)
11 - 11 (M-S)
HOPE COVE, KINGSBRIDGE
Tel: (0548) 561214

Boddingtons Bitter   (H)
Flowers Original   (H)

AC CA CI DB DF FA ME ML OD PG PL RF
RS
Bar and restaurant close to beach. Parking
difficult in summer. Watch out for the pet
parrot!

HORNDON

ELEPHANTS NEST (Map Ref B5)
11:30 - 2:30 ; 6:30 - 11 (M-S)
HORNDON, MARY TAVY, TAVISTOCK
(TURN OFF A386 AT MARY TAVY,
FOLLOW SIGNS TO MOOR), OS:
SX517800
Tel: (0822) 810273

Boddingtons Bitter   (H)
Palmers BB   (H)
St Austell HSD   (H)
Thwaites Craftsman Ale   (H)
Webster's Yorkshire Bitter   (H)

AC CD CH CI (BULMER TRADITIONAL)
CP DB DM FA GD LM (FOLK CLUB) ME
ML OD PG QP RF RM (QUIET
BACKGROUND) RS SN
Splendid moorland pub named after a
former landlord's beard. A very large
garden with lots of animals. Stone walled
bar with a roaring fire in winter. Well
known for its excellent food and convivial
atmosphere.

HORNS CROSS

HOOPS INN (Map Ref B3)
HORNS CROSS, Nr. BIDEFORD,
Tel: (0237) 451222

Boddingtons Bitter   (H)
Flowers IPA   (H)
Flowers Original   (H)

HORRABRIDGE

LEAPING SALMON INN (Map Ref B6)
11 - 3 ; 6 - 11. (M-S)
WHITCHURCH ROAD, HORRABRIDGE, YELVERTON
Tel: (0822) 852939

Draught Bass	(H)
Courage Best Bitter	(H)
Courage Directors	(H)

CP GD ME ML OD PB PG RF
Popular with the fishing fraternity. The garden overlooks the car park and is not suitable for children. Well inside pub.

LONDON INN (Map Ref B6)
HORRABRIDGE, TAVISTOCK
Tel: (0822) 853567

Draught Bass	(H)
Flowers IPA	(H)

HORSEBRIDGE

ROYAL INN (Map Ref B6)
12 - 3 ; 7 - 11. (M-S)
HORSEBRIDGE, Nr. TAVISTOCK (OFF A384, 6 MILES WEST OF TAVISTOCK), OS: SX401749
Tel: (082287) 214

Draught Bass	(H)
Tamar	(H)
Horsebridge Best	(H)
Heller	(H)
Marston's Pedigree	(H)

CA CP ME ML OD PB PG QP RF
Characterful homebrew pub on the banks of the Tamar, a former c15 nunnery.

IDDESLEIGH

DUKE OF YORK (Map Ref C4)
11:30 - 3 ; 6:30 - 11. (M-S)
IDDESLEIGH, Nr. WINKLEIGH,
Tel: (0837) 810253

Cotleigh Tawny	(G)
Hook Norton Old Hooky	(G)
Wadworth 6X	(G)

AC CC ME ML OD PG QP RF
12th century thatched village pub with a superb inglenook fireplace, genuine beams and an old stillage behind the bar. Definitely nothing modern. All food is prepared on the premises, but no food Mondays.

IDE

HUNTSMAN INN (Map Ref E5)
11 - 3:30 ; 6 - 11. (M-S)
2, HIGH ST, IDE, Nr. EXETER,
Tel: (0392) 72779

Boddingtons Bitter	(H)
Marston's Pedigree	(H)
Whitbread WCPA	(H)

BB CA CI CP DB DF (ACCESS) GD ME ML OD PG QP RF
Thatched village inn beside a ford. Boasts the longest pub sign in Britain. Pub dates back to at least 1564.

POACHERS INN (Map Ref E5)
11 - 3 ; 5:30 - 11. (M-S)
55, HIGH STREET, IDE, Nr. EXETER,
Tel: (0392) 73847

Brains Dark	(H)
Flowers IPA	(H)

CA CD (EUCHRE) CP DB DF (ACCESS) FA GD ML OD PB PG PL QP RF
Pleasant village two-bar pub. Unpretentious.

TWISTED OAK (Map Ref E5)
11 - 2:30 ; 6 - 11. (M-S)
LITTLE JOHN'S CROSS HILL, IDE, EXETER,
Tel: (0392) 73666

Draught Bass	(H)
Boddingtons Bitter	(H)
Flowers IPA	(H)

CA CP DB DF FA (IN RESTAURANT) GD ME ML OD PB PG PL RS ST
Plush, lounge bar, well appointed and tastefully furnished. Pub is home to 1 darts, 2 pool, and 16 skittle teams.

ILFRACOMBE

BUNCH OF GRAPES (Map Ref B1)
11 - 11. (M-S)
36, HIGH STREET, ILFRACOMBE,
Tel: (0271) 863276

Marston's Pedigree	(H)
Ruddles Best Bitter	(H)
Ushers Best Bitter	(H)

LM (OCCASIONAL) ML PG
Victorian pub in a Victorian street. The inside has been redesigned as a mix of 18th and 20th century, good collection of trophies.

COACH HOUSE INN (Map Ref B1)
BICCLESCOMBE PARK, ILFRACOMBE,
Tel: (0271) 864160

Draught Bass (H)

GEORGE AND DRAGON (Map Ref B1)
12 - 3 ; 7 - 11 (M-S (W), VARIABLE IN SUMMER)
4, FORE STREET, ILFRACOMBE,
Tel: (0271) 863851

Courage Best Bitter (H)
Courage Directors (H)
Ushers
    Founders (H)
    Best Bitter (H)

FA ME ML
Pleasant old-fashioned atmosphere, though not as olde worlde as its 600 year pedigree might suggest.

HELE BAY HOTEL (Map Ref B1)
WATERMOUTH ROAD, HELE,
ILFRACOMBE,
Tel: (0271) 863726

Draught Bass (H)
Flowers IPA (H)

LONDON & PARIS (Map Ref B1)
11 - 3 ; 6:30 - 11. (M-S, VARIABLE IN SUMMER)
155, HIGH STREET, ILFRACOMBE,
Tel: (0271) 863559

Tetley Bitter (H)

FA ME ML
Comfortable lounge bar and restaurant at end of High Street. Beer range changes regularly.

MERMAID INN (Map Ref B1)
SEA FRONT, ILFRACOMBE,
Tel: (0271) 863870

John Smith's Bitter (H)
Ruddles County (H)

PIER HOTEL (Map Ref B1)
THE PIER, ILFRACOMBE, DEVONSHIRE.
Tel: (0271) 863918

Flowers IPA (H)

PRINCE ALBERT (Map Ref B1)
3, HIGH STREET, ILFRACOMBE,
Tel: (0271) 867301

John Smith's Bitter (H)

PRINCE OF WALES (Map Ref B1)
2, FORE STREET, ILFRACOMBE,
Tel: (0271) 866391

John Smith's Bitter (H)

QUEENS (Map Ref B1)
HIGH STREET, ILFRACOMBE,
Tel: (0271) 864303

Courage Best Bitter (H)
Courage Directors (H)

ROYAL BRITANNIA HOTEL (Map Ref B1)
11 - 11. (M-S)
BROAD STREET, ILFRACOMBE,
Tel: (0271) 862939

Courage Best Bitter (H)
John Smith's Bitter (H)

AC FA ME ML OD PG QP RF
Comfortable harbourside hotel.

SANDPIPER INN (Map Ref B1)
THE QUAY, ILFRACOMBE,
Tel: (0271) 865260

John Smith's Bitter (H)

SHIP AND PILOT INN (Map Ref B1)
10, BROAD STREET, ILFRACOMBE,
Tel: (0271) 863562

Flowers IPA (H)

THE LAMB (Map Ref B1)
11 - 3 ; 6 - 11. (M-S)
HIGH STREET, ILFRACOMBE,
Tel: (0271) 863708

Draught Bass (H)

ML OD PB PG
Victorian town pub, with a large public bar to rear.

VICTORIA (Map Ref B1)
HIGH STREET, ILFRACOMBE,
Tel: (0271) 863753

Ushers Best Bitter (H)

WAVERLEY (Map Ref B1)
12 - 11. (M-S (W), 11 - 11 (S))
19, ST. JAMES PLACE, ILFRACOMBE,
Tel: (0271) 862681

Courage Best Bitter (H)
Ushers 1824 Particular (H)
Ushers Best Bitter (H)

FA ME (SUMMER ONLY) ML PB PG
Large pub near the harbour with a theme
based on the last sea-going paddle steamer
'WAVERLEY'

WELLINGTON ARMS (Map Ref B1)
11 - 3:30 5 - 11. (M-S)
66, HIGH STREET, ILFRACOMBE,
Tel: (0271) 862206

Courage Best Bitter (H)
Courage Directors (H)

FA ME (SUMMER ONLY) ML OD PB PG
QP RF
Beamed, town pub with Iron Duke theme.

WHEEL INN (Map Ref B1)
2, THE PROMENADE, ILFRACOMBE,
Tel: (0271) 862545

Courage Best Bitter (H)

ILSINGTON

CARPENTERS ARMS (Map Ref D5)
11 - 2:30 ; 6 - 11. (M-S)
ILSINGTON, BOVEY TRACEY
Tel: (0364) 661215

Flowers IPA (G)

CI FA ME ML OD PG QP RF
Typical village local, but well worth a visit.
Well run, by very experienced landlords.
Very friendly atmosphere.

Duke of York, Iddesleigh

INSTOW

QUAY (Map Ref B2)
11:30 - 2:30 ; 6 - 11. (M-S (W),
VARIES IN SUMMER) MARINE PARADE,
INSTOW, BIDEFORD,
Tel: (0271) 860665

Flowers IPA (H)
Flowers Original (H)

AC ME ML OD
Small, one bar pub overlooking the
Torridge estuary. Guest beer.

WAYFARER (Map Ref B2)
LANE END ROAD, INSTOW, Nr.
BIDEFORD,
Tel: (0271) 860342

Flowers IPA (H)
Flowers Original (H)

IPPLEPEN

PLOUGH INN (Map Ref E6)
11 - 3 ; 6 - 11. (M-S)
FORE STREET, IPPLEPEN, NEWTON
ABBOT
Tel: (0803) 812118

Courage Best Bitter (H)
John Smith's Bitter (H)

WELLINGTON (Map Ref E6)
11 - 2:30 ; 6 - 11. (M-F, 11 - 11 Sat)
FORE STREET, IPPLEPEN, NEWTON
ABBOT
Tel: (0803) 812375

Courage Best Bitter (H)
John Smith's Bitter (H)
Wadworth 6X (H)
Guest Beer Regular (H)

CA CD (EUCHRE) CP DF FA GD ME ML
OD PB PG RF
Village centre pub, popular with locals.
Large garden with barbecue for own use.

IVYBRIDGE

BRIDGE INN (Map Ref C7)
11 - 3 ; 6 - 11. (M-Th. 11 - 11 F, Sat)
HARFORD ROAD, IVYBRIDGE
Tel: (0752) 897086

Courage Best Bitter (H)

PG PL RF
Basic, friendly pub with an active pool
room.

IMPERIAL INN (Map Ref C7)
11 - 3 ; 6 - 11. (M-Th. 11 - 11 F, Sat)
28, WESTERN ROAD, IVYBRIDGE
Tel: (0752) 892269

Courage Best Bitter	(H)
Ruddles Best Bitter	(H)
Wadworth 6X	(H)
Guest Beer Regular	(H)

CA CH CI CP DF FA ME ML OD PG RF
Good, old fashioned, pub with excellent
food and a large range of guest ales
including those from local breweries.
Separate children's area.

OLD SMITHY (Map Ref C7)
11 - 3 ; 6 - 11. (M-W; 11 - 11 Th-Sat)
45, FORE STREET, IVYBRIDGE

Courage Best Bitter	(H)
Courage Directors	(H)
John Smith's Bitter	(H)

ML PG
Friendly pub, in the town centre, which
caters for all age groups.

SPORTSMANS INN (Map Ref C7)
12 - 3 ; 7 - 11. (M-S)
EXETER ROAD, IVYBRIDGE
Tel: (0752) 892280

Boddingtons Bitter	(H)
Furgusons Dartmoor Best Bitter	(H)
Castle Eden Ale	(H)
Flowers IPA	(H)
Flowers Original	(H)

AC CP FA ME ML PB PG
The only pub in the town with a separate
public bar.

KENN

LEY ARMS (Map Ref E5)
11 - 3 ; 6 - 11:30. (M-S, 11 - 3 Sun)
KENN, EXETER, (1/2ml FROM
KENNFORD SERVICES ON A38.)
Tel: (0392) 832341

Draught Bass	(H)
Furgusons Dartmoor Strong	(H)
Wadworth 6X	(H)
Flowers IPA	(H)

CC CD CP DF DM FA ME ML QP RF
c13 thatched village pub with excellent
carvery menu and family atmosphere. 20p
off beer on Fridays.

KENNFORD

ANCHOR (Map Ref E5)
11 - 12. (M-S)
KENNFORD, EXETER, (OFF A38 NEAR
KENNFORD SERVICES.)
Tel: (0392) 832344

Courage Best Bitter	(H)
John Smith's Bitter	(H)
Ruddles County	(H)
Wadworth 6X	(H)

AC CP FA ME ML RF
Large village pub with friendly
atmosphere. At present (28/12/92) being
managed for Receivers.

SEVEN STARS (Map Ref E5)
KENNFORD, EXETER, (OFF A38, IN
VILLAGE CENTRE.)
Tel: (0392) 833246

Boddingtons Bitter	(H)
Wadworth 6X	(E)
Flowers IPA	(H)

THE GISSONS ARMS, (Map Ref E5)
11 - 11. (M-S)
KENNFORD, EXETER, (OFF A38, NEAR
KENNFORD SERVICES.)
Tel: (0392) 832444

Draught Bass	(H)
Furgusons Dartmoor Best Bitter	(H)
Tetley Walker Bitter	(H)
Flowers IPA	(H)

AC CP FA GD ME ML OD QP RS
Good restaurant, cosy friendly
atmosphere. BBQs in summer. Renovated
after fire.

KENTISBEARE

KEEPERS COTTAGE INN (Map Ref F4)
11 - 3 ; 5 - 11. (M-F.(W) 11 - 11 (S). 11 - 11 Sat ALL YEAR)
KENTISBEARE, CULLOMPTON, (ON A373 3mls EAST OF CULLOMPTON.),
OS: ST064066
Tel: (08846) 247

Draught Bass	(G)
Cotleigh Tawny	(G)
Otter Ale	(G)
Wadworth 6X	(G)

CA CC CD CP DB FA GD (CHILDRENS PLAY AREA) ME ML OD PG QP RF RS ST
c16 former beer and cider house, farm, and petrol station! Thatched roof and cob/stone walls. Internally very little remaining of origional decor, but has been tastefully modernised over the years. Good, homecooked meals. A guest beer always available.

WYNDHAM ARMS (Map Ref F4)
11 - 2:30 ; 6 - 11 (M-S)
HIGH STREET, KENTISBEARE, CULLOMPTON, (CENTRE OF VILLAGE, NEXT TO CHURCH.),
Tel: (08846) 327

Exe Valley Dob's Best Bitter	(H)
Marston's Pedigree	(H)
Otter Ale	(H)
Flowers IPA	(H)

CA CC CD CP DB DF FA GD ME ML MR OD PG PL RF SN ST
Large, busy but very friendly village pub. Restaurant and bar snacks - home made. c14 inn or farmhouse with large inglenook fireplace. Unusually good for a Whitbread house - worth a visit.

KENTON

DEVON ARMS HOTEL (Map Ref E5)
11 - 3 ; 5 - 11. (M-F. 11 - 11 Sat.)
FORE STREET, KENTON, EXETER, (ON A379 BETWEEN EXMINSTER AND STARCROSS.)
Tel: (0626) 890213

Draught Bass	(H)
Boddingtons Bitter	(H)
Furgusons Dartmoor Best Bitter	(H)
Guest Beer Occasional	(H)

AC CD CI (BULMERS WEST COUNTRY) CP DF DM FA GD ME ML OD PB PG ST
Large village pub with good food.

DOLPHIN INN (Map Ref E5)
11:30 - 3 ; 5 - 11. (11.30 - 11 SATURDAY)
FORE STREET, KENTON, EXETER, (ON A379 IN KENTON VILLAGE)
Tel: (0626) 891371

Draught Bass	(H)
Charrington IPA	(H)
Guest Beer Occasional	(H)

CA CC CD CI (LOCAL FARM) DB DF DM FA GD ME ML OD PB PG RF SN
Refurbished village pub with garden, restaurant and family room. Parking adjacent in the council car park.

KILMINGTON

NEW INN (Map Ref G4)
11 - 3 ; 7 - 11 (M-S (W), 1030 - 11 M-S (S))
THE HILL, KILMINGTON, AXMINSTER,
Tel: (0297) 33376

Palmers BB	(H)
IPA	(H)

CA CP DF FA GD ME ML OD PB PG QP
Palmers western outpost is a fine, friendly village inn just off the A35. Fine beers carefully vented through a water trap - not cask breathers. Superb views from garden.

KINGS NYMPTON

GROVE INN (Map Ref C3)
12 - 3 ; 7 - 11. (M-S)
KINGS NYMPTON, UMBERLEIGH,
Tel: (0769) 80406

Courage Best Bitter	(H)

CC CP DF FA ME ML OD PB QP
Grade 2 listed village inn with one large bar and a homely lounge/TV room.

KINGSBRIDGE

CRAB SHELL INN (Map Ref D8)
11 - 11. (M-S)
EMBANKMENT ROAD, KINGSBRIDGE
Tel: (0548) 852345

Draught Bass	(H)
Whitbread Best Bitter	(H)
Flowers IPA	(H)

CA CP DF FA ME ML OD PB PG QP RF RS
Very old waterside pub and world famous restaurant specialising in fresh fish fare. Seating on the waterfront with wonderful estuary views. FREE mooring for patrons boats. Crab fishing off quay.

DODBROOKE INN (Map Ref D8)
CHURCH STREET, KINGSBRIDGE
Tel: (0548) 2068

Draught Bass	(H)
Boddingtons Bitter	(H)
Marston's Pedigree	(H)

KING OF PRUSSIA (Map Ref D8)
10:30 - 2:30 ; 5 - 11. (M-F, 10.30 - 3.30 Sat
(W), 11-11 M-S (S))
2, CHURCH STREET, KINGSBRIDGE
Tel: (0548) 852099

Whitbread Best Bitter	(H)
Flowers Original	(H)
Guest Beer Regular	(H)

CA CI DF FA ML OD PG RF
Friendly locals bar with a large contingent
of youngsters.

SHIP & PLOUGH (Map Ref D8)
11 - 11. (M-S)
THE PROMENADE, KINGSBRIDGE
Tel: (0548) 852485

Draught Bass	(H)
Blewitt's Best Bitter	(H)
Guest Beer Regular	(H)

AC FA ME ML OD PG RF
Spacious bar with convivial atmosphere
and an attractive wood burning stove.
Pub dates back to 1784. Good value food.
Landlord is in the process of setting up a
micro-brewery just outside the town.

KINGSKERSWELL

BARN OWL (Map Ref E6)
11:30 - 2:30 ; 6:30 - 11 (M-S)
ALLER ROAD, KINGSKERSWELL,
NEWTON ABBOT
Tel: (0803) 872130

Furgusons Dartmoor Best Bitter	(H)
Ind Coope Burton Ale	(H)

AC CP DF ME ML OD PB RF RS
A converted farmhouse, with 2
oak-beamed bars. Reputation for good
food in both bars and restaurant.

BICKLEY MILL INN (Map Ref E6)
11 -2:30 ; 6 - 11 (M-S)
STONEYCOMBE, KINGSKERSWELL,
NEWTON ABBOT, OS: SX864665
Tel: (0803) 873201

Draught Bass	(H)
Greene King IPA	(H)
Wadworth 6X	(H)

AC CC CH CP DF FA ME ML OD RF
Large 13th century converted mill house
with terraced gardens. Good food and live
music on Saturday nights.

HARE & HOUNDS (Map Ref E6)
11 - 3 ; 6 - 11 (M-S)
TORQUAY ROAD, KINGSKERSWELL,
NEWTON ABBOT
Tel: (0803) 873119

Draught Bass	(H)
Eldridge Pope Hardy Country	(H)
Flowers IPA	(H)

CP DF FA ME ML OD
Large eating house, popular with tourists.
Good disabled facilities.

PARK INN (Map Ref E6)
15, COLES LANE, KINGSKERSWELL,
NEWTON ABBOT
Tel: (0803) 872216

Courage Best Bitter (H)

SLOOP (Map Ref E6)
NEWTON ROAD, KINGSKERSWELL
NEWTON ABBOT
Tel: (0803) 872979

Draught Bass	(H)
Courage Best Bitter	(H)

KINGSTEIGNTON

BELL INN (Map Ref E6)
11 - 2:30 ; 5 - 11. (M-F, OPENS AT 6P.M.
SAT. EVENINGS)
29, FORE STREET, KINGSTEIGN- TON,
NEWTON ABBOT
Tel: (0626) 56483

Courage Best Bitter	(H)
Courage Directors	(H)

CC CP FA ME ML OD PG RF
Traditional village pub, refurbished in
1987. Caters for families and couples with
an accent on food.

DEWDROP INN (Map Ref E6)
66, FORE STREET, KINGSTEIGNTON
Tel: (0626) 52786

Draught Bass	(H)
Flowers Original	(H)

OLD RYDON (Map Ref E6)
11 - 2:30 ; 6 - 11. (M-S)
RYDON LANE, KINGSTEIGNTON,
NEWTON ABBOT, OS: SX875737
Tel: (0626) 54626

Draught Bass	(H)
Wadworth 6X	(H)

CP DF FA GD ME ML OD QP RF RS
Superb old world pub with an upstairs
drinking area, cosy corners, a good fire,
excellent food and a fine garden. Small,
olde worlde, Grade 2 listed, pub built in
1560. Bar has a minstrels gallery, and a
large conservatory included in the eating
area. A separate restaurant provides 'Haute
Cuisine' food, whilst the main bar has a
continuously changing menu from all
continents. Well worth a visit, but go early
as it is a very popular eating place.

PASSAGE HOUSE INN (Map Ref E6)
HACKNEY LANE, KINGSTEIGNTON
NEWTON ABBOT
Tel: (0626) 55515

Draught Bass	(H)
Marston's Pedigree	(H)
Flowers IPA	(H)

SANDYGATE INN (Map Ref E6)
11 - 2:30 ; 5:30 - 11. (M-F, 6 - 11 Sat)
KINGSTEIGNTON, NEWTON ABBOT
Tel: (0626) 54679

Flowers Original	(H)

CP DF FA ME ML OD PB PG RS (DINING
ROOM)
c17, oak beamed, popular pub, with good
value home-made food in the dining room.

TEN TORS INN (Map Ref E6)
EXETER ROAD, KINGSTEIGNTON,
NEWTON ABBOT
Tel: (0626) 65434

Draught Bass	(H)
Tetley Bitter	(H)

KINGSTON

DOLPHIN INN (Map Ref C7)
11 - 3 ; 6 - 11. (M-S)
KINGSTON, Nr. BIGBURY
Tel: (0548) 810314

Ushers Founders	(H)

CD (EUCHRE) CH CP FA GD ME ML OD
PG QP
A large low beamed pub with a strong
smell of food cooking on the charcoal grill.
Family room, gents and garden are all
across the road.

KINGSWEAR

STEAM PACKET INN (Map Ref E7)
11:30 - 3 ; 6 - 11. (M-S, VARIES IN
SUMMER)
FORE STREET, KINGSWEAR,
DARTMOUTH
Tel: (0803) 752208

Courage Best Bitter	(H)
Ushers Best Bitter	(H)
Wadworth 6X	(H)

BR (KINGSWEAR -SOUTH DEVON
RAILWAY) CA DF ME ML PG QP
Friendly, locals pub.

KNOWLE

EBRINGTON ARMS (Map Ref B2)
KNOWLE, Nr. BARNSTAPLE, (OFF A361,
1 MILE NORTH OF BRAUNTON)
Tel: (0271) 812166

Draught Bass	(H)

CP ME ML OD RF
Old, multi-roomed, village pub.

The Dartmoor Inn, Lydford

KNOWLE (E)

BRITANNIA (Map Ref F5)
11 - 2 ; 6 - 10:30. (M-Th. 6 - 11 F, Sat. 12 - 2
Sun)
KNOWLE VILLAGE, BUDLEIGH
SALTERTON, (MIDDLE OF VILLAGE ON
B3178), OS: SY0582

Draught Bass (G)

CD CP QP RF
Present pub built in 1930's to replace
original thatched pub,on site of carpark.
Decor still as original. Locally known as
'The Dog & Donkey' and has the well
earned reputation of serving the best Bass
in the area. Landlady probably one of the
oldest in the country - in her eighties.

KNOWSTONE

MASONS ARMS (Map Ref D3)
11 - 3 ; 7 - 11. (M-S)
Nr. SOUTH MOLTON,
Tel: (03984) 231

Cotleigh Tawny (H)
Hall And Woodhouse Badger Best Bitter
(H)

AC CA CP FA ME ML OD PB PG QP RF
Charming c16 Grade 2 listed inn on the
edge of Exmoor, and on the Two Moors
Way footpath. Pub boasts a beautiful
thatched roof over rendered stone walls,
with a superb , unspoilt interior including
an impressive fireplace.

LAMERTON

BLACKSMITHS ARMS (Map Ref B5)
LAMERTON, TAVISTOCK
Tel: (0822) 612962

Draught Bass (H)

LANDKEY

CASTLE INN (Map Ref C2)
LANDKEY, Nr. BARNSTAPLE.

Flowers IPA (H)

LANDSCOVE

LIVE AND LET LIVE (Map Ref D6)
11:30 - 11. (M-S)
LANDSCOVE, NEWTON ABBOT
Tel: (080426) 663

Furgusons Dartmoor Best Bitter (H)
Ind Coope Burton Ale (H)

CA CP DF FA ME ML OD PG QP RF
Pleasant small, quiet, pub in a tiny hamlet,
over 200 years old. Home-cooked food and
country wines. The 'Landscove Ale' is
Dartmoor Best. BEWARE! - the
Thompson's porter is KEG.

LANGTREE

GREEN DRAGON (Map Ref B3)
DRAGON HILL, LANGTREE, Nr.
TORRINGTON,
Tel: (08055) 342

Draught Bass (H)

LAPFORD

MALTSCOOP INN (Map Ref D3)
11:30 - 2:30 ; 6 - 11. (M-S)
LAPFORD, Nr. CREDITON,
Tel: (0363) 83330 ᴏ₁ᴣᴄᴣ ᴃᴣᴣᴣᴏ

Adnams Broadside (G)
Butcombe Bitter (H)
Gibbs Mew Premium (H)
Hook Norton Best Bitter (H)
Wadworth 6X (G)

AC BR (LAPFORD) CA CC DB DF
(ACCESS ONLY) FA (RESTAURANT
ONLY) GD LM ME ML OD (PATIO) PB PG
PL QP RF RS ST
Real village inn with wooden stillage
behind bar and an old inglenook fireplace.
Disabled access to the gents. Live music
some Sunday nights. Well worth a visit!

LIVERTON

WELCOME STRANGER (Map Ref D6)
12 - 3 ; 6 - 11. (M-S)
LIVERTON, NEWTON ABBOT
Tel: (0626) 821224

Courage Best Bitter (H)
Ushers (H)
    Best Bitter (H)
    Founders

CA CP DF FA ME ML OD PG QP RF
Large one bar pub set alone on the old
main road, with good views.

LODDISWELL

LODDISWELL INN (Map Ref D7)
LODDISWELL, KINGSBRIDGE,
OS: SX721484
Tel: (0548) 550308

Ushers	**(H)**
Best Bitter	**(H)**
Founders	**(H)**

LONGDOWN

LAMB INN (Map Ref E5)
11 - 2:30 ; 6 - 11 (M-S)
LONGDOWN, Nr. EXETER, (ON B3121)
Tel: (0392) 81226

Furgusons Dartmoor Best Bitter	**(H)**
Ind Coope Burton Ale	**(H)**
Morland Old Speckled Hen	**(H)**
Guest Beer Occasional	**(H)**

CP DB ME ML OD (PATIO) RF
Pleasantly refurbished victorian inn.
Restaurant type food and snacks.

LOWER ASHTON

MANOR INN (Map Ref E5)
12 - 2:30 ; 6 - 11. (T-S. CLOSED ALL DAY
MONDAY)
LOWER ASHTON, (JUST OFF B3193 ON
EAST SIDE.)
Tel: (0647) 53204

Draught Bass	**(H)**
Cotleigh Tawny	**(H)**
Wadworth 6X	**(G)**
Guest Beer Regular	**(H)**

CA CC CP GD ME ML OD PB PG QP RF
A typical unspoilt country pub. The public
bar comprises of a wooden floor, a few
tables and chairs, dartboard, open fire and
a small bar area. The lounge is slightly
more comfortable but still has a rustic
atmosphere. The beer range varies.

THE MANOR INN

LOWER ASHTON, DEVON · Tel. (0647) 52301

HOME COOKING
☆
REAL ALES
Cotleigh Tawny Bitter
Huntsman Royal Oak
(both hand pumped)
Wadworth 6X
(gravity feed)
☆
GARDEN
☆
CAR PARK

LUNDY ISLAND

MARISCO TAVERN (Map Ref A1)
(WHENEVER BOAT VISITS)
LUNDY ISLAND, BRISTOL CHANNEL
(TAKE THE BOAT FROM ILFRACOMBE
(S) OR BIDEFORD ALL YEAR),
OS: SS138440
Tel: (0237) 431831

Marisco Tavern	
John 'O's	**(H)**
Old Light	**(H)**
Old Light Special	**(H)**

CA (MUST BE BOOKED IN ADVANCE)
FA ML QP RF
Devon's remotest pub, 12 miles from the
nearest road. The pub serves as the village
shop, and has its own brewery, which is
being refurbished at time of survey. (2/93)
The pub has granite floors, carved wooden
balcony, and relics from the many ships
wrecked off the island. Well worth a visit -
can be done in a day.

LUPPITT

LUPPITT INN (Map Ref F4)
12 - 2 ; 7 - 11. (M-S)
LUPPITT, Nr. HONITON,
Tel: (0404) 891613

Otter Bitter	**(H)**

Farmhouse bar.

LUSTLEIGH

CLEAVE (Map Ref D5)
11 -3 ; 7 -11. (M-S (W), 11-11 (S))
LUSTLEIGH, BOVEY TRACEY
Tel: (06477) 223

Draught Bass	**(H)**
Whitbread WCPA	**(H)**
Flowers Original	**(H)**

AC CP DF FA ME ML OD PB QP RF
15th century thatched inn in the heart of
Lustleigh with a cosy lounge bar and a
vast, granite inglenook fireplace and
separate dining granite walled dining
room.

LUTON

ELIZABETHAN INN (Map Ref E5)
11 - 3 ; 6 - 11. (M-S)
LUTON, Nr. NEWTON ABBOT,
OS: SX903768
Tel: (0626) 775428

Cornish Royal Wessex	(H)
Furgusons Dartmoor Strong	(H)
Flowers IPA	(H)

CA CC CH CP FA ME ML OD PB RF
400 year old pub with low ceilings in a
cosy public bar. Wood panelled lounge
and family lounge.

LUTTON

MOUNTAIN INN (Map Ref C7)
11 - 3 ; 6 - 11. (Th-Sat. 7 - 11 M-W)
LUTTON, CORNWOOD, IVYBRIDGE
Tel: (075537) 247

Furgusons Dartmoor Strong	(H)
Ind Coope Burton Ale	(H)
Wadworth 6X	(H)
Guest Beer Regular	(H)

CI (SUMMER ONLY) CP ME ML OD PG
RF
Cottage style bar and furnishings with
exposed cob walls, a large granite fire
place. Set in a sleepy village where car
parking requires good manners. House
beer - Mountain Ale - is Burton Ale.

LYDFORD

CASTLE INN (Map Ref B5)
11:30 - 3 ; 6 - 11. (M-S)
LYDFORD, Nr. TAVISTOCK, OS: SX509848
Tel: (082282) 242

Draught Bass	(H)
Furgusons Dartmoor Best Bitter	(H)
Palmers IPA	(H)
Palmers Best Bitter	(H)
Guest Beer Regular	(G)

AC CA CC CP DF FA GD ME ML OD PB
PG QP RF
Stone flagged 16th century inn near the
castle, with a pleasant and welcoming
atmosphere. Two-roomed pub with a large
stone fireplace, low ceilings, and a garden
ideal for children.

DARTMOOR INN (Map Ref B5)
11:30 - 2:30 ; 6:30 - 11. (M-S (W) 11 - 3, 6 - 11
(S))
LYDFORD, Nr. TAVISTOCK (ON A386, AT
JUNCTION OF ROAD FROM LYDFORD),
OS: SX523852
Tel: (0822821) 221

Draught Bass	(H)
St Austell Tinners	(H)

AC CA CC CP FA ME ML OD PG RF
Charm and atmosphere in this family run
pub situated on Dartmoor. A bridle path
leads across the moor from the side of the
pub.

MANOR INN (Map Ref B5)
11 - 3 ; 6 - 11. (M-S)
LYDFORD, Nr. TAVISTOCK (1 MILE
SOUTH OF LYDFORD, AT MOUTH OF
GORGE), OS: SX503832
Tel: (082282) 208

Draught Bass	(H)
Wadworth 6X	(H)

AC CA CC CH CP DF FA ME ML OD PG
PL QP RF
Stone walled inn by gorge and stream,
with a 'Dirty Duck' bar and pool room.

LYMPSTONE

GLOBE INN (Map Ref E5)
11 - 2:30 ; 6 - 11. (M-S)
THE STRAND, LYMPSTONE, Nr.
EXMOUTH, (TOWARDS HARBOUR
FROM B.R. STATION),
Tel: (0395) 263166

Draught Bass	(H)
Boddingtons Bitter	(H)
Flowers IPA	(H)

BR (Lympstone) DB DM FA ME ML PB QP
Village pub situated near quay/harbour.
Famous for seafood meals.

NUTWELL LODGE (Map Ref E5)
EXMOUTH ROAD, LYMPSTONE, Nr.
EXMOUTH, (ON A376, 1/2 MILE SOUTH
OF EXTON.), OS: SX990858
Tel: (0392) 875180

Draught Bass	(H)
Furgusons Dartmoor Best Bitter	(H)

REDWING (Map Ref E5)
11 - 2:30 ; 6 - 11. (M-S)
CHURCH ROAD, LYMPSTONE, Nr.
EXMOUTH, (HALF-WAY ALONG
CHURCH ROAD FROM CHURCH TO
STATION.), Tel: (0395) 222156

| Flowers IPA | (H) |
| Flowers Original | (H) |

BR (Lympstone) CI CP DB FA GD ME ML
OD PB PG
Friendly, unpretentious village pub.

SWAN INN (Map Ref E5)
THE STRAND, LYMPSTONE, Nr.
EXMOUTH, (CORNER OF STATION
APPROACH AND THE STRAND.),
Tel: (0395) 272284

| Draught Bass | (H) |
| Flowers IPA | (H) |

**YE OLDE SADDLERS ARMS, (Map
Ref E5)**
11 - 2:30 ; 6 - 11. (M-S (W), 11 - 11 (S))
EXMOUTH ROAD, LYMPSTONE,
EXMOUTH, (ON A376 AT JUNCTION
WITH LONGMEADOW ROAD.),
Tel: (0395) 272798

Courage Best Bitter	(H)
Ruddles Best Bitter	(H)
Ushers Best Bitter	(H)

CA CA CP CP DB FA GD ME ML OD PG
PL QP RS SN
Large roadside pub with bias towards
restaurant facilities. Well known for its
good menu.

LYNBRIDGE

**OLDE COTTAGE INNE (Map Ref
D1)**
12 - 3 ; 6:30 - 11. (M-S)
LYNBRIDGE, LYNTON, Tel: (0598) 53570

Draught Bass	(H)
Butcombe Bitter	(H)
(SUMMER ONLY)	
Guest Beer Occasional	(H)

AC CA CC CP ME ML OD QP RF
Old world pub with accomodation,
situated on the banks of the West Lyn
River.

LYNMOUTH

RISING SUN HOTEL (Map Ref D1)
11 - 2:30 ; 6 - 11. (M-S (W), VARIABLE IN
SUMMER)
MARS HILL, LYNMOUTH,
Tel: (0598) 53223

| Ruddles Best Bitter | (H) |
| Ruddles County | (H) |

AC ME ML
Picturesque thatched hotel on the seafront.

**VILLAGE INN AT LYNMOUTH
(Map Ref D1)**
11 - 2:30 ; 7 - 11. (M-S (W), 11 - 11 (S))
LYNMOUTH STREET, LYNMOUTH,
Tel: (0598) 52354

Castle Eden Ale	(H)
(SUMMER ONLY)	
Flowers Original	(H)

AC FA ME ML OD RF
Comfortable lounge bar.

LYNTON

CROWN HOTEL (Map Ref D1)
11 - 11. (M-S)
SINAI HILL, LYNTON,
Tel: (0598) 52253

| Draught Bass | (H) |

AC CP FA ME ML OD PB PG RS
(EVENINGS ONLY)
18th century coaching inn with public,
lounge bar and outside drinking area. Bar
food and an A LA Carte restaurant in the
evenings.

GLOBE (Map Ref D1)
17, LEE ROAD, LYNTON,
Tel: (0598) 53350

| Draught Bass | (H) |

QUEENS HOTEL (Map Ref D1)
11 - 11. (M-S) QUEEN STREET, LYNTON,
Tel: (0598) 52625

Butcombe Bitter	(H)
Courage Directors	(H)
Ruddles County	(H)
Guest Beer Regular	(H)
(SUMMER ONLY)	

AC FA ME (SUMMER ONLY) ML
(SUMMER ONLY) PG RF
Comfortable town pub with enthusiastic
landlord, and good variety of guest ales.

ROYAL CASTLE HOTEL (Map Ref D1)
11 -3 ; 6:30 - 11. (M-S (W), 6-11 (S))
CASTLE HILL, LYNTON,
Tel: (0598) 52348

Butcombe Bitter	(H)
Exmoor Ale	(H)
(SUMMER ONLY)	
Tetley Bitter	(H)

AC CP FA ME ML OD QP
Elegant clifftop hotel with spectacular views along the Bristol Channel.

STAG & STABLE BAR (Map Ref D1)
(ONLY OPEN IN SUMMER) VALLEY OF THE ROCKS HOTEL, LEE ROAD, LYNTON,
Tel: (0598) 52349

Courage Directors	(H)

MAIDENCOMBE

THATCHED TAVERN (Map Ref E6)
11 - 3 ; 6 - 11. (M-S)
STEEP HILL, MAIDENCOMBE, TORQUAY
Tel: (0803) 329155

Ind Coope Burton Ale	(H)
Tetley Bitter	(H)

AC CA DF FA GD ME ML NS OD QP
Thatched c16 inn overlooking Torbay. Winner of 'Pub Garden of the Year' for last 3 years.

MALBOROUGH

OLD INN (Map Ref D8)

Draught Bass	(H)
Courage Best Bitter	(H)
Smiles Best Bitter	(H)

CH CI CP FA ME ML OD PB PG RF
Pub in two distinct parts - one for drinking and one for eating. Both envelope the U-shaped bar. Les Routier noted.

ROYAL OAK (Map Ref D8)
11 - 3 ; 5 - 11 (M-S)
HIGHER TOWN, MALBOROUGH, TOTNES
Tel: (0548) 561481

Courage Best Bitter	(H)
Ushers 1824 Particular	(G)
Ushers Founders	(H)

AC CC CI FA PG RF
Horseshoe shaped bar, good pub grub (traditional). A regular local trade. Undergoing refurbishment at time of survey (12/92).

MANATON

KESTOR INN (Map Ref D5)
11 - 3 ; 6:30 - 11. (M-S)
MANATON, Nr. BOVEY TRACEY
Tel: (064722) 204

Wadworth 6X	(H)
Flowers Original	(H)
Guest Beer Regular	(H)

AC CH CP DF FA ME ML OD PG RF RS
Extensively refurbished in a modern style with a separate restaurant.

MARLDON

OLDE SMOKEY HOUSE (Map Ref E6)
VICKERAGE ROAD, MARLDON, Nr. TORQUAY
Tel: (0803) 557630

Courage Best Bitter	(H)
Courage Directors	(H)
John Smith's Bitter	(H)

MARSH

COTTAGE INN (Map Ref G4)
MARSH, Nr. HONITON,.
Tel: (0460) 234339

Draught Bass	(H)
John Smith's Bitter	(H)

FLINTLOCK INN (Map Ref G4)
11 - 2:30 ; 6:30 - 11. (M-S)
MARSH, Nr. HONITON,
Tel: (0460) 234403

Guest Beer Regular	(H)

CA CC CP DF FA ME ML PG RF Free house with a continuously changing beer menu, taking advantage of the extensive range of beers now available in the west country.

MARY TAVY

MARY TAVY INN (Map Ref B5)
11:30 - 3 ; 6 - 11. (M-S (W). 11 - 3 (S))
LANE HEAD, MARY TAVY, Nr. TAVISTOCK
Tel: (0822) 810326

Draught Bass	(H)
St Austell Tinners	(H)

HSD (H) AC CA CC CH CP DF FA ME ML OD PB PG QP RF
Large roadside c16 inn, at the edge of the moor, with a pleasant and welcoming atmosphere and a large stone fireplace.

ROYAL STANDARD (Map Ref B5)
MARY TAVY, Nr. TAVISTOCK
Tel: (0822) 810289

Draught Bass	(H)
Palmers BB	(H)

MEAVY

ROYAL OAK INN (Map Ref C6)
11 - 2 ; 6 - 11. (M-S)
MEAVY, Nr YELVERTON
Tel: (0822) 852944

Draught Bass	(H)
Boddingtons Bitter	(H)
Castle Eden Ale	(H)
Guest Beer Regular	(H)

CA CC ME ML OD PB PG QP RF
Classic, c15 country pub near the village
green next to the church. Popular with
walkers, ramblers and country folk. The
public bar has a slate floor, and an
inglenook fireplace. One of two pubs in the
country owned by the local parish council.

MEMBURY

LONGBRIDGE INN (Map Ref G4)
11 - 3 ; 6:30 - 11. (M-S)
MEMBURY, Nr AXMINSTER,
Tel: (0404) 88366

Exmoor Ale	(H)

CP DF FA ME ML OD PG QP RF
Small country family owned pub in the
Yarty valley. Separate restaurant, but no
food on Mondays. Two skittle alleys.

MERTON

MALT SCOOP (Map Ref C3)
12 - 2 ; 7 - 11. (M-S)
MERTON, Nr. TORRINGTON,
Tel: (08053) 260

Butcombe Bitter	(H)

CP
Basic traditional village pub which has
been in the same family since 1906.

MILTON ABBOT

EDGCUMBE ARMS (Map Ref B5)
11 - 3 ; 6 - 11. (M-S)
FORE STREET, MILTON ABBOT
Tel: (0822) 87229

Boddingtons Bitter	(H)
Wadworth 6X	(H)

CC CP ME ML OD PB QP RF
Welcoming, convivial roadside pub with
an impressive fireplace. Guest beers in
summer.

MILTON COOMBE

WHO'D HAVE THOUGHT IT (Map Ref B6)
11:30 - 2:30 ; 6:30 - 11. (M-F. 11.30 - 3 Sat)
MILTON COOMBE, YELVERTON,
OS: SX488660
Tel: (0822) 853313

Draught Bass	(H)
Blackawton Headstrong	(H)
Eldridge Pope Royal Oak	(H)
Marston's Pedigree	(H)
Wadworth 6X	(H)

CA CI CP DF GD ME ML OD QP
Beautiful 3 roomed 16th century inn,
picturesquely situated in a steep wooded
valley and a pleasantly chaotic village
close to Lopwell dam. Extensive bar
snacks and main meals.

MODBURY

EXETER INN (Map Ref C7)
11 - 2:30 ; 6:45 - 11. (M-S (W). 11 - 11 (S))
BROAD STREET, MODBURY
Tel: (0548) 830239

Courage Directors	(H)
John Smith's Bitter	(H)
Marston's Pedigree	(H)
Ruddles Best Bitter	(H)

AC CD (EUCHRE) CP DB FA LM
(OCCASIONAL) ME ML OD PG RF
14th century inn very popular with
youngsters and pensioners alike.
Occasional jazz.

MODBURY INN (Map Ref C7)
11:30 - 3 ; 5:30 - 11. (M-Th. 11 - 11 F, Sat)
BROWNSTON STREET, MODBURY
Tel: (0548) 830439

Draught Bass	(H)
Blackawton Bitter	(G)
Flowers IPA	(H)

AC CD (EUCHRE) DB FA ME ML OD PB
PG RS
Large hotel with restaurant.

MOLLAND

BLACKCOCK (Map Ref D2)
11 - 11. (M-S)
MOLLAND, Nr. SOUTH MOLTON,
Tel: (07697) 297

Cotleigh
  Harrier   (H)
  Tawny   (H)
Guest Beer Regular   (H)
(SUMMER ONLY)

AC CA CC CP DF FA ME ML OD PG RF
Pleasant village inn with accomodation
and an indoor swimming pool. Home
cooked grub. Live music at weekends.
Guest beers.

LONDON INN (Map Ref D2)
12 - 3 ; 7 - 11. (M-S)
MOLLAND, Nr. SOUTH MOLTON.
Tel: (07697) 269

Draught Bass   (G)
Flowers IPA   (G)

AC CC CP FA ME ML OD PB PG QP RF
Traditional Devon inn on the lower reaches
of Exmoor, one of a dying breed of proper
pubs.

MONKLEIGH

BELL INN (Map Ref B3)
MONKLEIGH, Nr. BIDEFORD,
Tel: (0805) 22338

Flowers IPA   (G)
Guest Beer Regular   (G)

CP ML OD RF
Friendly village pub with a guest ale, and
an enthusiastic landlord.

MONKTON

MONKTON COURT INN (Map Ref G3)
MONKTON, Nr. HONITON, (ON A30 TO
EAST OF HONITON.)
Tel: (0404) 42309

Otter Bitter   (H)
Webster's Yorkshire Bitter   (H)

MORCHARD BISHOP

LONDON INN (Map Ref D4)
12 - 2:30 ; 6:30 - 11. (M-S)
MORCHARD BISHOP, Nr. CREDITON,
Tel: (03637) 222

Fullers London Pride   (H)
Fullers ESB   (H)
Wadworth 6X   (H)
Flowers IPA   (H)

CA CD (CRIB) CP DB DF (ACCESS ONLY)
FA GD ME ML OD PG PL QP RF ST
Large, tastefully modernised, c16 village
pub. Separate skittle alley.

MORELEIGH

NEW INN (Map Ref D7)
12 - 2 ; 6:30 - 11. (M-S)
MORLEIGH, Nr. HALWELL,
KINGSBRIDGE (ON B3207, 1 MILE WEST
OF HALWELL), OS: SX765527
Tel: (0548) 82326

Palmers IPA   (G)

CI CP ME ML PB PG QP RF
Excellent traditional village pub off the
beaten track. Not fancy, not spoilt not
modernised. Has a reputation for fine
steaks and is highly recommended.

MORETONHAMPSTEAD

UNION INN (Map Ref D5)
11 - 11. (M-S)
10, FORD STREET,
MORETONHAMPSTEAD
Tel: (0647) 40199

Boddingtons Bitter   (H)
Eldridge Pope Hardy Country   (H)
Flowers Original   (H)

CP FA ME ML OD PG
A lively town centre locals pub, c15 in
origin. Formerly an old coaching inn with
stables to the rear. Only pub in the town
with a car park.

MORTEHOE

CHICHESTER ARMS (Map Ref B1)
11 - 2:30 ; 6 - 11. (M-S (W), VARIABLE IN
SUMMER)
MORTEHOE,
Tel: (0271) 870411
Ruddles County   (H)
Ushers Best Bitter   (H)
CA CP FA ME ML OD PG
Large, comfortable pub, with separate
skittle alley, situated at top of a steep hill
overlooking Woolacombe Bay.

SHIP AGROUND (Map Ref B1)
11 - 3 ; 5:30 - 11 (M-S (W), VARIABLE IN
SUMMER)
THE SQUARE, MORTEHOE,
ILFRACOMBE,
Tel: (0271) 870856

Boddingtons Bitter	(H)
Butcombe Bitter	(H)
Guest Beer Regular	(H)

CA FA ME ML OD PG RF
Traditional Devon inn on the lower reaches
of Exmoor, one of a dying breed of proper
pubs with a menagerie in the front
passage. Pub was converted from old
cottages situated next to village church.
Ideal for coastal walks and golden sandy
beaches. Constantly changing guest ales.

MUDDIFORD

MUDDIFORD INN (Map Ref C2)
12 - 2:30 ; 7 - 11. (M-S (W), 11 - 11 (S))
MUDDIFORD, Nr. BARNSTAPLE, (ON
B3230, 3mls NORTH OF BARNSTAPLE)
Tel: (0271) 850243

Ushers Best Bitter	(H)
Webster's Yorkshire Bitter	(H)

CP FA ME (SUMMER ONLY) ML
(SUMMER ONLY) OD
Large, old fashioned pub, with pleasant
gardens, now under new ownership.

MUSBURY

GOLDEN HIND (Map Ref G4)
11 - 2:30 ; 6 - 11. (M-S)
MUSBURY, (ON MUSBURY BYPASS AT
CORNER OF ROAD INTO VILLAGE.),
OS: SY272946 Tel: (0297) 55241

3 Draught Bass	(H)

CA CI CP DB FA GD ME ML OD PB PG
QP RF SN
Small cosy pub on main Axminster to
Seaton road.

NADDERWATER

ROYAL OAK (Map Ref E4)
11 - 3 ; 5:30 - 11. (M-F. 11 - 11 Sat)
NADDERWATER, Nr. EXETER, (ON OLD
TEDBURN ROAD VIA WHITESTONE.)
Tel: (0392) 72352

Draught Bass	(H)
Boddingtons Bitter	(H)
Flowers Original	(H)

DB GD (SWINGS FOR CHILDREN) ML
(EXCEPT TUES.) OD PB
Two-bar village local.

NEWTON ABBOT

DARTMOUTH INN (Map Ref E6)
11 - 11. (M-S)
63, EAST STREET, NEWTON ABBOT
Tel: (0626) 53451

Draught Bass	(H)
Guest Beer Regular	(H)

BR (NEWTON ABBOT) CD (EUCHRE) CI
DB FA OD PG PL
Old pub on main road, with a major guest
ale emphasis. Over 300, mainly
independent, ales generally over 4% ABV
have been stocked and always at the same
price. Often there are 18 different ales sold
during a week.

GOLDEN LION (Map Ref E6)
MARKET STREET, NEWTON ABBOT
Tel: (0626) 67062

Furgusons Dartmoor Best Bitter	(H)
Ind Coope Burton Ale	(H)

HEAVITREE ARMS (Map Ref E6)
11 - 11 (M-S)
HIGHWEEK ROAD, NEWTON ABBOT
Tel: (0626) 53116

Draught Bass	(H)

CD CI OD PG PL SK ST
Busy estate pub popular for pool and the
full size snooker table. Occasional live
music.

66

QUEENS HOTEL (Map Ref E6)
11 - 2:30 ; 5 - 11. (M-F, 11 - 11 Sat)
QUEEN STREET, NEWTON ABBOT
Tel: (0626) 63133

Draught Bass	(H)
Mill Janner's Ale	(H)
(CALLED QUEENS ALE)	
Tetley Bitter	(H)

AC BR (NEWTON ABBOT - OPPOSITE)
CP DF ME ML QP RF
Large hotel opposite the railway station
renowned for the quality of its Bass. Very
friendly atmosphere.

RAILWAY INN (Map Ref E6)
197, QUEEN STREET, NEWTON ABBOT
Tel: (0626) 54166

| Boddingtons Bitter | (H) |

WHITE HART INN (Map Ref E6)
8, EAST STREET, NEWTON ABBOT
Tel: (0626) 63910

| Flowers IPA | (H) |

WOLBOROUGH INN (Map Ref E6)
11 - 2 ; 6 -11. (M-F, 7 - 11 SAT EVENING)
WOLBOROUGH STREET, NEWTON
ABBOT
Tel: (0626) 61667

| Flowers IPA | (H) |

AC CD (EUCHRE) DB ML PG PL
Small one bar pub on the edge of town.
Very sporty.

NEWTON POPPLEFORD

CANNON INN (Map Ref F5)
11:30 - 2:30 ; 6:30 - 11. (M-S. 12 - 2.30 Sun.)
HIGH STREET, NEWTON POPPLEFORD
Tel: (0395) 68266
| Cornish Royal Wessex | (H) |
| Marston's Pedigree | (H) |
AC CC CI (TAUNTON) CP DB FA
(LOUNGE ONLY) ME ML OD PB PG
Inn with a dining room and a skittle alley.
Two bar friendly local.

EXETER INN (Map Ref F5)
11 - 3 ; 6 - 11. (M-S)
HIGH STREET, NEWTON POPPLEFORD
DEVONSHIRE.
Tel: (0395) 68295

| Flowers IPA | (H) |

CC CI (TAUNTON) DB DF FA ME ML OD
PB PG ST
Comfortable one bar village local.

NEWTON ST. CYRES

BEER ENGINE (Map Ref E4)
11:30 - 2:30; 6: - 11: (SAT 11 - 11)
NEWTON ST. CYRES, EXETER.
Tel: (0392) 851282

Beer Engine		
Rail Ale	(H)
Piston Bitter	(H)
Sleeper	(H)

BR (NEWTON ST. CYRES) CC CP GD ME
ML OD RF
Friendly and deservedly popular home
brew pub near the railway station. At
weekends the downstairs bar is opened
and the brewery may be viewed. Good
value food including locally made
sausages and cheeses. Live entertainment
every weekend.

Pub and Brewery
THE BEER ENGINE
Newton St. Cyres Exeter EX5 5AX. Exeter 851282

BEAUTIFUL BEERS BREWED ON THE PREMISES
Rail Ale   Piston Bitter   Sleeper Heavy

GOOD PUB FOOD ALWAYS AVAILABLE
CHILDREN WELCOME
LIVE MUSIC AT THE WEEKEND
Beer Garden

CROWN AND SCEPTRE (Map Ref E4)
NEWTON ST. CYRES, EXETER.
Tel: (0392) 851278

Draught Bass	**(H)**
Eldridge Pope Hardy Country	**(H)**

NEWTON TRACEY

HUNTERS INN (Map Ref C2)
11 - 3 ; 7 - 11. (M-S)
NEWTON TRACEY, Nr. BARNSTAPLE.
Tel: (0271) 858339

Marston's Pedigree	**(H)**
Flowers IPA	**(H)**

CC CP DF FA ME ML OD PG RF
Popular hostelry with a reputation for
good food. The old part of the pub is very
cosy.

NOMANSLAND

MOUNT PLEASANT INN (Map Ref D3)
11 - 2:30 ; 6 - 11. (M-F, 11 - 11 Sat)
NOMANSLAND, Nr. TIVERTON (ON A373 NORTH WEST OF TIVERTON)
Tel: (0884) 860271

Boddingtons Bitter	**(H)**
Flowers Original	**(H)**

CA CP DF FA ME ML OD PG RF RS
Sympathetically modernised one bar pub,
which was once the village smithy. Has a
restaurant attached.

NORTH BOVEY

RING OF BELLS (Map Ref D5)
11 - 3 ; 6 - 11 (M-S)
NORTH BOVEY, BOVEY TRACEY
Tel: (0647) 40375

Furgusons Dartmoor Best Bitter	**(H)**
Ind Coope Burton Ale	**(H)**
Wadworth 6X	**(H)**
Guest Beer Regular	**(H)**
(SUMMER ONLY)	

AC CA FA ME ML OD PB PG RF
c13, grade 1 listed, thatched inn,
completely unmodernised. Set in a pretty
village off the beaten track. - well worth
the effort of finding.

NORTH MOLTON

MINERS ARMS (Map Ref D2)
NORTH MOLTON, Nr. BARNSTAPLE,
Tel: (05984) 316

Draught Bass	**(H)**

CP ME ML RS
Comfortable lounge bar and separate
restaurant.

POLTIMORE ARMS (Map Ref D2)
NORTH MOLTON, Nr. BARNSTAPLE,
Tel: (05984) 338

Courage Directors	**(H)**
Flowers Original	**(H)**

NORTH TAWTON

GREEN DRAGON (Map Ref C4)
12 - 3 ; 7 - 11. (M-S)
NORTH TAWTON, Nr. OKEHAMPTON,

Boddingtons Bitter	**(H)**

CP PB PG RF Comfortable two-roomed
pub.

NORTHAM

KINGSLEY INN (Map Ref B2)
FORE STREET, NORTHAM, Nr.
BIDEFORD,
Tel: (0237) 474221

Flowers IPA	**(H)**
Flowers Original	**(H)**

NOSS MAYO

OLD SHIP INN (Map Ref C7)
11 - 3 ; 6 - 11. (M-F. 11 - 11 Sat)
NOSS MAYO, NEWTON FERRERS
Tel: (0752) 872387

Furgusons Dartmoor Best Bitter	**(H)**
Wadworth 6X	**(H)**

CA CD (EUCHRE) CH CP DB FA ME ML
OD PG PL
Old fashioned, oak beamed, single bar
pubton waters edge of River Yealm.

SWAN INN (Map Ref C7)
11 - 3 ; 6 - 11. (M-S (W), 11 - 11 (S))
PILLORY HILL, NOSS MAYO, NEWTON
FERRERS
Tel: (0752) 872392

Courage Best Bitter	(H)
Ushers Best Bitter	(H)
Ushers Founders	(H)

CA CD (EUCHRE) CP DB FA (EATING
AREA ONLY) ME ML OD PG (QUIZ) RF
Large, single bar local, overlooking River
Yealm. Quiz night on Thursdays.

OAKFORD

RED LION HOTEL (Map Ref E3)
12 - 3 ; 7 - 11. (M-S (W). 11 - 11 (S))
ROOKERY HILL, OAKFORD, Nr.
TIVERTON,
Tel: (03985) 219

Boddingtons Bitter	(H)
Butcombe Bitter	(H)
Guest Beer Regular	(H)

AC CA DB FA ME ML OD PG (QUIZ) PL
RF RM (BACKGROUND) SH
Old shooting and fishing inn in centre of
village.

OKEHAMPTON

PLUME OF FEATHERS (Map Ref C4)
10:30 - 3:30 ; 5:30 - 11. (HOURS MAY
VARY) 38, FORE STREET,
OKEHAMPTON,
Tel: (0837) 52815

Courage Best Bitter	(H)
Courage Directors	(H)
Guest Beer Regular	(H)

AC CA CP DF ME ML PB PG
Pleasant town centre pub, busy at
lunchtimes. Good value B & B. Interesting
collection of archive photos in front bar. At
least two, usually independent, guest ales
available.

WHITE HART HOTEL (Map Ref C4)
10:30 - 11. (M-S)
FORE STREET, OKEHAMPTON,
Tel: (0837) 54514

Draught Bass	(H)
Cotleigh Tawny	(H)
Guest Beer Regular	(H)

AC CA CD (CRIB) FA ME ML QP
Attractive town pub, popular with the
other town's publicans.

OTTERTON

KINGS ARMS (Map Ref F5)
11 - 3 ; 5:30 - 11 (M-S)
FORE STREET, OTTERTON, (ON MAIN
STREET IN MIDDLE OF VILLAGE),
Tel: (0395) 68416

Draught Bass	(H)
Flowers IPA	(H)

CA CI (GREEN VALLEY CYDER) CP DB
DF DM FA GD ME ML OD PL QP RF SN
ST
Recently modernised village pub with
large separate games room.

OTTERY ST. MARY

LAMB & FLAG (Map Ref F4)
11 - 11. (M-S)
BATTS LANE, OTTERY ST. MARY.
Tel: (0404) 812616

Flowers IPA	(H)

CI (TAUNTON) DB DF (LOUNGE ONLY)
FA (SKITTLE ROOM ONLY) ME ML PB
PG QP ST
Lively town local with a skittle alley.

LONDON INN (Map Ref F4)
10:30 - 2 ; 5:30 - 11. (M-S)
GOLD STREET, OTTERY ST. MARY.
Tel: (0404) 814763

Draught Bass	(H)
Guest Beer Regular	(H)

AC CI (INCH'S) CP DB DF FA ME ML MR
(2 FUNCTION ROOMS) OD PB PG PL QP
RF ST
18th century old coaching house with
genuine oak beams and horse brasses.
Olde worlde restaurant, two function
rooms, skittle alley and a pool room.
Guest beers.

PLUME OF FEATHERS (Map Ref F4)
10:30 - 3 ; 5:30 - 11. (M-S)
YONDER STREET, OTTERY ST. MARY .
Tel: (0404) 812395

Cornish Royal Wessex	(H)

CC CD CI (TAUNTON) CP DB DF FA
(LOUNGE ONLY) OD PB PG RF SN
(LUNCHTIME ONLY)
Popular and lively local.

STAFFORD HOTEL (Map Ref F4)
11 - 11. (M-S)
5, CORNHILL, OTTERY ST. MARY.
Tel: (0404) 812025

Draught Bass	(H)

AC CD DB FA ME ML OD PG
Downstairs hotel bar and bistro, with take away pizzas.

VOLUNTEER (Map Ref F4)
10:30 - 3 ; 5 - 11. (M-T (W), 11 - 11 F, Sat. 11-11 M-S (S))
BROAD STREET, TOWN SQUARE, OTTERY ST. MARY.
Tel: (0404) 812445

Cornish Royal Wessex	(H)
Eldridge Pope Royal Oak	(H)
Flowers IPA	(H)

AC CC CD (EUCHRE) CI FA (IF EATING) ME ML OD PB PG RF
Traditional old town pub.

PAIGNTON

COACH HOUSE (Map Ref E6)
11 - 11. (M-S)
32, CHURCH STREET, PAIGNTON
Tel: (0803) 558766

Courage Best Bitter	(H)
Courage Directors	(H)
John Smith's Bitter	(H)

BR (PAIGNTON) CI CP DF FA LM ME ML OD PG
Old style pub, with oak beams, set near the town centre. A former coaching house, now provides a warm , friendly atmosphere, good food, and weekend live entertainment.

OLD MANOR INN (Map Ref E6)
11 - 11. (M-S)
10, OLD TORQUAY ROAD, PAIGNTON
Tel: (0803) 551157

Boddingtons Bitter	(H)
Wadworth 6X	(H)
Flowers IPA	(H)
Flowers Original	(H)
Guest Beer Regular	(H)

DF FA ME ML OD PG RF
Grade 2 listed, former coaching inn, with original oak beams.

POLSHAM ARMS (Map Ref E6)
11 - 11. (M-S)
35, LOWER POLSHAM ROAD, PAIGNTON
Tel: (0803) 558360

Draught Bass	(H)
Boddingtons Bitter	(H)
Castle Eden Ale	(H)
Flowers IPA	(H)
Guest Beer Regular	(H)

BR (PAIGNTON) CP FA OD PB PG QP (LOUNGE) SN
c16 pub, with two separate bars, and a friendly atmosphere. Garden has a pets corner.

TOM COBLEY INN (Map Ref E6)
12 - 3 ; 5:30 - 11. (M-W, 11 - 3 Th, 11 - 11 F, Sat)
FOXHOLE ROAD, PAIGNTON
Tel: (0803) 551518

Draught Bass (H)

VICTORIA HOTEL (Map Ref E6)
11 - 11. (M-S)
31, CHURCH STREET, PAIGNTON
Tel: (0803) 551214

Boddingtons Bitter	(H)
Flowers IPA	(H)
Guest Beer Regular	(H)

AC BR (PAIGNTON) FA ME ML OD PB PG
Old fashioned, pub, with a friendly atmosphere. Good home-cooked food at reasonable prices, as are the accommodation rates. BBQs on patio in summer.

WATERSIDE HOTEL (Map Ref E6)
11 - 11. (M-S)
128, DARTMOUTH ROAD, GOODRINGTON, PAIGNTON
Tel: (0803) 551113

Courage Best Bitter	(H)
Courage Directors	(H)
John Smith's Bitter	(H)
Guest Beer Regular	(H)

AC BR (SOUTH DEVON RAILWAY) DF FA LM ME ML OD PG RS
Busy roadside inn, tastefully decorated, and games orientated. Live music usually once a week.

PARKHAM

BELL INN (Map Ref B3)
11 - 3 ; 6 - 11. (M-S (S), VARIABLE IN
WINTER)
PARKHAM. Nr. BIDEFORD,.OS: SS387212
Tel: (0237) 451201

Draught Bass	**(H)**
Fullers London Pride	**(H)**
(SUMMER ONLY)	
Flowers IPA	**(H)**

CA CP ME ML QP RF
Delightful thatchrd inn at edge of a
thriving village. Low beamed interior and
a grandfather clock set into one wall.

PARRACOMBE

FOX AND GOOSE INNE (Map Ref C1)
12 - 2:30 ; 7 - 11. (M-S)
PARRACOMBE, Nr. LYNTON.
Tel: (05983) 402

Draught Bass	**(H)**

AC CP ME ML PG
Old coaching inn in small village just off
A39.

HUNTERS INN (Map Ref C1)
11 - 2:30 ; 7 - 11. (M-S (W), 11 - 11
SUMMER)
HEDDONS MOUTH, PARRACOMBE.
OS: SS655482
Tel: (05983) 230

Exmoor Ale	**(H)**
Wadworth 6X	**(H)**
Flowers Original	**(H)**
Guest Beer Occasional	**(H)**

AC CP DF FA ME ML OD RF
Built as a hunting lodge in a beautiful
valley in 1901. Still retains its original
charm and character. Draught cider in
summer only. Signposted off the A399.
The hotel is close to the coastal walks, and
its grounds are patrolled by peacocks.

PAYHEMBURY

SIX BELLS (Map Ref F4)
12 - 2:30 ; 6 - 11. (M-S)
PAYHEMBURY, Nr. HONITON
Tel: (0404) 84261

Draught Bass	**(H)**
Charrington IPA	**(H)**
Wadworth 6X	**(H)**

CA CP DF FA ME (NOT SUNDAY,
MONDAY) ML (NOTMONDAY) OD PB
PG QP RF
Quiet village pub.

PENNYMOOR

CRUWYS ARMS (Map Ref E3)
12 - 2:30 ; 5:30 - 11. (F, 11 - 11 Sat, CLOSED
M-W (W) & T (S))
PENNYMOOR, Nr. TIVERTON
Tel: (0363) 866662

Flowers IPA	**(H)**
Guest Beer Regular	**(H)**

DF FA ME ML (NOT SUNDAY) OD RF
c16 village pub.

PETER TAVY

PETER TAVY INN (Map Ref B5)
11:30 - 2:30; 6:30 - 11.   (M-S)
PETER TAVY, Nr. TAVISTOCK, OS:
SX514776
Tel: (0822) 810348

Furgusons Dartmoor Best Bitter	**(G)**
Marston's Pedigree	**(G)**
Castle Eden Ale	**(G)**
Guest Beer Regular	**(G)**

CC CP ME ML OD QP RF RS
c15 moorland inn, formerly a farm cottage
and a blacksmith's shop. Frank ' Mad
Axeman' Mitchell, the only person to
escape from Dartmoor Prison and not be
recaptured, is reputed to have stayed here.
His bills being paid by the Kray brothers
prior to murdering him. Typical moorland
pub with low ceilings and flagstones.
Excellent vegetarian food, expensive but
nice.

PLYMOUTH

ABBEY HOTEL (Map Ref B7)
11 - 11. (M-S)
5, ST. ANDREWS STREET, PLYMOUTH
Tel: (0752) 661624

Draught Bass	(H)
Courage Best Bitter	(H)
John Smith's Bitter	(H)

BR (PLYMOUTH) DF ML
Bright, breezy two-bar pub with some
interesting fittings. Next to the
Magistrate's court.

ABBOT'S WAY (Map Ref B7)
11 - 3 ; 5 - 11. (M-Th, 11 - 11 F, Sat)
SOUTHWAY DRIVE, SOUTHWAY,
PLYMOUTH
Tel: (0752) 774481

Wadworth 6X	(H)

CP LM ME ML OD PG (TABLE
FOOTBALL) PL
Large noisy estate pub, video juke box,
gaming machines & pool dominated.
Comfortably furbished, sizeable speakers
in one area indicate a powerful disco.

ADMIRAL BENBOW (Map Ref B7)
11 - 3 ; 7 - 11. (M-S)
28, BENBOW STREET, DEVONPORT,
PLYMOUTH
Tel: (0752) 561655

Ushers Best Bitter	(H)

ADMIRAL MACBRIDE (Map Ref B7)
10 - 11. (M-S)
1, THE BARBICAN, PLYMOUTH
Tel: (0752) 262054

Courage Best Bitter	(H)
Wadworth 6X	(H)
Guest Beer Regular	(H)

CD (EUCHRE) CI DB LM PG
Large, single-bar pub, overlooking
Mayflower Steps. Live music on Friday
and Saturday nights, and disco on Sunday
nights.

ALBERT GATE (ALBERT) (Map Ref B7)
11:30 - 11. (M-S)
32, CHARLOTTE STREET, DEVONPORT,
PLYMOUTH
Tel: (0752)

Boddingtons Bitter	(H)

ANCHORAGE (Map Ref B7)
11 - 11. (M-S)
203, BILLACOMBE ROAD,
BILLACOMBE, PLYMOUTH
Tel: (0752) 403877

Draught Bass	(H)
Summerskills Whistle Belly Vengeance	(H)

ARCHER INN (Map Ref B7)
12 - 3 ; 7 - 11. (M-Th, 11 - 11 F, Sat)
11, ARCHER TERRACE, NORTH ROAD
WEST, PLYMOUTH
Tel: (0752) 667654

Draught Bass	(H)

BR (NORTH ROAD WEST) DB
Pleasantly revamped back street local with
a two-part bar just off the City centre.

AVONDALE ARMS (Map Ref B7)
10 - 11. (M-S)
206, KEYHAM ROAD, PLYMOUTH
Tel: (0752)

Boddingtons Bitter	(H)
St Austell HSD	(H)

BR (KEYHAM) DB ME ML PB
A two-bar pub , often frequented by
dockyard personnel, with numerous naval
photographs. Open for breakfast from 7am.

BANK (Map Ref B7)
11 - 11. (M-S)
OLD GEORGE STREET, PLYMOUTH
Tel: (0752) 672100

Furgusons Dartmoor Best Bitter	(H)
Tetley Bitter	(H)

BR (PLYMOUTH) ME ML OD
When the local branch of Allied breweries
converted the bank by the theatre into a
pub it was intended as their showpiece.
The interior lends itself to the grandiose
Victoriana school of pub design and the
conservatory and patio area at the back
could work well. A hefty injection of good
taste could yet make it a classic. The only
known pub with its own radio station -
Bank F.M., which can be seen in operation.

BARBICAN ARMS (Map Ref B7)
11:30 - 3 ; 6:30 - 11. (M-S)
20, LOOE STREET, BARBICAN
Tel: (0752) 662485

Furgusons Dartmoor Best Bitter	(H)

BLACK PRINCE (Map Ref B7)
11 - 11. (M-S)
8, LAIRA PLACE, ST. JUDES
Tel: (0752) 660503

Courage Best Bitter (H)

CD (EUCHRE) DB DF DM FA GD OD PG
PL RF
Local pub in a residential area.

BLOCKHOUSE INN (Map Ref B7)
10 - 11. (M-S)
59/61, DEVONPORT ROAD, STOKE
Tel: (0752) 567107

Blackawton 44 Special (H)

BR (DEVONPORT) CD DB DF FA PG PL
Pleasant, comfortable pub in the shopping
area of Stoke.

BLUE BIRD (Map Ref B7)
11 - 11. (M-S)
164, EGGBUCKLAND ROAD, HIGHER
COMPTON
Tel: (0752) 774367

Boddingtons Bitter (H)
Flowers Original (H)

DB DF FA ML (M-F ONLY) OD PG PL
Established pub, extensively modernised
inside, and the only one in the area part of
the national 'Twin Network' computer
quiz game.

BREAKWATER INN (Map Ref B7)
12 - 1. (M-S (MUSIC LICENSE))
BREAKWATER HILL, COXSIDE
Tel: (0752) 664556

Draught Bass (H)
Courage Directors (H)
Marston's Pedigree (H)
Ruddles County (H)
Wadworth 6X (H)

GD LM PG PL
Open from midday, with live
entertainment in the evenings.

BRETON ARMS (Map Ref B7)
BUCKWELL STREET, BRETONSIDE
Tel: (0752) 266054

Draught Bass (H)

BREWERY TAP (Map Ref B7)
11 - 2:30 ; 6 - 11. (M-S)
52, EDGECUMBE AVENUE,
STONEHOUSE
Tel: (0752) 262536

Courage Best Bitter (H)
John Smith's Bitter (H)
Wadworth 6X (H)

CI ME ML PG
Comfortable 'L' shaped bar with
momentoes of the now demolished Regent
brewery which used to stand behind and is
now a private car park. Constantly
changing cider menu.

BRISTOL CASTLE (Map Ref B7)
11 - 3 ; 6 - 11. (M-Th. 11 - 4, 6 - 11 F, Sat)
6, DUNCAN STREET, DEVONPORT
Tel: (0752) 563155

Courage Best Bitter (H)

CD (EUCHRE) CP DB DF DM FA OD PB
PG PL
A small, two-bar local, with a well
furnished lounge.

BRITANNIA (Map Ref B7)
11 - 2:30 ; 6 - 11. (M-F. 11 - 3, 6.30 - 11 Sat) 2,
WOLSELEY ROAD, MILEHOUSE
Tel: 90752) 605054

Courage Best Bitter (H)
John Smith's Bitter (H)
Guest Beer Regular (H)

DF LM MR RF
Large, pub near bus depot and central
park. Expansive lounge bar and separate
function room. live entertainment
Thur-Sun. evenings.

BRITANNIA INN (Map Ref B7)
12 - 3:30 ; 6:30 - 11. (M-F. 12 - 4 Sat)
16, OCTAGON STREET, STONEHOUSE
Tel: (0752) 665796

John Smith's Bitter (H)

BR (PLYMOUTH) CD (EUCHRE) DB DF
FA PB PL
Small, two-bar, town pub with well
furnished lounge.

BROWN BEAR (Map Ref B7)
11 - 3 ; 5:30 - 11. (M & T, 11 - 11 Wed - Sat)
20, CHAPEL STREET, DEVONPORT
Tel: (0752) 564663

Courage Best Bitter	(H)
Ushers Founders	(H)
Ushers Best Bitter	(H)

BR (DEVONPORT) CD (EUCHRE) CP DF
FA ME ML OD PG RS
Main road local which has moved slightly
upmarket with a restaurant extension
complementing the existing bar.

BUTCHER'S ARMS (Map Ref B7)
11 - 4 ; 7 - 11. (M-Th; 11 - 11 F, Sat)
160, CREMYLL STREET, STONEHOUSE
Tel: (0752) 660510

Guest Beer Regular	(H)

DB DF OD PG PL
Small, single-bar pub with a childrens play
area in garden at rear. Guest beer changed
monthly. Many darts trophies displayed.

CASEY'S (Map Ref B7)
11 - 3 ; 5:30 - 11. (M-S)
35, MARLBOROUGH STREET,
DEVONPORT
Tel: (0752) 563309

Whitbread Best Bitter	(H)

CHARLIES CIRCUS (Map Ref B7)
11 - 11 (M-F. 6 - 11 Sat)
1/2, THE MONEY CENTRE, DRAKES
CIRCUS, PLYMOUTH
Tel: (0752) 262288

Boddingtons Bitter	(H)

BR (PLYMOUTH) ML (12-2 ONLY)
City centre pub with disco upstairs.

CHERRY TREE (Map Ref B7)
11 - 11. (M-S)
291, HAM DRIVE, PENNYCROSS
Tel: (0752) 771981

Worthington Best Bitter	(H)
John Smith's Bitter	(H)

DB DF LM PB PG PL
Large, three-bar pub, with live
entertainment at weekends.

CHINA HOUSE (Map Ref B7)
11:30 - 3 ; 5 - 11. (M-S)
SUTTON WHARF, SUTTON ROAD,
COXSIDE
Tel: (0752) 260930

Furgusons Dartmoor Best Bitter	(H)
Dartmoor Strong	(H)
Wadworth 6X	(H)

CP FA ME ML OD RF
A gem of a pub, well worth finding. Built
inside the shell of a disused wharehouse, it
gives great views across Plymouth Sound.

CLARENCE HOTEL (Map Ref B7)
11 - 3 ; 7 - 11. (M-S)
31, CLARENCE PLACE, STONEHOUSE
Tel: (0752) 603827

Ushers Founders	(H)
Ushers Best Bitter	(H)

SN
Small friendly locals pub.

CLIFTON HOTEL (Map Ref B7)
11:30 - 3 ; 7 - 11. (M-S)
35, CLIFTON STREET, GREENBANK
Tel: (0752) 266563

Draught Bass	(H)
Furgusons Dartmoor Strong	(H)
Summerskills Best Bitter	(H)
Tetley Bitter	(H)
Guest Beer Regular	(H)

BR (PLYMOUTH) DF ME ML PG
Warm, friendly, pub with an old wall clock
that is never right. (not even twice a day?).

CLIPPER (Map Ref B7)
11 - 3 ; 7 - 11. (M-S)
65, UNION STREET, PLYMOUTH
Tel: (0752)

Courage Best Bitter	(H)

COLONIAL (Map Ref B7)
12 - 3 ; 5 - 11. (M-Th. 11 - 11 F, Sat)
SEVEN STARS LANE, TAMERTON
FOLIOT
Tel: (0752) 772693

Tetley Bitter	(H)

ML OD
Pub with an interesting internal design.

COMMERCIAL INN (Map Ref B7)
11 - 11. (M-S)
75, LAMBHAY HILL, BARBICAN
Tel: (0752) 668697

Furgusons Dartmoor Best Bitter   (H)

CD (EUCHRE) DB FA ML
Small, one-bar pub with emphasis on food
at lunchtimes.

COMPLEX (Map Ref B7)
11 - 11. (M-S)
6, KEYHAM ROAD, KEYHAM
Tel: (0752)

Courage Best Bitter   (H)
Courage Directors   (H)
Ruddles County   (H)
St Austell XXXX Mild   (H)
Wadworth 6X   (H)

BR (KEYHAM) LM ME ML OD PB
Sizeable two bar pub oft frequented by
dockyard and navy personnel. Guest
beers, and live music four times a week.

COMPTON INN (Map Ref B7)
12 - 2:30 ; 6 - 11. (M-F, 11.30 - 11 Sat)
77, PRIORY ROAD, LOWER COMPTON
Tel: (0752) 266962

Courage Best Bitter   (H)
Courage Directors   (H)

CH DB FA ME (ON REQUEST) ML OD PG
PL
Attractive pub, tucked away in an old and
quiet suburb.

CORNER HOUSE (Map Ref B7)
10 - 11. (M-S)
111, NEW GEORGE STREET, PLYMOUTH
Tel: (0752) 668759

Boddingtons Bitter   (H)
Flowers Original   (H)

BR (PLYMOUTH) DF ML
Large city centre pub.

CORNWALLS GATE (Map Ref B7)
11 - 3 ; 6 - 11. (M-S)
71, NORMANDY WAY, ST. BUDEAUX
Tel: (0752) 363838

Courage Best Bitter   (H

DISTILLERY (Map Ref B7)
11 - 2:30 ; 6:30 - 11. (M-S)
SOUTHSIDE STREET, BARBICAN
Tel: (0752)

Boddingtons Bitter   (H)
Flowers IPA   (H)

DOG & DUCK (Map Ref B7)
11 - 3 ; 7 - 11. (M-S, 12-3 F, Sat) 14/16,
ASHLEY PLACE, PLYMOUTH
Tel: (0752) 660614

Brains Dark   (H)
Marston's Pedigree   (H)
Flowers IPA   (H)

BR (PLYMOUTH) CD (EUCHRE) DB OD
One-roomed, locals pub, with strong darts
and euchre teams.

DOLPHIN HOTEL (Map Ref B7)
10 - 11 (M-S)
14, THE BARBICAN, BARBICAN
Tel: (0752) 660876

Draught Bass   (G)
RF

Spartan dockside hostelry frequented by
fishermen. Opposite the disused GWR
quayside station, alongside which fishing
vessels moor. Archetypal Plymouth. The
last unaltered pub on the historic Barbican;
a time-warp for the serious, appreciative,
drinker.

DUKE OF SOMERSET (Map Ref B7)
11 - 11. (M-S)
14, WOLSDON STREET, STONE - HOUSE
Tel: (0752) 266074

Theakston XB   (H)
Old Peculier   (H)
Young's Bitter   (H)

LM PG
Typical, back street, locals pub with
entertainment on Sunday nights.

EAGLE TAVERN (Map Ref B7)
11 - 11. (M-S)
COMMERCIAL ROAD, COXSIDE
Tel: 0752) 661974
DB ME (IF REQUESTED)
ML (IF REQUESTED)
Basic but pleasant locals pub.

EDGCOMBE HOTEL (Map Ref B7)
11 - 11. (M-S)
2, MOLESWORTH ROAD, STOKE
Tel: (0752) 569334

Draught Bass   (H)

FALCON (Map Ref B7)
11 - 3 ; 6 - 11. (M-F, 11-11 Sat)
22, MELVILLE ROAD, FORD
Tel: (0752) 561894

Furgusons Dartmoor Best Bitter   (H)

ML PB PG Basic locals pub.

FALSTAFF (Map Ref B7)
DUNNETT ROAD, SOUTHWAY
Tel: (0752) 775934

Courage Best Bitter	(H)

FAREHAM INN (Map Ref B7)
12 - 11. (M-S)
6, COMMERCIAL ROAD, COXSIDE
Tel: (0752) 664420

St Austell HSD	(H)

Basic, back street pub, with beer from the wood and various ciders. Worth a visit.

FELLOWSHIP INN (Map Ref B7)
7, TREVETHICK ROAD, KINGS
TAMERTON
Tel: (0752) 362439

Courage Best Bitter	(H)
Summerskills Best Bitter	(H)

FERRY HOUSE INN (Map Ref B7)
11 - 11. (M-S)
888, WOLSELEY ROAD, ST. BUDEAUX
Tel: (0752) 361659

Courage Best Bitter	(H)
Ushers Best Bitter	(H)

DB FA ME ML PG RF
Splendid views over the Tamar estuary.

FERRYBOAT INN (Map Ref B7)
11:30 - 3 ; 6:30 - 11.(M-F, 11-11 Sat)
1, TAMAR STREET, DEVONPORT Tel:
(0752) 561824

Draught Bass	(H)

AC CP DB FA ME ML OD PG PL
Nearest pub to the Torpoint Ferry.

FIRST & LAST (Map Ref B7)
11 - 2:30 ; 6:30 - 11 (M-S)
162, EXETER STREET, PLYMOUTH
Tel: (0752) 660059

Courage Best Bitter	(H)
Courage Directors	(H)

FISHERMAN'S ARMS (Map Ref B7)
11 - 3 ; 6 - 11. (M-F (W), 11-11 Sat & M-S (S))
31, LAMBHAY STREET, BARBICAN
Tel: (0752) 661457

St Austell HSD	(H)

CI FA ME ML OD PB PG
200 year old pub on the Barbican, and the only one selling HSD.

FORD HOTEL (Map Ref B7)
11 - 3 ; 6 - 11. (M-Th, 11-11 F, Sat)
155, ALEXANDRA ROAD, FORD
Tel: (0752) 562728

Courage Best Bitter	(H)
Wadworth 6X	(H)

ML PB PG
Two-bar, split level, locals pub, with a games area.

FORTESCUE HOTEL (Map Ref B7)
11 - 11. (M-S)
37, MUTLEY PLAIN, PLYMOUTH
Tel: (0752) 660673

Furgusons Dartmoor Best Bitter	(H)
Dartmoor Strong	(H)
Wadworth 6X	(H)

BR ML OD
Busy city centre pub, with a downstairs drinking area.

FOSTERS INTER'NL PUB (Map Ref B7)
89/91, UNION STREET, PLYMOUTH
Tel: (0752)

Courage Best Bitter	(H)

QUEEN ANNE'S BATTERY,
PLYMOUTH
Tel: (0752) 257772

Furgusons Dartmoor Best Bitter	(H)

CP DF FA ME ML OD
A small, well furnished, modern bar, overlooking The marina and Plymouth Sound. Formerly named 'Atlantic Challenge Bar'.

FRIENDSHIP INN (STOKE) (Map Ref B7)
11 - 11. (M-S)
170, ALBERT ROAD, KEYHAM
Tel: (0752) 563055

Ushers		
	Founders	(H)
	Best Bitter	(H)

BR (DEVONPORT) DB DF GD ME ML OD
PG RF

FRIENDSHIP INN (N. HILL) (Map Ref B7)
11 - 11. (M-S)
1, AMITY PLACE, NORTH HILL
Tel: (0752) 664958

Courage Best Bitter	(H)
Ushers Best Bitter	(H)

FROG & FRIGATE (Map Ref B7)
28, BISHOPS PLACE, WEST HOE
Tel: (0752) 262041

Courage Best Bitter	(H)
John Smith's Bitter	(H)

GEORGE COACH INN (Map Ref B7)
11:30 - 2:30 ; 5:30 - 11.(M-Th, 11.30 - 11 F, Sat)
399, TAVISTOCK ROAD, ROBOROUGH
Tel: (0752) 771527

Courage Best Bitter	(H)
Courage Directors	(H)
John Smith's Bitter	(H)

AC CI CP FA (RESTAURANT ONLY) GD
ME ML OD PB RS
Large roadside two bar inn with a
restaurant off the lounge. Public bar is
brash and lively, frequented by local estate
residents. The lounge is sedate.

GLEN (Map Ref B7)
12 - 11. (M-S)
GLENFIELD ROAD, GLENHOLT PARK
(OFF PLYMBRIDGE ROAD, NEAR
PLYMOUTH AIRPORT)
Tel: (0752) 776768

Courage Best Bitter	(H)
Furgusons Dartmoor Best Bitter	(H)

CC CP DB DF FA ME ML MR OD PG PL
RF ST
This huge sprawling establishment was
formerly a private club. Boasts a skittle
alley, dance floor, and function room. Good
pub meals.

GOLDEN HIND (Map Ref B7)
11 - 3 ; 6 - 11. (M-F, 11-11 Sat)
260, MANNAMEAD ROAD, HARTLEY
(JUNCTION OF A38, A386, B3250)
Tel: (0752) 771072

Courage Best Bitter	(H)
Flowers Original	(H)

DB DF ME ML PB PG PL
Large, busy pub by Manadon roundabout.

GOOD COMPANIONS (Map Ref B7)
11 - 11. (M-S)
17, MAYFLOWER STREET, PLYMOUTH
Tel: (0752) 669751

Flowers IPA	(H)

GRAND DUCHESS (Map Ref B7)
11 - 11. (M-S)
34, GIBBON STREET, NORTH HILL
Tel: (0752) 660630

Courage Best Bitter	(H)
Courage Directors	(H)

DB ML OD PG
Well furnished pub, frequented by
students.

GRAND HOTEL (Map Ref B7)
ELLIOT STREET, THE HOE
Tel: (0752) 661195

Courage Best Bitter	(H)
Courage Directors	(H)

GRENVILLE HOTEL (Map Ref B7)
11 - 3 ; 6 - 11. (M-Th, 11-11 F, Sat)
GRENVILLE ROAD, St. JUDES
Tel: (0752) 661344

Courage Best Bitter	(H)

DB DF ML PB PG PL
Quiet pub in a residential area.

HALF MOON INN (Map Ref B7)
11 - 3 ; 7 - 11. (M-Wed, 11-11 Th - Sat)
59, PEMBROKE STREET, DEVONPORT
Tel: (0752) 561138

John Smith's Bitter	(H)

DB FA PG
Small, backstreet, local's pub.

HERBERT (Map Ref B7)
11 - 11. (M-S)
1, HERBERT STREET, DEVONPORT
Tel: (0752) 563154

Courage Best Bitter	(H)
Ushers	
Founders	(H)
Best Bitter	(H)

BR (DOCKYARD) ML OD
One bar pub set amid back streets,
overlooking main railway line,
comfortably furnished.

HILL PARK HOTEL (Map Ref B7)
11 - 11. (M-S)
32, HILLPARK CRESCENT, GREENBANK
Tel: (0752) 662688

Courage Best Bitter	(H)
Courage Directors	(H)
Wadworth 6X	(H)

BR (PLYMOUTH) CD (EUCHRE) DF ME
ML OD PB PG
Large, two-bar, estate pub with occasional
weekend disco.

INDIAN INN (Map Ref B7)
11 -3 ; 7 -11. (M-F, 6.30-11 Sat)
82, DEVONPORT ROAD, STOKE
Tel: (0752) 556438

Draught Bass	(H)

BR (DEVONPORT) DB FA ML (M-F
ONLY) OD PG
Small local on main road through Stoke
village, close to Devonport BR station.

**JAMES STREET SPIRIT VAULTS
(Map Ref B7)**
11 - 11. (M-S)
24, JAMES STREET, DEVONPORT
Tel: (0752) 667936

Furgusons Dartmoor Best Bitter	(H)
Dartmoor Strong	(H)
Wadworth 6X	(H)
ML	

Pub adjacent to university, much
frequented by students.

JOLLY MILLER (Map Ref B7)
11 - 2:30 ; 6 - 11. (M-Th, 11-11 F, Sat)
LEYPARK DRIVE, ESTOVER
Tel: (0752) 781919

Furgusons Dartmoor Best Bitter	(H)

DB FA (UNTIL 7pm) PG PL
Modern pub in shopping precinct.

KINGS HEAD (Map Ref B7)
11 - 11. (M-S)
21, BRETONSIDE, PLYMOUTH
Tel: (0752) 665619

Courage Best Bitter	(H)
Courage Directors	(H)
John Smith's Bitter	(H)
Marston's Pedigree	(H)
Ruddles County	(H)
Wadworth 6X	(H)

CD (EUCHRE) DM GD ML OD
Formerly named 'Hutton Longbar', this
pub was in existence in the early 1600's,
with the date 1629 carved into one of the

beams. Guiness was imported from Dublin
and bottled here until 3/2/1964. There is
an aviary in the garden.

LIFEBOAT INN (Map Ref B7)
12 - 3 ; 7 - 11. (M-S)
TORRIDGE WAY, EFFORD
Tel: (0752) 771588

Draught Bass	(H)
Courage Best Bitter	(H)

DB DF FA ME ML OD PB PG PL
Large, two-bar estate pub.

**LITTLE MUTTON MONSTER (Map
Ref B7)**
11- 2:30 ; 6 - 11. (M-S)
240, JAMES STREET, DEVONPORT
Tel: (0752) 560938

Courage Best Bitter	(H)
Marston's Pedigree	(H)
Ruddles County	(H)
St Austell HSD	(H)
Guest Beer Regular	(H)

GD ME ML OD PG (BAR SKITTLES) SH
200 year old pub adjoining the Naval
Dockyard, formerly named the 'Mutton
Cove Tavern'. Excellent value food, and
two guest ales.

LOPES ARMS (Map Ref B7)
27/29, TAVISTOCK ROAD, ROBOROUGH
Tel: (0752) 769633

Draught Bass	(H)
Courage Best Bitter	(H)
Courage Directors	(H)
John Smith's Bitter	(H)
Wadworth 6X	(H)

LORD BERESFORD (Map Ref B7)
11 - 3 ; 6 - 11. (M-S)
9, CUMBERLAND STREET, DEVONPORT
Tel: (0752) 561671

Courage Best Bitter	(H)

FA Basic, back street, local's pub.

LORD HIGH ADMIRAL (Map Ref B7)
11 - 11. (M-S)
33, STONEHOUSE STREET,
STONEHOUSE
Tel: (0752) 221508

Courage Best Bitter	(H)
Ushers Founders	(H)

CD (EUCHRE) CI DB DF FA OD PG PL
Single bar, town pub with strong local
trade.

LOUNGE (Map Ref B7)
11 - 2:30 ; 6 - 11. (M-S)
7, STOPFORD PLACE, STOKE
Tel: (0752) 561330

Draught Bass	(G)
Worthington Best Bitter	(G)
Guest Beer Regular	(G)

BR (DEVONPORT) GD ME ML OD QP
Plush, back street local with wood
panelled, split-level lounge bar and a
"lived-in" atmosphere. One of the few
outlets in the area for bottle conditioned
beers.

LUGGER (Map Ref B7)
11:30 - 3 ; 7 - 11. (M-W. 11.30-4, 7-11 Th-Sat)
12, ALBANY STREET, DEVONPORT
Tel: (0752) 563801

Furgusons Dartmoor Best Bitter	(H)
Fergusons Dartmoor Strong	(H)

BR (DEVONPORT) ML OD PB
Lively public bar, and a comfortable
lounge bar whose walls are adorned with
wartime artifacts.

MASONIC INN (Map Ref B7)
10 - 11.(M-S)
65, DEVONPORT ROAD, STOKE
Tel: (0752) 607257

Courage Best Bitter	(H)
Summerskills Best Bitter	(H)
Guest Beer Regular	(H)

BR (DEVONPORT) DB FA ME ML PG PL
Recently refurbished and re-opened pub in
a busy shopping locality. Guest beer
usually another of the Summerskill's range.

MAYFLOWER INN (Map Ref B7)
LAKESIDE DRIVE, ERNESETTLE
Tel: (0752) 362484

Guest Beer Regular	(H)

MECHANICS ARMS (Map Ref B7)
11 - 3 ; 5 - 11. (M-Th, 11-11 F, Sat)
31, STONEHOUSE STREET,
STONEHOUSE
Tel: (0752) 660176

St Austell HSD	(H)

LM ML (NOT SUNDAY) PG
Small, one bar, corner hostelry, in a busy
industrial area but with a family
atmosphere. Music hall piano concerts? on
Sunday evenings.

MILLBRIDGE INN (Map Ref B7)
11 - 11. (M-S)
23, MOLESWORTH ROAD, STOKE
Tel: (0752) 563056

Courage Bitter Ale	(H)
Courage Best Bitter	(H)
Marston's Pedigree	(H)
Ruddles County	(H)
Wadworth 6X	(H)

BR (DEVONPORT) CI GD OD RF
Medium sized, two-roomed, local's pub
with Bitter Ale sold as 'Firkin Ale'.

MINERVA (Map Ref B7)
12 - 3 ; 7 - 11. (M-F, 11-11 Sat)
31, LOOE STREET, BARBICAN
Tel: (0752) 669065

Courage Best Bitter	(G)

CI DB DF OD
Said to be the oldest pub in Plymouth. In a
mews area between the bus station and the
Barbican, a few doors away from Plymouth
Arts Centre. Long slim front bar and cosy
back room with darts. Occasionally
drowned by muzak, but otherwise pretty
good.

MOUNT PLEASANT HOTEL (Map Ref B7)
11 - 2:30 ; 7 - 11. (M-S)
MILLBAY ROAD, PLYMOUTH
Tel: (0752) 665807

Draught Bass	(H)

MUTLEY TAVERN (Map Ref B7)
10 - 11. (M-S)
14, FURZE HILL ROAD, MUTLEY
Tel: (0752) 668616

Courage Best Bitter	(H)
Wadworth 6X	(H)

AC BR (PLYMOUTH) ML PG
Recently refurbished local's pub.

NAVY INN (Map Ref B7)
11 - 11. (M-S)
34, SOUTHSIDE STREET, BARBICAN
Tel: (0752) 661864

Worthington Best Bitter	(H)
Courage Best Bitter	(H)
Courage Directors	(H)

DF LM ML
Large, single bar pub, with lively night
time trade. Separate games room.

NEW MARKET (Map Ref B7)
10 - 11. (M-S, 7 - 10.30 ONLY SUNDAY)
2, MARKET WAY, PLYMOUTH
Tel: (0752) 662643

Courage Best Bitter	(H)
Courage Directors	(H)
John Smith's Bitter	(H)

BR (PLYMOUTH) CP ME ML (12-10)
1960's open plan lounge in an
unsalvageably modern building.

NEW PARK INN (Map Ref B7)
12 - 3 ; 7 - 11. (M-S)
36, CAMPERDOWN STREET,
DEVONPORT
Tel: (0752) 562056

Courage Best Bitter	(H)
Ushers Best Bitter	(H)

BR (DOCKYARD) CD CI DB PG PL
A small, friendly, one-bar local's pub.

NOTTINGHAM (Map Ref B7)
12 - 3 ; 6 - 11. (M-S)
1, NOTTINGHAM PLACE, MUTLEY
Tel: (0752) 665895

Furgusons Dartmoor Best Bitter	(H)

BR (PLYMOUTH) ML PB PG
Basic pub.

OLD FRIARY (Map Ref B7)
11 - 11. (M-S)
51/53, BRETONSIDE, PLYMOUTH
Tel: (0752) 664554

John Smith's Bitter	(H)

AC DF PG
Small bar with a larger lounge.

OLD ROAD INN (Map Ref B7)
12 - 3 ; 6 - 11. (M-Th, 12-11 F, Sat)
296, OLD LAIRA ROAD, LIPSON VALE
Tel: (0752) 665683

Courage Best Bitter	(H)
Courage Directors	(H)

DB DF OD PB PG PL
Two-bar pub on the old Exeter Road.

PEAR TREE INN (Map Ref B7)
11 - 2 :30 ; 6 - 11. (M-S)
7, DEVONPORT ROAD, STOKE
Tel: (0752) 563260

Courage Best Bitter	(H)
Ushers Best Bitter	(H)

BR (DEVONPORT) FA PG
One roomed horsehoe shaped bar on the
main road.

PEN & PARCHMENT (Map Ref B7)
11 - 11. (M-S)
15, ST. ANDREWS STREET, PLYMOUTH
Tel: (0752) 661263

Boddingtons Bitter	(H)
Marston's Pedigree	(H)
Flowers IPA	(H)

BR (PLYMOUTH) DB DF ML
Smart compact one room side street bar.
situated behind the law courts and across
from the 16th century merchants house.

PENNYCOMEQUICK (Map Ref B7)
12 - 2:30 ; 7 - 11. (M-F, 11-3, 7-11 Sat)
CENTRAL PARK AVENUE, PLYMOUTH
Tel: (0752) 661412

Furgusons Dartmoor Best Bitter	(H)

BR (PLYMOUTH) ML OD PB PG
Popular pub with a busy public bar and
incredibly ordinary lounge. Friendly, with
a reputation for well kept ale.

PHOENIX TAVERN (Map Ref B7)
12 - 3 ; 7 - 11. (M-S)
9, PHOENIX STREET, PLYMOUTH
Tel: (0752) 222523

Draught Bass	(H)

ML
Smartly appointed, one roomed,
downtown bar with a potent juke box.

PRINCE ALFRED (Map Ref B7)
2, CLARENCE PLACE, STONEHOUSE
Tel: (0752) 663842

Courage Best Bitter	(H)

PRINCE MAURICE (Map Ref B7)
11 - 3 ; 7 - 11. (M-F, 11-11 Sat)
3, CHURCH HILL, EGGBUCKLAND
Tel: (0752) 771515

Draught Bass	(H)
Courage Best Bitter	(H)
John Smith's Bitter	(H)
Wadworth 6X	(H)
Guest Beer Regular	(H)

CP FA (IN SNUG) OD PG RF SN
c16 former farmhouse, now well
appointed, with snacks only available
during both sessions. Families welcomed
in the snug.

PROVIDENCE INN (Map Ref B7)
11 - 11.(M-S)
20, PROVIDENCE STREET, NORTH HILL
Tel: (0752) 228178

Eldridge Pope Royal Oak	(H)
Summerskills Whistle Belly Vengeance	
	(H)

DF FA ME (6-9pm) ML PG
One-room, back street local's pub.

PYM ARMS (Map Ref B7)
11 - 3 ; 6 - 11. (M-S)
16, PYM STREET, DEVONPORT
Tel: (0752) 561823

Draught Bass	(H)
Worthington Best Bitter	(H)
Charrington IPA	(H)
St Austell XXXX Mild	(H)
HSD	(G)
Wadworth 6X	(G)

BR (DEVONPORT) CI ML PG
Fitted out with 'genuine' fake beams which
defy the normal constraints of
construction. Heavily populated by
students in term-time. Has the only real
mild for miles around; a beer drinkers
paradise. Situated near the naval dockyard,
it holds regular beer festivals, and always
has guest beers on.

JOIN NOW

QUEENS DOCK TAVERN (Map Ref B7)
11:30 - 3 ; 6:30 - 11. (M-S)
57, CHARLOTTE STREET, KEYHAM
Tel: (0752) 567061

Draught Bass	(H)
Flowers Original	(H)

BR (KEYHAM) CD (EUCHRE) DB DF GD
OD PG PL
A large, single-bar, local's pub, well
furnished.

RAILWAY INN (Map Ref B7)
11 - 11. (M-S)
122, ALBERT ROAD, STOKE
Tel: (0752) 561155

Courage Directors	(H)

REVENUE INN (Map Ref B7)
10 - 11. (M-S)
32, MARLBOROUGH STREET,
DEVONPORT
Tel: (0752) 561479

St Austell HSD	(H)

CD (EUCHRE) DB PG
Friendly, local's pub.

RISING SUN INN (Map Ref B7)
11 - 2:30 ; 6 - 11. (M-F; 11 - 3, 6 - 11 Sat)
138, EGGBUCKLAND ROAD, HIGHER
COMPTON
Tel: (0752) 774359

Courage Best Bitter	(H)
Courage Directors	(H)

DB DF FA ML (M-F ONLY) OD PB PG QP
(LOUNGE ONLY) RF
Pleasant, suburban, two-bar pub.

**ROYAL ALBERT BRIDGE INN (Map
Ref B7)**
11 - 11. (M-S)
930, WOLSELEY ROAD, ST. BUDEAUX
Tel: (0752) 361108

Draught Bass	(H)
Courage Best Bitter	(H)

CD DB DM FA ME ML OD PG
Friendly, riverside local, under Brunel's
railway bridge, giving a pleasant view
across the River Tamar to Cornwall.

ROYAL SOVEREIGN (Map Ref B7)
11 - 11. (M-S)
174, UNION STREET, STONEHOUSE
Tel: (0752) 253226

Courage Best Bitter	**(H)**
Wadworth 6X	**(H)**
Guest Beer Regular	**(H)**

CI
Fun pub with a friendly atmosphere; a
sense of humour is a MUST!.

SEVEN STARS INN (Map Ref B7)
11 - 3 ; 6 - 11. (M-S)
SEVEN STARS LANE, TAMERTON
FOLIOT
Tel: (0752) 772901

Courage Best Bitter	**(H)**
Courage Directors	**(H)**

CP FA ME ML OD RF
Small village pub overtaken by suburbia.
A new conservatory is at the rear and
children are allowed in the restaurant area
only.

SEYMOUR ARMS (Map Ref B7)
11:30 - 11. (M-S) 10,
NORTH STREET, PLYMOUTH
Tel: (0752) 664215

Tetley Bitter	**(H)**
Guest Beer Regular	**(H)**

FA ME (6-7pm) ML PG
Friendly, locals pub, popular with the art
college.

SHIP INN (Map Ref B7)
11 - 2:30 ; 6 - 11. (M-S (W); 11 - 11 (S))
12, THE QUAY, BARBICAN
Tel: (0752) 667604

Ruddles Best Bitter	**(H)**
Ruddles County	**(H)**

FA (RESTAURANT ONLY) ME ML RS
Large, single bar, pub with an upstairs
carvery/restaurant and family room.

SHIPWRIGHTS ARMS (Map Ref B7)
11 - 3 ; 6 - 11.
(M-S; EXCEPT FRIDAY - 5.30-11)
13, SUTTON ROAD, COXSIDE
Tel: (0752) 665804

Courage Best Bitter	**(H)**
Courage Directors	**(H)**

ML OD PG RF
Comfortable pub near the city centre and
the historic Barbican. Old piano sessions
on weekend evenings.

SIPPERS (Map Ref B7)
11 - 11. (M-S)
18, MILLBAY ROAD, PLYMOUTH
Tel: (0752) 670668

Boddingtons Bitter	**(H)**
Flowers Original	**(H)**

BR (PLYMOUTH) ME (UNTIL 8.30pm) ML
OD PG (CORNISH SNOOKER !)
Brick walled interior of this split level
tavern is well matched by the flagged
floor. Has many nautical exhibits and an
inetersting explanation of the pubs name.

STAR OF THE WEST (Map Ref B7)
11 - 11. (M-S)
7, BROWNLOW STREET, STONEHOUSE
Tel: (0752) 229037
CI OD PG
Traditional Devonshire cyder house in the
city centre.

STOKE INN (Map Ref B7)
11 - 3 ; 7 - 11. (M-Th; 11-3, 6.30-11 F, Sat) 43,
DEVONPORT ROAD, STOKE
Tel: (0752) 561084

Draught Bass	**(H)**

BR (DEVONPORT) CD (EUCHRE) CP DB
FA (FUNCTION ROOM) GD OD PG

**STONE MASONS ARMS (Map Ref
B7)**
11 - 3 ; 6 - 11. (M-W; 11-11 Th-Sat)
145, ALBERT ROAD, DEVONPORT
Tel: (0752) 607179

Furgusons Dartmoor Best Bitter	**(H)**

BR (DEVONPORT) ML OD
Basic pub.

STOPFORD ARMS (Map Ref B7)
11 - 2:30 ; 6 - 11. (M-S; 11-3 Sat)
172, DEVONPORT ROAD, STOKE
Tel: (0752) 562915

Courage Best Bitter	**(H)**
Guest Beer Regular	**(H)**

BR (DEVONPORT) ML (NOT SUNDAY)
PB PG
Clean and tidy, small city local with a
'village ' atmosphere. Large selection of
pure malt whiskeys.

SWAN INN (Map Ref B7)
12 - 3 ; 7 - 11. (M-W; 12-3, 7-12 Th-Sat)
6, CORNWALL BEACH, DEVONPORT
Tel: (0752) 568761

Draught Bass	(H)
Ruddles Best Bitter	(H)
Ruddles County	(H)
St Austell HSD	(H)
Wadworth 6X	(H)
Webster's Yorkshire Bitter	(H)

FA ME ML OD PG RF
Stone walled interior split level drinking
house. Emphasis on music, situated by the
Tamar with good views of sunsets, weather
permitting.

TAMAR HOTEL (Map Ref B7)
11 - 2:30 ; 6 - 11. (M-S)
1, MORSHEAD ROAD, CROWNHILL
Tel: (0752) 771445

Draught Bass	(H)
Boddingtons Bitter	(H)
Courage Best Bitter	(H)

CP PB
Large, spacious estate pub, formerly
named 'Trader Jacks'.

TAP & BARREL (Map Ref B7)
11 - 11. (M-S)
ASHFORD CRESCENT, MUTLEY
Tel: (0752) 663603

Courage Best Bitter	(H)
Courage Directors	(H)
John Smith's Bitter	(H)
Wadworth 6X	(H)

CP DB FA ME ML OD PG PL
Modern estate pub incongruously situated
amidst an established residential area.

TERMINUS HOTEL (Map Ref B7)
11 - 11. (M-S)
1, PARADISE PLACE, STOKE
Tel: (0752) 560869

Ushers Founders	(H)
Ushers Best Bitter	(H)

AC BR (DEVONPORT) CD (EUCHRE) CI
DB DF FA GD ME ML OD PG (UCKERS)
PL
A friendly, well furnished, single bar pub.
Note the fish tank at the end of the bar?

THE MALL (Map Ref B7)
10 - 11. (M-S)
156, CORNWALL STREET, PLYMOUTH
Tel: (0752) 266158

Furgusons Dartmoor Best Bitter	(H)
Tetley Bitter	(H)

BR (PLYMOUTH) FA ML Good pub for
weary shoppers, with excellent lunchtime
food.

THISTLE PARK TAVERN (Map Ref B7)
11 - 11. (M-S)
1, SUTTON ROAD, COXSIDE
Tel: (0752) 667677

Eldridge Pope Royal Oak	(H)
Greene King Abbot	(H)
Marston's Pedigree	(H)
Ruddles County	(H)
St Austell Crippledick (XMAS ONLY)	(H)
St Austell HSD	(H)
Wadworth 6X	(H)
Guest Beer Regular	(H)

PG RF
Warm, friendly atmosphere in a pub which
holds 2 beer festivals a year: May-day bank
holiday, and the last weekend in October.
Regular guest ales.

THREE CROWNS (Map Ref B7)
11 - 3 ; 7 - 11 (M-S (W); 11-11 (S))
11, THE PARADE, BARBICAN
Tel: (0752) 229324

Worthington Best Bitter	(H)
Courage Best Bitter	(H)
Courage Directors (H)	

ME ML OD
Comfortable one bar pub in the Barbican
area.

THREE FERRETS (Map Ref B7)
11 - 11. (M-S)
38, CHARLOTTE STREET, DEVONPORT
Tel: (0752) 561259

Courage Best Bitter	(H)
John Smith's Bitter	(H)
Ushers Best Bitter	(H)
Guest Beer Regular	(H)

BR (DEVONPORT) DB LM ML OD
One-bar pub, formerly the 'Grapes Tavern',
with various nightly entertainments.
Courage Directors is sold under the house
name of 'Ferret Ale'.

TRAFALGAR INN (Map Ref B7)
12 - 11. (M-S (W); 11.30-11 (S)) 62,
EBRINGTON STREET, PLYMOUTH
Tel: (0752) 262059

Courage Best Bitter	**(H)**
John Smith's Bitter	**(H)**
Ruddles County	**(H)**

BR (PLYMOUTH) DB PG PL
Large, Victorian, town pub with wood
panelled bar and ornate, embossed ceiling.

TRELAWNY HOTEL (Map Ref B7)
11 - 11. (M-S)
640, WOLSELEY ROAD, ST. BUDEAUX
Tel: (0752) 361623

Courage Best Bitter	**(H)**

DB DF ME ML PG

UNITY (Map Ref B7)
11 - 11. (M-S) EASTLAKE STREET,
PLYMOUTH
Tel: (0752) 262622

Furgusons Dartmoor Best Bitter	**(H)**
Ind Coope Burton Ale	**(H)**

ML
Excellent food pub for shoppers. There is a
conservatory on one side.

VALLETORT INN (Map Ref B7)
12 - 11. (M-S)
1A, CLAREMONT STREET, PLYMOUTH
Tel: (0752) 600402

Flowers Original	**(H)**

BR (PLYMOUTH) CI CP DF ME ML OD
PB PG (TABLE FOOTBALL) PL
Two bar pub with a large public bar, and a
well furnished lounge bar.

VICTUALLING OFFICE TAVERN
(Map Ref B7)
11 - 11. (M-S)
10, CREMYLL STREET, STONEHOUSE
Tel: (0752) 669372

Courage Best Bitter	**(G)**

AC CD (EUCHRE) DB DF FA PG PL RF
Large, single-bar pub with military
memorabilia.

VINE HOTEL (Map Ref B7)
11 - 11. (M-S)
5, ADMIRALS HARD, STONEHOUSE
Tel: (0752) 664804

Courage Best Bitter	**(H)**

CD (EUCHRE) CP DB FA PG (CHESS) PL
A single L-shaped bar with timber beamed
ceiling.

WATERLOO INN (Map Ref B7)
11 - 11. (M-S)
30, WATERLOO STREET, STOKE
Tel: (0752) 550090

Draught Bass	**(H)**
Worthington Best Bitter	**(H)**
Summerskills Best Bitter	**(H)**

DF FA ME (UNTIL 8.30pm) ML OD PG

WELLINGTON HOTEL (Map Ref B7)
11 - 11. (M-S)
21, WELLINGTON STREET,
GREENBANK
Tel: (0752) 661133

Courage Best Bitter	**(H)**
Courage Directors	**(H)**
Summerskills Best Bitter	**(H)**
Wadworth 6X	**(H)**

ML PB Back street pub with a busy locals
trade in public bar.

WESTERN HOTEL (Map Ref B7)
10:30 - 11. (M-S)
1, FORE STREET, DEVONPORT
Tel: (0752) 563838

St Austell HSD	**(H)**

AC BR (DEVONPORT) CD (EUCHRE) DF
FA GD ME ML OD PG
Large, open-plan pub with separate games
room. Friendly staff and regulars.

**WESTERN MILL HOTEL (Map Ref
B7)**
11 - 11. (M-S)
57, BRIDWELL ROAD, ST. BUDEAUX
Tel: (0752) 361552

Draught Bass	**(H)**

BR (ST. BUDEAUX) DF OD PG
Basic, local's pub with a games room
downstairs.

WINDMILL INN (Map Ref B7)
12 - 2:30 ; 6 - 11. (M-Th; 11-11 F, Sat)
THURLSTONE WALK, BAMPTON
ROAD, LEIGHAM
Tel: (0752) 777462

Courage Best Bitter	(H)

CP DB DF ME ML OD PB PG PL
Large estate pub with adjoining sports club.

WOODLAND FORT INN (Map Ref B7)
11 - 11. (M-S)
50, BUTT PARK ROAD, HONICKNOWLE
Tel: (0752) 774541

Courage Best Bitter	(H)

DB ML OD PB PG PL
Basic, two-bar pub in an established
residential area.

WOODSIDE (Map Ref B7)
11 - 3 ; 6 - 11. (M-Th; 11-11 F, Sat)
12, GASKIN STREET, PLYMOUTH
Tel: (0752) 669700

Furgusons Dartmoor Best Bitter	(H)
Dartmoor Strong	(H)
Tetley Bitter	(H)
Wadworth 6X	(H)

BR (PLYMOUTH) CI DB GD ME (UNTIL
9pm) ML OD PG PL
Good, basic pub with superb views across
Plymouth Sound.

PLYMPTON

COLEBROOK INN (Map Ref C7)
11 - 3 ; 6 - 11. (M-F; 11-4, 6-11 Sat)
COLEBROOK VILLAGE, PLYMPTON
Tel: (0752) 336267

Draught Bass	(H)
Courage Best Bitter	(H)
John Smith's Bitter	(H)

FA ME ML OD PB PG QP RF
Formerly 4 cottages, built in 1714, situated
alongside the brook where fishing boats
landed their catches.

HELE ARMS (Map Ref C7)
11 - 3 ; 6 - 11. (M-S)
34, MARKET ROAD, PLYMPTON
Tel: (0752) 336054

Courage Best Bitter	(H)
John Smith's Bitter	(H)

ML PB
Basic two roomed pub.

LONDON INN (Map Ref C7)
12 - 3 ; 7 - 11. (M-Th, 11-11 F, Sat)
8, CHURCH ROAD, PLYMPTON
Tel: (0752) 337025

Courage Best Bitter	(H)
John Smith's Bitter	(H)
Ruddles County	(H)
Summerskills Whistle Belly	
Vengeance	(H)
Flowers Original	(H)
Guest Beer Regular	(H)

CP DF FA ML OD PB PG QP (LOUNGE)
RF

LYNEHAM INN (Map Ref C7)
11 - 3 ; 6 - 11. (M-Th; 11-11 F, Sat)
Tel: (0752) 336955

Draught Bass	(H)
Courage Best Bitter	(H)
Wadworth 6X	(H)

CA CP FA ME ML OD PG QP
Multi-roomed pub, with a children's play
area.

POST OFFICE INN (Map Ref C7)
10 - 11. (M-S)
39, BRIDGEQUAY, PLYMPTON
Tel: (0752) 337051

Boddingtons Bitter	(H)
Flowers IPA	(H)

ML PG
Large, one-room pub, with a comfortable
atmosphere.

SIR JOSHUA REYNOLDS (Map Ref C7)
10:30 - 11. (M-S)
25, RIDGEWAY, PLYMPTON
Tel: (0752) 336982

Courage Best Bitter	(H)
Eldridge Pope Royal Oak	(H)

CP ME ML PB PG
Roomy, two-bar pub.

UNICORN (Map Ref C7)
11:30 - 3 ; 6 - 11. (M-Th; 11-11 F, Sat)
PLYMOUTH ROAD, PLYMPTON
Tel: (0752) 336877

Furgusons Dartmoor Best Bitter	(H)
Wadworth 6X	(H)

CP FA ME ML OD PB
Lively bar, and a good place to eat.
Pre-booking is advisable.

UNION INN (Map Ref C7)
11 - 3 ; 6 - 11: (M-S)
17, UNDERWOOD ROAD, PLYMPTON
Tel: (0752) 337294

Courage Best Bitter	(H)
John Smith's Bitter	(H)

CP ME ML PB QP
Peaceful pub with an interesting collection
of naval memorabilia.

PLYMSTOCK

BLUE PETER (Map Ref B7)
11 - 3 ; 6 - 11. (M-Th; 11-11 F, Sat)
68, POMPHLETT ROAD, PLYMSTOCK
Tel: (0752) 402388

Courage Best Bitter	(H)

CP DB DF ME ML OD PB PG PL RF
Two-bar estate pub.

BORINGDON ARMS (Map Ref B7)
11:30 - 3 ; 5:30 - 11. (M-Th (W); 11-11 F, Sat
(W) & M-S (S))
BORINGDON TERRACE, TURNCHAPEL,
Tel: (0752) 402053

Draught Bass	(H)
Butcombe Bitter	(H)
Fullers London Pride	(H)
St Austell HSD	(H)
Summerskills Whistle Belly Vengeance	(H)
Summerskills Ninja	(H)

AC CD DM FA GD ME ML OD PB PG
(BACKGAMMON) RF
Friendly, two-bar, ex-quarrymaster's
house, with many artifacts on display.
Regular beer festivals, and guest ales.

DRAKES DRUM (Map Ref B7)
11 - 11. (M-S)
19, RADFORD PARK ROAD,
PLYMSTOCK
Tel: (0752) 402613

Courage Bitter Ale	(H)
Courage Best Bitter	(H)
John Smith's Bitter	(H)
Wadworth 6X	(H)

CD (EUCHRE) CP DF DM ME ML OD PB
PG
Large suburban pub.

ELBURTON HOTEL (Map Ref B7)
221, BILLACOMBE ROAD, PLYMSTOCK
Tel: (0752) 403213

Courage Best Bitter	(H)
John Smith's Bitter	(H)

KINGS ARMS (Map Ref B7)
11 - 3 ; 6 - 11. (M-Th; 11-11 F, Sat)
THE QUAY, ORESTON, PLYMSTOCK
Tel: (0752) 401277

Boddingtons Bitter	(H)
Flowers Original	(H)

MORLEY ARMS (Map Ref B7)
11 - 2:30 ; 5:30 - 11. (M-Th; 11-11 F, Sat)
BILLACOMBE ROAD, POMPHLETT
Tel: (0752) 401191

Butcombe Bitter	(H)
Courage Best Bitter	(H)
John Smith's Bitter	(H)

NEW INN (Map Ref B7)
11 - 11. (M-S)
BORINGDON ROAD, TURNCHAPEL
Tel: (0752) 402765

Boddingtons Bitter	(H)
Guest Beer Regular	(H)

FA ME ML OD PG QP RF
200 year old, historic, waterfront inn which
can be reached by the water taxi from the
Barbican. Patrons can beach or moor their
boats in front of the inn.

PLYMSTOCK INN (Map Ref B7)
11 - 3 ; 5:30 - 11. (M-Th; 11-11 F, Sat)
22, CHURCH ROAD, PLYMSTOCK
Tel: (0752) 402127

Draught Bass	(H)

ROYAL OAK (Map Ref B7)
11 - 2:30 ; 7 - 11. (M-S)
LAKE ROAD, HOOE, PLYMSTOCK
Tel: (0752) 403822

Butcombe Bitter	(H)
Courage Best Bitter	(H)

AC DB ME ML OD PG
Well positioned, wood panelled, local's
pub with good views across the tidal lake
and green.

**SHIPS TAVERN & KINGS HEAD
(Map Ref B7)**
11 - 3 ; 5:30 - 11. (M-S)
ARCADIA ROAD, ELBURTON
Tel: (0752) 401626

Draught Bass	(H)

CP DF (PORTABLE RAMP) ME ML OD PB
RS
Large, suburban restaurant/pub.

PLYMTREE

BLACKSMITHS ARMS (Map Ref F4)
6 - 11. (M-F; - 11-3, 6-11 Sat.) PLYMTREE,
Nr. CULLOMPTON.
Tel: (08847) 322

Boddingtons Bitter	(H)
Cotleigh Tawny	(H)
Wadworth 6X	(H)

DB FA ME ML (SAT & SUN ONLY) OD PG
RF ST
Traditional village local with one large bar
and separate skittle alley. NOT OPEN
weekday lunchtimes.

POSTBRIDGE

EAST DART HOTEL (Map Ref C5)
10:30 - 11: (M-S)
POSTBRIDGE, YELVERTON (ON B3212,
BETWEEN MORETONHAMPSTEAD
AND PRINCETOWN), OS: SX649790
Tel: (0822) 88213

Courage Best Bitter	(H)
Courage Directors	(H)
Webster's Yorkshire Bitter	(H)

WARREN HOUSE INN (Map Ref C5)
11 - 2:30 ; 6 - 11. (M-S (W); 11 - 11 (S))
POSTBRIDGE, YELVERTON (2 MILES
NORTH EAST OF POSTBRIDGE, ON
B3212), OS: SX674809
Tel: (0822) 88208

Gibbs Mew Bishop's Tipple	(H)
Wadworth 6X	(H)
Whitbread Best Bitter	(H)
Flowers Original	(H)

CA CI CP DB DM FA ME ML OD PG QP
RF
Originally a tin miners pub with good
moorland views, still has horse rails
outside for riders. Separate games/family
room. Log fire near bar is reputed to the
longest burning fire in the country; 100
years+. Ideally situated for Dartmoor
enthusiasts. Power is provided by the
pub's own generator.

POUNDSGATE

TAVISTOCK INN (Map Ref D6)
11 - 2:30 ; 6 - 11. (M-S (W), 11 - 3 ; 5-11 (S))
POUNDSGATE, NEWTON ABBOT
Tel: (03643) 251

Courage Best Bitter	(H)
Ushers Best Bitter	(H)

CA CP FA ME ML OD PG RF
Very old traditional granite moorland pub.
Rugged front bar, small side room and
plenty of room outside.

PRINCETOWN

DARTMOOR INN (Map Ref C6)
11 - 3 ; 6 - 11. (M-S)
MERRIVALE BRIDGE, PRINCETOWN,
YELVERTON
Tel: (082289) 340

Draught Bass	(H)
Worthington Best Bitter	(H)
Charrington IPA	(H)

AC CA CI CP ME ML OD PG RF RS
One-bar, pub, with a small games room
and a restaurant. Separate food counter.
Well located for Dartmoor enthusiasts.
Cider in summer.

DEVILS ELBOW HOTEL (Map Ref C6)
11 - 3 ; 7 - 11. (M-S)
THE SQUARE, PRINCETOWN
Tel: (082289) 232

Flowers IPA	(H)
Guest Beer Occasional	(H)

AC CA CI CP DF (BAR ONLY) FA ME ML
OD PG RF ST
Large pub with a skittle alley at rear. Guest
ales change every quarter, and cider in the
summer.

FOREST INN (Map Ref C6)
11 - 3 ; 6 - 11. (M-S)
HEXWORTHY, PRINCETOWN
Tel: (03643) 211

Furgusons Dartmoor Best Bitter	(H)
Palmers BB	(H)

AC CA CD CI CP FA (RESTAURANT
OMLY) ME ML OD PG QP RF RS
Large moorland inn and hotel, in a
spectacular Dartmoor location. Separate
restaurant area with excellent food.
Families welcome for meals. Walking,
fishing, riding facilities in the area.

PLUME OF FEATHERS (Map Ref C6)
11 - 11. (M-S)
THE SQUARE, PRINCETOWN
Tel: (082289) 240

Draught Bass	**(H)**
Worthington Best Bitter	**(H)**
Guest Beer Regular	**(H)**

AC CA CI CP FA ME ML OD PG RF ST
Traditional Dartmoor pub, built in 1785,
and Grade 2 listed. It has two bars, log
fires, exposed beams and granite walls.
There is a skittle alley available.

PRINCE OF WALES HOTEL (Map Ref C6)
11 - 3 ; 6:30 - 11. (M-S) TAVISTOCK ROAD,
PRINCETOWN
Tel: (082289) 219

Draught Bass	**(H)**

AC CA CI CP FA ME ML OD PG RF
On the road to HM prison, popular with
warders and walkers alike.

TWO BRIDGES HOTEL (Map Ref C6)
11: -3 : ;6 : -11: (M-S(W); 11-11 (S))
TWO BRIDGES, PRINCETOWN (ON
B3212, 2 MILES NORTH-EAST OF
PRINCETOWN), OS: SX608749
Tel: (082289) 581

Courage Best Bitter	**(H)**
John Smith's Bitter	**(H)**

AC CA CI CP DF FA ME ML NS (IN
HOTEL) OD PB PG QP RF RS
Large hotel in the middle of Dartmoor,
with a no-smoking area in the hotel,
ideally situated for visitors to take
advantage of Dartmoor's many sights and
antiquaties. The friendly landlord is setting
up a micro-brewery in one of the hotel's
outbuildings, which should come on
stream in the autumn '93.

PRIXFORD

NEW RING O' BELLS (Map Ref C2)
PRIXFORD, Nr. BARNSTAPLE. (3 MILES
NORTH OF BARNSTAPLE), OS: SS549368
Tel: (0271) 43836

Flowers Original	**(H)**

PYWORTHY

MOLESWORTH ARMS (Map Ref A4)
11 - 2:30 ; 7 - 11. (M-S)
PYWORTHY, Nr. HOLSWORTHY.
OS: SS313029
Tel: (0409) 253513

Draught Bass	**(H)**
Worthington Best Bitter	**(H)**

RACKENFORD

STAG INN (Map Ref D3)
12 - 2:30 ; 6 - 11. (M-S)
RACKENFORD, Nr, SOUTH MOLTON.
Tel: (088488) 369

Cotleigh Tawny	**(H)**
Exmoor Gold (SUMMER ONLY)	**(H)**

AC CH CP DB FA ME ML OD PG RF
Thatched village inn with a darkened front
bar and a large back lounge with pool.
Ancient building of great potential,
reputedly Devon's oldest tunnel inn,
dating from AD 1237. Children are
admitted to the games room.

RATTERY

CHURCH HOUSE INN (Map Ref D6)
11 - 2:30 ; 6 - 11. (M-S)
RATTERY, SOUTH BRENT (OFF A38 AT
BUCKFASTLEIGH, 3 MILES SOUTH
WEST)
Tel: (0364) 42220

Furgusons Dartmoor Best Bitter	**(H)**
Tetley Bitter	**(H)**
Guest Beer Regular	**(H)**

AC CP ME ML OD QP RF
11th century pub with massive oak beams,
a great open fireplace and a spiral
staircase. Guest beers change weekly.
Reputation for good food.

**PROTECT
YOUR
PLEASURE**

RINGMORE

JOURNEY'S END INN (Map Ref C7)
11:30 - 3 ; 6:30 - 11. (M-S)
RINGMORE, Nr. KINGSBRIDGE
Tel: (0548) 810205

Adnams Broadside	(H)
Butcombe Bitter	(H)
Eldridge Pope Royal Oak	(H)
Exmoor Ale	(H)
Smiles Brewery Bitter	(H)
Wadworth 6X	(H)

AC BB CA CH CI CP (NEARBY) DB FA
ME ML OD PG QP RF RS
Old wood panelled, thatched bar with a
modern, wicker- filled restaurant extension
and an emphasis on good value food. Fine
range of well-kept real ales. Separate
games room with bar billiards.

ROCKBEARE

JACK-IN-THE-GREEN (Map Ref F4)
11 - 3 ; 6 - 11. (M-S) ROCKBEARE, Nr.
EXETER.
OS: SY023955
Tel: (0404) 822240

Courage Directors	(H)
John Smith's Bitter	(H)
Ruddle Best Bitter	(H)
Wadworth 6X	(H)

CA CD CH CP DF FA ME ML OD PB PG
QP RF ST
Busy main road pub with restaurant
facilities and friendly atmosphere. Beer
and food menus variable.

ROCKFORD

ROCKFORD INN (Map Ref D1)
12 - 2:30 ; 7 - 11. (M-S (W), VARIES IN
SUMMER)
ROCKFORD, BRENDON, Nr. LYNTON.
OS: SS756477
Tel: (05987) 214

Courage Best Bitter	(H)
John Smith's Bitter	(H)

AC CP ME ML PG QP RF
Old riverside inn, set deep in a wooded
valley on the edge of Exmoor. Good food.

SALCOMBE

FERRY INN (Map Ref D8)
11 - 3 ; 5:30 - 11. (M-S (W), 11-11 (S))
FORE STREET, SALCOMBE
Tel: (0548) 844000

Palmers	
BB	(H)
Tally Ho!	(H)
House Beer House Name	(H)

CA FA ME ML OD PB RF
3 bars in a terraced building which has
superb views over the estuary. Two-bar
pub and bistro, on waters edge, with a
large garden.

FORTESCUE INN (Map Ref D8)
11 - 11. (M-S) UNION STREET,
SALCOMBE
Tel: (0548) 842868

Courage Best Bitter	(H)
Furgusons Dartmoor Best Bitter	(H)
Guest Beer Regular	(H)

CA CD (EUCHRE) CI DF FA ME ML OD
PB PG (QUIZ) PL QP RF
Recent refurbishments have made this
large pub popular with youngsters. The
public bar is lively, with a quieter lounge.
Pub is about 250 years old, and has a
nautical theme with pictures and features.
Popular for meals.

SAMPFORD COURTENAY

COUNTRYMAN (Map Ref C4)
11 - 3 ; 6 - 11.
BEACON CROSS, ON B3215, (ON B3215,
2.5 MILES S.W. OF NORTH TAWTON),
OS: SX637994
Tel: (0837) 82206

Ruddles County	(H)
Ushers Best Bitter	(H)

CC CI CP DF FA ME ML OD PG QP RF
Superbly furnished country freehouse and
candlelit restaurant in 3.5 acres of gardens.
Must book for food at weekends. Guest
beers.

SAMPFORD PEVERELL

GLOBE INN (Map Ref F3)
11 - 11. (M-S)
16, LOWER TOWN, SAMPFORD
PEVERELL.
Tel: (0884) 821214

Cotleigh Tawny	(H)
Marston's Pedigree	(H)
Flowers IPA	(H)

BR (TIVERTON PARKWAY) CP FA ME ML
OD PG RF
Large roadside pub with an excellent
children's play area. Pub backs onto Grand
Western Canal. Occasional guest beers.

MERRIMEADE HOTEL (Map Ref F3)
11:30 - 2:30 ; 6 - 11. (M-F. 11-11 Sat)
1, LOWER TOWN, SAMPFORD
PEVERELL.
Tel: (0884) 820270

Cotleigh Tawny	(H)
Flowers Original	(H)

AC BR (TIVERTON PARKWAY) CP DF FA
GD ME ML OD PG RF
Busy main road hotel with a nice garden
and play area.

SANDFORD

LAMB INN (Map Ref D4)
12 - 3 ; 7 - 11. (M-S)
THE SQUARE, SANDFORD, Nr.
CREDITON.
Tel: (0363) 773676

Eldridge Pope Hardy Country	(H)
Flowers IPA	(H)

BB DB DF FA ML OD PB PG RF ST
c16 two-bar village inn, with a cobbled
forecourt, and friendly atmosphere.

ROSE AND CROWN (Map Ref D4)
11 - 3 ; 6:30 - 11. (M-S)
ROSE AND CROWN HILL, SANDFORD,
Nr. CREDITON, DEVONSHIRE.
Tel: (0363) 772056

Flowers IPA	(H)
Guest Beer Occasional	(H)

FA OD PG
Popular, friendly, local. At present being
run under receivership (1/2/93)

SCORRITON

TRADESMANS ARMS (Map Ref D6)
11 - 2 ; 7 - 11. (M-F, 11-2.30 Sat)
SCORRITON, BUCKFASTLEIGH,
OS: SX704685
Tel: (03643) 206

Furgusons Dartmoor Best Bitter	(H)
Wadworth 6X	(H)
Guest Beer Regular	(H)

CD CH CI DB DM FA ME ML OD PG RF
Set in an unspoilt village in the foothills of
Dartmoor, with a friendly, relaxing
atmosphere in the main bar and snug.
Family room has panoramic views of the
surrounding countryside.

SEATON

FAMOUS OLD GEORGE (Map Ref G5)
11 - 3 ; 5 - 11. (M-F, 11-11 Sat.)
THE SQUARE, SEATON. (IN SQUARE
ADJACENT TO SEA FRONT
ROUNDABOUT).
Tel: (0297) 21236

Cornish Royal Wessex	(H)
Wethered Winter Royal	(H)

CA CC DB DF DM ME ML PB PG PL QP
SN
Conciously old-world comfort and feel in a
town centre pub. Good food at sensible
prices.

FISHERMANS INN (Map Ref G5)
11 - 11.
MARINE PARADE, SEATON,. (BY SEA
FRONT ROUNDABOUT).
Tel: (0297) 20025

Draught Bass	(H)

AC CA DB ME ML OD PG PL QP RF SN
Friendly town centre pub on seafront.

HOOK AND PARROT (Map Ref G5)
11 - 11. (M-S)
THE ESPLANADE, SEATON. (ON SEA
FRONT NEAR ROUNDABOUT).
Tel: (0297) 20222

Draught Bass	(H)
Cornish Royal Wessex	(H)
Castle Eden Ale	(H)
Flowers Original	(H)

AC CA CC CH FA ME ML OD PG PL QP
RS SN ST (TABLE SKITTLES)
Seafront pub with terrace and cellar bar
(evenings only). Adjoining coffee shop
caters for children and drivers.

KINGS ARMS (Map Ref G5)
11:30 -2:30 ; 5:30 - 11. (M-F, 11-3 Sat., 11-11
F,Sat SUMMER)
FORE ST, SEATON. (ON TOP ROAD TO
COLYTON, 1/4ml. FROM TOWN
CENTRE.).
Tel: (0297) 23431

Draught Bass	(H)
Worthington Best Bitter	(H)
Guest Beer Occasional	(H)

BB CA CD DB FA GD ME ML OD PG QP
SH SN ST (ALSO TABLE SKITTLES)
Cheerful suburban pub on the road to
Colyford.

POLE ARMS HOTEL (Map Ref G5)
11 - 2:30 ; 5:30 - 11. (M-F, 11-11 Sat.)
FORE STREET, SEATON. (1/2 WAY
ALONG SEAWARDS 1-WAY SYSTEM, NR
COMMUNITY CENTRE.)
Tel: (0297) 20019

Draught Bass	(H)

SLEEPER (Map Ref G5)
11 - 2:30 ; 6:30 - 11. (M-T,S,. 1200 F (W).
11-3,6:30-11 M-S (S))
MARINE PLACE, SEATON. (JUST OFF
SEA FRONT BY ROUNDABOUT.),
Tel: (0297) 24380

Beer Engine		
	Rail Ale	(H)
	Piston Bitter	(H)
	Sleeper	(H)

BB CA CC DB FA ME ML PG (SHUBAR
(ROMANIAN)) PL QP SN
Large town centre pub with a room for all
seasons and a refreshing range of beers.

SEATON JUNCTION

SHUTE ARMS (Map Ref G4)
11 - 3 ; 6 - 11. (M-S)
SEATON JUNCTION, Nr. KILMINGTON.
Tel: (0297) 553850

Furgusons Dartmoor Best Bitter	(H)
Ruddles County	(H)

CA DF FA ME ML OD PB PG RF
Friendly village pub with wide range of
facilities.

SHALDON

CLIFFORD ARMS (Map Ref E6)
11- 2:30 ; 6 - 11. (M-F, 11-3, 6-11 Sat) 34,
FORE STREET, SHALDON
Tel: (0626) 872311

Draught Bass	(H)
Furgusons Dartmoor Best Bitter	(H)
Palmers BB	(H)

CH CI FA ME ML OD
Traditional style pub, specialising in
home-cooked food, especially fish and
seafood.

FERRYBOAT INN (Map Ref E6)
THE STRAND, SHALDON
Tel: (0626) 872340

Courage Best Bitter	(H)
Courage Directors	(H)
John Smith's Bitter	(H)

NESS HOUSE HOTEL (Map Ref E6)
Tel: (0626) 873480

Palmers BB	(H)
Wadworth 6X (SUMMER ONLY)	(H)
Old Timer (WINTER ONLY)	(H)

ROYAL STANDARD HOTEL
(Map Ref E6)
FORE STREET, SHALDON
Tel: (0626) 872442

Boddingtons Bitter	(H)
Marston's Pedigree	(H)

SHIPWRIGHTS ARMS (Map Ref E6)
11 - 3 ; 5 - 1. (M-S (W), VARIABLE IN
SUMMER)
RINGMORE ROAD, SHALDON
Tel: (0626) 873237

Courage Best Bitter	(H)
Courage Directors	(H)
John Smith's Bitter	(H)

CA CP DF FA ME ML OD PB PG RF
Well run, refurbished with a nautical
flavour. Good, reasonably priced food in a
c17 pub, situated in a prominent position
overlooking the River Teign estuary.

SHAUGH PRIOR

MOORLAND HOTEL (Map Ref C6)
12 - 3 ; 7 - 11. (M-S) WOTTER, SHAUGH
PRIOR, OS: SX552621
Tel: (075539) 228

Boddingtons Bitter	**(H)**
Guest Beer Regular	**(H)**

AC CA CC CI (SUMMER ONLY) CP DF
FA ME ML OD PB PG
A family run freehouse/hotel on the edge
of Dartmoor, overlooking the Hoe, with a
well furnished public bar.

WHITE THORN INN (Map Ref C6)
11:30 -2:30 ; 6 - 11. (M-S)
SHAUGH PRIOR, PLYMOUTH
Tel: (075539) 245

Courage Best Bitter	**(H)**
John Smith's Bitter	**(H)**
Ushers Founders	**(H)**
Ushers Best Bitter	**(H)**

SHEBBEAR

DEVILS STONE INN (Map Ref B3)
SHEBBEAR, Nr. HOLSWORTHY.
OS: SS439093
Tel: (040928) 210

Boddingtons Bitter	**(H)**
Flowers Original	**(H)**

SHEEPWASH

HALF MOON (Map Ref B4)
11:30 - 2:30 ; 6 - 11. (M-S)
THE SQUARE, SHEEPWASH, Nr.
HATHERLEIGH.
OS: SS487064
Tel: (040923) 376

Draught Bass	**(H)**
Worthington Best Bitter	**(H)**
Courage Best Bitter	**(H)**

AC CP FA ME ML OD PG QP RF RS
Long established village inn, specialising
in breaks for anglers. Lunchtime bar-food,
evening restaurant.

SHOBROOKE

RED LION INN (Map Ref E4)
11:30 -2:30 ; 6:30 - 11. (Tues-Sat. 8-11 Mon)
SHOBROOKE, Nr. CREDITON.
Tel: (0363) 772340

Courage Directors	**(H)**
John Smith's Bitter	**(H)**
Wadworth 6X	**(H)**

AC CA CP DF FA ME ML OD PB PG RF RS
SN
Pleasant village pub with restaurant and
reputation for good food.

SIDBURY

HARE AND HOUNDS (Map Ref F4)
10:30 - 11. (M-S)
PUTTS CORNER, SIDBURY, Nr.
HONITON (ON A375 BETWEEN
SIDMOUTH AND HONITON),
OS: SY145962
Tel: (0404) 41760

Draught Bass	**(H)**
Boddingtons Bitter	**(H)**
Marston's Pedigree	**(H)**
Castle Eden Castle Eden Porter	**(G)**

CA CI (LOCAL FARM) CP DB DF FA LM
ME ML OD PB PG PL RF ST
With its own water and electricity and its
own bakery, this pub is already almost self
sufficient, but there are plans for a brewery
as well in a purpose built brewery. Every
2nd Sunday there is a car boot sale. Live
jazz on Sundays. Comfortable setees and
armchairs around an open fire in the
lounge. Good food.

RED LION (Map Ref F5)
11 - 2:30 ; 6 - 11. (SAT. LUNCH 11-3)
FORE STREET, SIDBURY, SIDMOUTH.
Tel: (0395) 597313

Whitbread Best Bitter	**(H)**
Flowers Original	**(H)**

AC CC DB ME ML OD PG ST
A smart one bar pub with a skittle alley
and friendly staff.

SIDFORD

BLUE BALL INN (Map Ref F5)
10:30 - 2:30 ; 5:30 - 11. (M-S)
SIDFORD, SIDMOUTH.
Tel: (0395) 514062

Boddingtons Bitter	(H)
Cornish Royal Wessex	(H)
Marston's Pedigree	(H)

AC CH CI (TAUNTON) CP DB FA ME ML
OD PB PG QP RF
Three bar whitewashed cob and thatch pub
with a large inglenook fireplace in the
public bar. Comfortable lounge. Pretty
garden with outdoor food service area, but
watch small children as the gates open
directly onto the main road.

RISING SUN (Map Ref F5)
10:30 - 3 ; 6 - 11. (M-S)
SCHOOL STREET, SIDFORD, SIDMOUTH
Tel: (0395) 513722

Draught Bass	(H)
Boddingtons Mild	(H)
Castle Eden Ale	(H)

AC CD CI (TAUNTON) DB DF (TOILETS)
FA (IF EATING) ME ML OD PB PG RF ST
Recently refurbished village pub with
basic public bar, and cosy lounge bar.
Friendly staff.

SIDMOUTH

ANCHOR (Map Ref F5)
11 - 11. (M-S)
OLD FORE STREET, SIDMOUTH.
Tel: (0395) 514129

Draught Bass	(H)
Flowers Original	(H)

CI CP DB DF LM (REGULAR) ME ML OD
PB PG RF
A typical Devenish pub with lots of
hanging bric-a-brac.

BALFOUR ARMS (Map Ref F5)
11- 2:30 ; 5:30 - 11. (M-S)
26, WOOLBROOK ROAD, SIDMOUTH.
Tel: (0395) 512993

Draught Bass	(H)
Cornish Royal Wessex	(H)
Flowers Original	(H)

CD CI (TAUNTON) DB DF DM FA ME ML
OD PG
Cosmopolitan 3 bar town pub, on the
Exeter bus route out of town.

BLACK HORSE (Map Ref F5)
11 - 11. (M-S)
FORE STREET, SIDMOUTH.
Tel: (0395) 513676

Flowers IPA	(H)
Flowers Original	(H)

CD DB DF FA (IF EATING) ME ML PB PG
Spacious two bar town pub.

BOWD INN (Map Ref F5)
11 - 3 ; 5 - 11. (M-S)
BOWD CROSS, SIDMOUTH (JUNCTION
OF A3052 & B3176), OS: SY106901
Tel: (0395) 513328

Draught Bass	(H)
Boddingtons Bitter	(H)
Marston's Pedigree	(H)

BB CA CH CP DF (ACCESS ONLY) FA GD
ME ML OD PG QP RF RM
(BACKGROUND)
Old pub, with many of the original oak
beams. Very food orientated with a good
menu which lives up to its reputation.

DOVE INN (Map Ref F5)
11 - 3 ; 6 - 11. (11-11 Sat (W), 11-11 M-S (S))
DOVE LANE, SIDMOUTH.
Tel: (0395) 513445

Marston's Pedigree	(H)
Flowers IPA	(H)

AC CD CI (TAUNTON) DB DM FA ME
ML PB
A genuine two bar local of the old
fashioned type.

DUKE OF MARLBOROUGH HOTEL (Map Ref F5)
11 - 11. (M-S) ESPLANADE, SIDMOUTH.
Tel: (0395) 513320

Courage Best Bitter	(H)
Courage Directors	(H)

MERMAID BAR (Map Ref F5)
10:30 - 3 ; 6 - 11. (M-S)
ESPLANADE, SIDMOUTH.
Tel: (0395) 513047

Draught Bass	(H)
Furgusons Dartmoor Best Bitter	(H)
Wadworth 6X	(H)

AC CD ME ML
Very noisy downstairs bar with upbeat
MUSIK.

NEW TAVERN (Map Ref F5)
8 -11. (M-S)
FORE STREET, SIDMOUTH.
Tel: (0395) 512827

Draught Bass   (H)

OLD SHIP (Map Ref F5)
10:30 - 3 ; 6 - 11. (M-S)
OLD FORE STREET, SIDMOUTH.
Tel: (0395) 512127

Draught Bass   (H)
Boddingtons Bitter   (H)
Castle Eden Ale   (H)

ME ML QP RF RS
Pannelled and beamed old pub with
smuggling associations. Very busy in
summer. Separate upstairs restaurant with
skeleton of wattle and daub wall. Don't
mistake the water trough for the loo!

RADWAY (Map Ref F5)
11 - 3 ; 7 - 11. (M-S)
1, RADWAY PLACE, SIDMOUTH,
DEVONSHIRE.
Tel: (0395) 578305

Cornish Royal Wessex   (H)
Flowers IPA   (H)

RIVIERA HOTEL (Map Ref F5)
11 - 2:30 ; 6 - 11. (M-S)
ESPLANADE, SIDMOUTH.
Tel: (0395) 515201

Draught Bass   (H)

SWAN INN (Map Ref F5)
11 - 2:30 ; 6 - 11. (M-S)
37, YORK STREET, SIDMOUTH.
Tel: (0395) 512849

Cornish Royal Wessex   (H)
Whitbread WCPA   (H)

CD DB DF DM ME ML OD PB PG QP
Two bar locals pub tucked away within 100
yards of the sea front. Well worth finding.

TAPPERS BAR (Map Ref F5)
12 - 2:30 ; 7 - 11. (M-S)
ROYAL YORK & FAULKNER HOTEL,
ESPLANADE, SIDMOUTH.
Tel: (0395) 513043

Wadworth 6X   (H)

AC FA ML
Comfortable downstairs hotel bar, with
friendly staff.

TUDOR ROSE (Map Ref F5)
10:30 - 2:30 ; 5:30 - 11. (M-S)
HIGH STREET, SIDMOUTH.
Tel: (0395) 514720

Draught Bass   (H)

VOLUNTEER (Map Ref F5)
11- 2 ; 7 - 11. (M-S (W), 6.30-11 (S))
52, TEMPLE STREET, SIDMOUTH,
Tel: (0395) 512498

Cornish Royal Wessex   (H)
Flowers IPA   (H)

SILVERTON

LAMB INN (Map Ref E4)
11 - 2:30 ; 7 - 11. (M-S)
47, FORE STREET, SILVERTON.
Tel: (0392) 860272

Draught Bass   (H)
Worthington Best Bitter   (H)

SILVERTON INN (Map Ref E4)
12 - 3 ; 5:30 - 11. (M-F. 11-11 Sat)
FORE STREET, SILVERTON.
Tel: (0392) 860196

Draught Bass   (H)
Exe Valley Dob's Best Bitter   (H)

FA ME ML OD RF RS
Recently modernised interior, now with
restaurant upstairs.

The Lamb Inn, Silverton

THREE TUNS (Map Ref E4)
11:30 - 3 ; 5:30 - 11. (M-S)
14, EXETER ROAD, SILVERTON.
Tel: (0392) 860352

Courage Best Bitter	(H)
Courage Directors	(H)
Fuller London Pride	(H)
John Smith's Bitter	(H)
Wadworth 6X	(H)

AC CP DF FA ME OD RF
One of Devon's older pubs, a 15th Century
inn of character.

SLAPTON

QUEENS ARMS (Map Ref D7)
11:30 - 3 ; 6 - 11. (M-S)
SLAPTON, KINGSBRIDGE
Tel: (0548) 580800

Furgusons Dartmoor Best Bitter	(H)
Palmers IPA	(H)
Wadworth 6X	(H)
Guest Beer Regular	(H)

CA CI CP DF FA ME ML OD PG QP RF
Comfortable village locals pub, with a
friendly landlord, and excellent
home-cooked food. Many CAMRA
souveniers on display.

TOWER INN (Map Ref D7)
11 - 3 ; 6 - 11. (M-S)
SLAPTON, KINGSBRIDGE
Tel: (0548) 580216

Eldridge Pope Royal Oak	(H)
Exmoor Ale	(H)
Gibbs Mew Bishop's Tipple	(H)
Hall And Woodhouse Tanglefoot	(H)
Palmers IPA	(H)
Wadworth 6X	(H)

AC CA CC CP DF FA ME ML OD PG QP
RF
14th century classic pub overlooked by an
ancient crumbling tower. A central bar
flanked by a lounge and a food bar.
Popular in summer, very small car park.
Interior tastefully decorated with small
bats (flying sort). Beer prices are high, but
the quality is also high. - Worth a visit.

SMALLRIDGE

RIDGEWAY INN (Map Ref G4)
11:30 - 2:30 ; 6:45 - 11. (M-S)
SMALLRIDGE, AXMINSTER.
(SIGNPOSTED FROM A358 AXMINSTER
TO CHARD ROAD) Tel: (0297) 32171

Otter Ale	(H)
Guest Beer Occasional	(H)

AC CC CP DF FA ME ML OD PB PG RF
Cheerful village inn off the beaten track.
Well worth searching for.

SOUTH BRENT

ANCHOR HOTEL (Map Ref D7)
SOUTH BRENT, ASHBURTON
Tel: (0364) 73135

Draught Bass (G)

ROYAL OAK (Map Ref D7)
11 - 2 ; 6 - 11. (M-F, 11 - 11 Sat)
STATION ROAD, SOUTH BRENT
Tel: (0364) 72133

Furgusons Dartmoor Best Bitter	(H)
Dartmoor Strong	(H)
Wadworth 6X	(H)
Guest Beer Occasional	(H)

AC CA CI DM FA ME ML OD PG ST
2nd oldest pub in village, built in 1830,
used to be used as the local law court. Pub
is the H.Q. for 5 football and 23 skittle
teams, who knock down over 250,000 pins
every year.

SOUTH MOLTON

KINGS ARMS (Map Ref D2)
KING STREET, SOUTH MOLTON,
Tel: (0769) 572679

Draught Bass	(H)

TOWN ARMS (Map Ref D2)
11 - 3 ; 6 - 11. (M-S)
EAST STREET, SOUTH MOLTON.
Tel: (07695) 2531

Gibbs Mew	
Local Line	(H)
Salisbury Bitter	(H)

AC CP ME ML OD PG QP RF
Small, quiet, town centre local, with
attractive stained glass windows.

SOUTH POOL

MILLBROOK INN (Map Ref D8)
11 - 3 ; 5:30 - 11. (M-S)
SOUTH POOL, KINGSBRIDGE
Tel: (0548) 531581

Draught Bass	(G)
John Smith's Bitter	(H)
Ruddles Best Bitter	(H)

CA CD (EUCHRE) CI DB DF FA ME ML
OD PB PG QP
There are two bars and a tiny terrace. Small
pub near river that really does babble.The
front room is the village bar, compact and
warm. The rear bar is more like a sitting
room with chintzy furnishings and a few
dining tables. Outside there is a tidal
pond with ducks. Pub gets very busy,
especially at high tides, so go early.

SOUTH TAWTON

SEVEN STARS INN (Map Ref C4)
11 - 3 ; 6 - 11. (M-S (W)
VARIABLE IN SUMMER)
SOUTH TAWTON, Nr. OKEHAMPTON.
Tel: (0837) 840292

Eldridge Pope Royal Oak	(H)
Palmers IPA	(H)
Guest Beer Regular	(H)

AC ME ML OD RF
Stone built village pub with one bar and a
restaurant. One guest beer always
available.

SOUTH ZEAL

OXENHAM ARMS (Map Ref C4)
11 - 2:30 ; 6 - 11. (M-S, 12 - 2.30 Sun)
SOUTH ZEAL, Nr. OKEHAMPTON.
Tel: (0837) 840244

Draught Bass	(G)
St Austell Tinners	(G)

AC CA CC CP FA ME ML OD QP RF
Granite built village inn with a genuine old
world feel. Strongly recommended.
Draught cider in summer.

SPARKWELL

TREBY ARMS (Map Ref C7)
11 - 3 ; 6:30 - 11. (M-S)
SPARKWELL, IVYBRIDGE
Tel: (0752) 537363

Draught Bass	(H)
Boddingtons Bitter	(H)
Wadworth 6X	(H)
Guest Beer Regular	(H)
(weekends)	

CA CP ME (NOT MON. EVE.) ML OD PG
RF
Compact and cosy village local with an
interesting bottle collection. Pub originates
from about 1750, and is set in a picturesque
village near a well known wild life park.
(worth a visit) Guest beers at weekends.

SPREYTON

TOM COBLEY TAVERN (Map Ref D4)
6 -11. (T-F (W), 7-11 M (W), Sat (W) 12-3)
SPREYTON, Nr CREDITON,
DEVONSHIRE., OS: SX698968
Tel: (064723) 314

Cotleigh Tawny	(G)
Exe Valley Dob's Best Bitter	(G)
Greene King Abbot	(G)

AC CC CD CP DB DF DM FA
(RESTAURANT ONLY) ME ML (SUMMER
ONLY) OD PG (TABLE TENNIS) QP RF RS
SH
Quiet village local, superb function room
with an inside barbecue. Home made food,
but no food on weekdays except in
summer.

ST ANN'S CHAPEL
PICKWICK INN (Map Ref C7)
11- 3 ; 6:30 - 11. (M-S)
ST. ANN'S CHAPEL, BIGBURY
Tel: (0548) 810241

Draught Bass	(H)
Charrington IP	(H)

AC CA CD (EUCHRE) CP DB DF FA ME
ML OD PG
The pub stands on the site of the Chapel of
St. Ann, which now forms part of the inn.
Recently refurbished with a large carvery
restaurant.

ST. GILES-IN-THE-WOOD

CRANFORD INN (Map Ref C3)
ST. GILES-IN-THE-HEATH, Nr.
TORRINGTON.
Tel: (0805) 23309

Draught Bass   (H)

STARCROSS

ATMOSPHERIC RAILWAY
(Map Ref E5)
11:30 - 2:30 ; 6:30 - 11.   (M-S (W), 11-2.30,
6-11 (S))
STARCROSS, EXETER.
Tel: (0626) 890335

Draught Bass   (H)
Boddingtons Bitter   (H)
Eldridge Pope Hardy Country   (H)
Whitbread Best Bitter   (H)

ME ML OD ST
Comfortable pub with a slightly excessive
railway theme. Pub takes its name from
Brunel's railway that used a vacuum in a
leather pipe between the rails to pull the
trains along. The only remaining example
of this system is in the form of a pumping
house (now a museum) opposite the pub.

COURTENAY ARMS (Map Ref E5)
11 - 11.   (M-S)
STARCROSS, EXETER.
Tel: (0626) 890246

Draught Bass   (H)
Ind Coope Burton Ale   (H)
Theakston Old Peculier   (H)

STAVERTON

SEA TROUT INN (Map Ref D6)
11 - 2:30 ; 6 - 11:   (M-S)
STAVERTON, TOTNES
Tel: (0803) 762274

Draught Bass   (G)
Furgusons Dartmoor Best Bitter   (H)
Wadworth 6X   (H)
Guest Beer Regular   (H)

AC BR (DART VALLEY RAILWAY) CA CP
DF FA ME ML OD PB PG RF
Pleasant country pub with a restaurant.

STIBB CROSS

UNION INN (Map Ref B3)
12 - 3 ; 7 - 11.   (M-S)
STIBB CROSS, Nr. TORRINGTON.
Tel: (08055) 253

Draught Bass   (H)

CP ME ML OD PG RF
Convivial bar and restaurant.

STOCKLAND

KINGS ARMS (Map Ref G4)
12 - 3 ; 6:30 - 11.   (M-S)
STOCKLAND, Nr. AXMINSTER.
Tel: (0404) 88361

Exmoor Ale   (H)
Hall & Woodhouse Badger Best Bitter   (H)
Ruddles County   (H)
Ushers Best Bitter   (H)

AC CC CP DF FA ME (NOT SUNDAY) ML
OD PG QP
Carefully enlarged and modernised
friendly free house with a spotless cellar.
No food Sunday evenings.

STOKE CANNON

STOKE CANNON INN (Map Ref E4)
11 - 2:30 ; 6 - 11.
HIGH STREET, STOKE CANNON,
EXETER. (ON A396 IN VILLAGE),
OS: SX938979
Tel: (0392) 841200

Draught Bass   (H)
Boddingtons Bitter   (H)

CC CP GD ME ML OD PB PG QP RF
Welcoming village pub, retaining many of
it's original features.

STOKE FLEMING

GREEN DRAGON (Map Ref E7)
11 - 3 ; 5:30 - 11. (M-S (W), 11-11 (S))
CHURCH ROAD, STOKE FLEMING,
OS: SX862484
Tel: (0803) 770238

Draught Bass   (H)
Boddingtons Bitter   (H)
Flowers IPA   (H)

CH CI DB FA GD ME ML (WEEKENS
ONLY (W), DAILY (S)) OD PG RF RS
Old, oak beamed pub with inglenook
fireplace, separate restaurant. Large garden
with childrens' equipment.

LONDON INN (Map Ref E7)
11 - 11. (M-S)
DARTMOUTH ROAD, STOKE FLEMING
Tel: (0803) 770397

Eldridge Pope Hardy Country	(H)
Flowers IPA	(H)
Guest Beer Regular	(H)

CA CH DF FA GD ME ML OD PG RF
c17 coaching house, Grade 2 listed, with
family/games room and beer garden.

STOKENHAM

CHURCH HOUSE INN (Map Ref D8)
11 - 11. (M-S)
STOKENHAM, KINGSBRIDGE,
OS: SX807428
Tel: (0548) 580253

Draught Bass	(H)
Boddingtons Bitter	(H)
Flowers IPA	(H)

CC CD (EUCHRE) CH CI CP FA GD ME
ML OD PG (JENGA)
RS Roomy village pub run by garrulous,
enterprising landlord. The menu features
genuinely local fresh fish and 300 varieties
of jacket potato. BBQs in summer.

TRADESMANS ARMS (Map Ref D8)
12 - 2:30 ; 7 - 11. (M-S)
STOKENHAM, KINGSBRIDGE

Tel: (0548) 580313

Draught Bass	(H)
Guest Beer Regular	(H)

CA CI CP DF ME ML OD QP RF
Pretty thatched village pub that stocks 115
malt whiskies, and has at least 2 guest ales
at most times. There is NO keg bitter in the
pub, but as the landlord has an aversion to
'national' porters, Thompson's Porter is
available, but this is KEG.

Ye Old Union Inn, Stibb Cross

STRETE

KINGS ARMS (Map Ref D7)
11:30 - 2:30 ; 6:30 - 11. (M-S (W), 11-2.30,
6-11 (S))
STRETE, KINGSBRIDGE,
OS: SX841468
Tel: (0803) 770377

Draught Bass	(H)
Eldridge Pope Royal Oak	(H)
(SUMMER ONLY)	
Flowers Original	(H)

CD (EUCHRE) CH CP FA GD ME ML OD
PG RF RS
Basic, but worthy village pub with a good
sea view from the dining room. The pub
has some unusual decorative ironwork.

SWIMBRIDGE

JACK RUSSELL (Map Ref C2)
11:30 - 2:30 ; 6 - 11. (M-S)
SWIMBRIDGE, Nr. BARNSTAPLE.
Tel: (0271) 830366

John Smith's Bitter	(H)
Ushers Best Bitter	(H)

CP FA ME ML OD PB PG RF
Country inn with two bars and a games
room. A separate dining room provides an
A La Carte menu. The pub's name derives
from a former local parson who was
responsible for the Jack Russell breed of
dogs. (patron saint of postmen!!)

TALATON

TALATON INN (Map Ref F4)
12 - 2:30 ; 7 - 11. (M-S)
TALATON, Nr. HONITON.
Tel: (0404) 822214

Wadworth 6X	(H)

CD CH CP DB FA ME ML OD PB PG QP
ST
Popular friendly village pub with a
separate restaurant serving good value
home cooked food.

TAVISTOCK

CORNISH ARMS (Map Ref B6)
11 - 3 ; 5:30 - 11. (M-Th, Sat; 11-11 Fri)
WEST STREET, TAVISTOCK
Tel: (0822) 612145

Courage Best Bitter	(H)
Ruddle Best Bitter	(H)

ME ML OD PB PG
Sizeable effervescent 2 bar town pub with
considerable dining area.

COTTAGE INN (Map Ref B6)
PACKWOOD ROAD, TAVISTOCK
Tel: (0822) 617181

Courage Best Bitter	(H)
Ushers Best Bitter	(H)
Ushers Founders	(H)

MARKET INN (Map Ref B6)
2, WHITCHURCH ROAD, TAVISTOCK
Tel: (0822) 613556

Courage Best Bitter	(H)
Ushers Best Bitter	(H)

ORDOLPH ARMS (Map Ref B6)
KILWORTHY HILL, TAVISTOCK
Tel: (0822) 615048

Draught Bass	(H)
Boddingtons Bitter	(H)
Furgusons Dartmoor Best Bitter	(H)

QUEENS HEAD HOTEL (Map Ref B6)
11 - 3 ; 6 - 11. (ALL DAY WEDS, FRI &
SAT)
WEST STREET, TAVISTOCK
Tel: (0822) 613048

Draught Bass	(H)

TAVISTOCK INN (Map Ref B6)
11 - 3 ; 5:30 - 11 (M-S)
BROOK STREET, TAVISTOCK
Tel: (0822) 612661

Courage Best Bitter	(H)
Founders	(H)
Best Bitter	(H)

Busy, friendly, local's, town pub.

UNION INN (Map Ref B6)
KING STREET, TAVISTOCK
Tel: (0822) 613115

Draught Bass	(H)

VIRTUOUS LADY (Map Ref B6)
PLYMOUTH ROAD, TAVISTOCK
Tel: (0822) 615811

Draught Bass	(H)

TEDBURN ST. MARY

KINGS ARMS HOTEL (Map Ref D4)
11 - 3 ; 6 - 11. (M-F. 11 - 11 Sat)
TEDBURN ST. MARY, EXETER.
Tel: (0647) 61224

Draught Bass	(H)
Courage Directors	(H)
John Smith's Bitter	(H)
Ruddles County	(H)

AC CA CC CI (BROMMELL'S) CP DF FA
ME ML OD PB PG RF RS
Well kept roadside inn which has a
separate restaurant with an extensive A
LA carte menu. Pleasant c15 country pub.

TEIGNMOUTH

BLUE ANCHOR INN (Map Ref E6)
11 - 11. (M-S)
TEIGN STREET, TEIGNMOUTH
Tel: (0626) 772741

Adnams Broadside	(H)
Boddingtons Bitter	(H)
Marston's Pedigree	(H)
Theakston Old Peculier	(H)

BR (TEIGNMOUTH) DF ME (NOT SUN.)
OD PG RF
Locals town centre pub close to the quay.
Very friendly atmosphere, and a good
selection of real ales. Open for breakfast at
8am.

GOLDEN LION INN (Map Ref E6)
12 - 3 ; 6 - 11. (M-S (W), 11 - 3 (S))
BITTON PARK ROAD, TEIGNMOUTH
Tel: (0626) 776442

Guest Beer Regular	(H)

BR (TEIGNMOUTH) ME ML PG
Two-bar local with pub games, and
occasional live entertainment.

THELBRIDGE

THELBRIDGE CROSS INN (Map Ref D3)
11:30 - 3 ; 6:30 - 11 (M-S)
THELBRIDGE, Nr. CREDITON.
(ON B3042), OS: SS790120 Tel: (0884) 860316

Draught Bass	**(H)**
Wadworth 6X	**(H)**
Guest Beer Regular	**(H)**

AC CA CC CP DF FA ME ML OD PB PG RF
Splendid, isolated but busy cross roads pub.

THORVERTON

DOLPHIN HOTEL (Map Ref E4)
11 - 3 ; 6 - 11. (M-S)
VILLAGE SQUARE, THORVERTON,
Tel: (0392) 860205

Boddingtons Bitter	**(H)**
Morland Old Speckled Hen	**(H)**
Flowers IPA	**(H)**
Flowers Original	**(H)**

AC CP DF FA ME ML OD PB PG QP RF
Friendly, comfortable country pub with A La carte restaurant.

EXETER INN (Map Ref E4)
11 - 3 ; 6 - 11. (M-S)
BULLEN STREET,THORVERTON, Nr. EXETER.
Tel: (0392) 860206

Courage Bitter Ale	**(H)**
Courage Best Bitter	**(H)**
Courage Directors	**(H)**

CA CP DF FA ME ML OD PG RF
Old coaching inn with superb collection of farm implements and it's own well. Skittle alley and function room available.

RUFFWELL HOTEL (Map Ref E4)
11 - 3 ; 6:30 - 11. (M-S)
THORVERTON, Nr. EXETER. (ON THE A396 BETWEEN REWE AND TIVERTON)
Tel: (0392) 860377

Flowers Original	**(H)**

CA CC CP FA ME ML MR OD PB PG RF
Old coaching inn on main Exeter - Tiverton road specialising in food. Function room available.

THROWLEIGH

NORTHMORE ARMS (Map Ref C5)
11 - 11. (M-S)
WONSON, THROWLEIGH, Nr. OKEHAMPTON. (3 MILES N.W. OF CHAGFORD), OS: SX673897
Tel: (064723) 428

Flowers IPA	**(G)**
Flowers Original	**(G)**

CC CP ME ML OD PG RF
Old fashioned local on fringe of Dartmoor. A good finishing point for walkers. Pub serves 3 villages / hamlets, and is hard to find, but worth the trouble.

THURLESTONE

VILLAGE INN (Map Ref C8)
11:30 - 2:30 ; 6 - 11. (M-S, 12 - 2.30 Sun)
THURLESTONE, KINGSBRIDGE
Tel: (0548) 560382

Draught Bass	**(H)**
Palmers BB	**(H)**
Wadworth 6X	**(H)**

CP DF FA ME ML OD PB QP
c16 village pub, with original oak beams.

TIPTON ST. JOHN

GOLDEN LION INN (Map Ref F5)
11 - 3 ; 6 - 11. (M-S)
TIPTON ST. JOHN, Nr. SIDMOUTH,
Tel: (0404) 812881

Draught Bass	**(H)**
Boddingtons Bitter	**(H)**
Eldridge Pope Hardy Country	**(H)**

AC CD DB DM FA ME ML OD PG RF
Comfortable, traditional village local.

The Kings Arms Inn, Tedburn St. Mary

TIVERTON

HALF MOON (Map Ref E3)
11 - 11. (M-S)
FORE STREET, TIVERTON,
Tel: (0884) 253543

Courage Best Bitter	(H)
Courage Directors	(H)
Webster's Yorkshire Bitter	(H)

DF FA ML MR PB PG
Large modern pub near market. Function room upstairs.

HARE AND HOUNDS (Map Ref E3)
11 - 3 ; 6:30 - 11. (M-F. 11 - 4, 6.30 - 11 Sat)
CHAPEL STREET, TIVERTON.
Tel: (0884) 252013

Boddingtons Bitter	(H)
Wadworth 6X	(H)

PRINCE BLUCHER (Map Ref E3)
11 - 2:30 ; 5 - 11. (M-Th. 11 - 11 F,Sat)
WESTEXE SOUTH, TIVERTON,
Tel: (0884) 252039

Flowers Original	(G)

PRINCE REGENT (Map Ref E3)
11 - 11. (M-S)
LOWMAN GREEN, TIVERTON.
Tel: (0884) 252882

John Smith's Bitter	(H)
Guest Beer Regular	(H)

AC CP DF FA (FOR MEALS ONLY) ME ML OD PB PG
Popular local near river Lowman and clock tower.

QUEENS HEAD (Map Ref E3)
11 - 11. (M-S)
CASTLE STREET, TIVERTON,
Tel: (0884) 254863

Cotleigh Tawny	(H)

DF FA PG (INCL BACKGAMMON)
Friendly town pub, popular for games.

RACEHORSE (Map Ref E3)
11 - 11. (M-S)
WELLBROOK STREET, TIVERTON.
Tel: (0884) 252606

Ruddles County	(H)
Ushers Best Bitter	(H)
Webster's Yorkshire Bitter	(H)

CP DF FA ME ML MR OD PG RF
Popular local with a large function room.

SEVEN STARS (Map Ref E3)
11 - 3 ; 6 - 11. (M-Th. 11 - 11 F,Sat)
BRIDGE STREET, TIVERTON,
Tel: (0884) 252070

John Smith's Bitter	(H)

WHITE BALL (Map Ref E3)
11 - 3 ; 6 - 11. (M-Th. 5.30 - 11 F, Sat.)
BRIDGE STREET, TIVERTON.
Tel: (0884) 259117

Draught Bass	(H)
Flowers Original	(H)

AC FA (LUNCHTIME ONLY) LM ML MR OD PB
Popular pub with large function room featuring live bands.

WHITE HORSE (Map Ref E3)
11 - 11. (M-S)
12, GOLD STREET, TIVERTON.
Tel: (0884) 252022

Draught Bass	(H)
Greene King IPA	(H)

AC DF ME ML OD PG
Small, friendly town centre pub, with good value food.

White Horse Inn, Tiverton

TOPSHAM

BRIDGE INN (Map Ref E5)
12 - 2 ; 6 - 10:30 (M-Th. 6 - 11 F, Sat)
BRIDGE HILL, TOPSHAM, EXETER.
Tel: (0392) 873862

Adnams Broadside	(G)
Branscombe Vale Branoc	(G)
Eldridge Pope Royal Oak	(G)
Exe Valley Devon Glory	(G)
Gibbs Mew Bishop's Tipple	(G)
Wadworth 6X	(G)

BR (TOPSHAM) CP OD PB QP RF
Well known pub, unchanged for many
years. Kept by the same family for
generations. The old barn at the rear was
once a brewery. Up to 15 real ales available
at most times.

DENLEY'S (Map Ref E5)
12 - 3 ; 6 - 11. (M-S)
62-64, HIGH STREET, TOPSHAM,
EXETER.
Tel: (0392) 875675

Draught Bass	(H)
Branscombe Vale Branoc	(H)
Castle Eden Ale	(H)

EXETER INN (Map Ref E5)
11:30 - 2:30 ; 6 - 11. (M-W. 11 - 2.30 Th, F. 11
- 11 Sat)
68, HIGH STREET, TOPSHAM, EXETER,
Tel: (0392) 873121

John Smith's Bitter	(H)

The Travellers Rest Inn, Whitestone.

GLOBE HOTEL (Map Ref E5)
11 - 11. (M-S)
34, FORE STREET, TOPSHAM, EXETER.
Tel: (0392) 873471

Draught Bass	(H)
Worthington Best Bitter	(H)
John Smith's Bitter	(H)
Ushers Best Bitter	(H)

AC BR (TOPSHAM) CH CP DF FA ME ML
MR PG (QUIZ) QP RS ST
c16 coaching house, Grade 2 listed, with
many of the original beams (and staff)
giving an olde worlde atmosphere, which
enhances the excellent beers and food.

LIGHTER INN (Map Ref E5)
11 - 11. (M-S)
THE QUAY, TOPSHAM, EXETER.
Tel: (0392) 875439

Hall And Woodhouse	
Badger Best Bitter	(H)
Hard Tackle	(H)
Tanglefoot	(H)

AC BR (TOPSHAM) CH CP FA ME ML
OD PG (QUIZ, CHARADES) QP
Roomy pub near the river, the only Hall
and Woodhouse tied house in Devon,
which serves good food and beer.

LORD NELSON (Map Ref E5)
11 - 2:30 ; 6 - 11. (M-F. 5.30 - 11 Sat)
HIGH STREET, TOPSHAM, EXETER.
Tel: (0392) 873314

Boddingtons Bitter	(H)
Wadworth 6X	(H)
Flowers Original	(H)

PASSAGE INN (Map Ref E5)
11 - 11. (M-S)
FERRY ROAD, TOPSHAM, EXETER.
Tel: (0392) 873653

Draught Bass	(H)
Eldridge Pope	
Hardy Country	(H)
Royal Oak	(H)
Marston's Pedigree	(H)
Flowers IPA	(H)

BR (TOPSHAM) CP DF (ACCESS ONLY)
FA (WEEKENDS ONLY) GD ME ML OD
QP
Pleasant split-level pub next to River Exe,
with a good menu.

SALUTATION (Map Ref E5)
11 - 11. (M-S)
68, FORE STREET, TOPSHAM, EXETER.
Tel: (0392) 873005

Draught Bass	(H)
Worthington Best Bitter	(H)
John Smith's Bitter	(H)

STEAM PACKET (Map Ref E5)
11 - 11. (M-S)
1, MONMOUTH HILL, TOPSHAM,
EXETER.
Tel: (03920 875085

Draught Bass	(H)
Boddingtons Bitter	(H)
Eldridge Pope Dorchester	(H)

AC BR (TOPSHAM) DB FA ME ML PB PG
Pleasant two-bar pub, with genial hosts,
providing good food and beer.

TORBRYAN

CHURCH HOUSE INN (Map Ref D6)
12 - 2:30 ; 7 - 11. (M-S (W), 11:30 - 3, 6 - 11
(S))
TORBRYAN, NEWTON ABBOT
Tel: (0626) 812372

Brains Dark	(H)
Marston's Pedigree	(H)
Marston's Owd Rodger	(H)
Flowers IPA	(H)
Flowers Original	(H)

AC CA CP DF FA ME ML OD PB QP RF RS
Superb example of a c13/14 traditional
Devon longhouse, with parts dating back
to c8. Many old interesting features. All
food is home-made.

TORCROSS

START BAY INN (Map Ref D8)
11:30 - 2:30 ; 6 - 11. (M-S) TORCROSS,
KINGSBRIDGE, OS: SX824422
Tel: (0548) 580553

Marston's Pedigree	(H)
Flowers IPA	(H)

CD (EUCHRE) CH CI CP DB FA ME ML
NS OD PG RF
Heavily food biased lounge bars in a pub
that is so close to the bay that seagull
protections had to be built in.

TORQUAY

CAFE ROYAL (Map Ref E6)
11 - 11. (M-S)
TORWOOD STREET, TORQUAY
Tel: (0803) 293124

Courage Best Bitter	(H)
Guest Beer Regular	(H)

AC DF (ACCESS ONLY) ME ML
Large, modern pub with a cocktail bar
upstairs. Busy at weekends - favourite
youngster's haunt.

CARY ARMS (Map Ref E6)
12 - 2:30 ; 7 - 11. (M-S) BEACH ROAD,
BABBACOMBE, TORQUAY, OS: SX930654
Tel: (0803) 327110

Furgusons Dartmoor Best Bitter	(H)
Dartmoor Strong	(H)

AC FA ME ML OD PL
Attractively situated overlooking
Babbacombe beach, with views across
Lyme Bay. Terraced garden below pub,
which has self catering flats and a
restaurant.

CROWN & SCEPTRE (Map Ref E6)
11 - 3 ; 5:30 - 11. (M-F, 11-4 Sat)
2, PETTITOR ROAD, TORQUAY
Tel: (0803) 328290

Courage Best Bitter	(H)
Courage Directors	(H)
John Smith's Bitter	(H)
Marston's Pedigree	(H)
Ruddles County	(H)
Guest Beer Regular	(H)

CP DF LM ML OD PB PG RF
300 year old popular local. Cockney
humour with a brusque landlord, overall
not a quiet pub. Folk oriented with
frequent live music. Pub located in a
preservation area. Well worth a visit (or
more) to see if the landlord is as pleasant
as the three resident dogs. When you have,
then try the well kept ales.

CYDER PRESS (Map Ref E6)
11 - 11. (M-S)
5/6, BRADDONS HILL ROAD WEST,
TORQUAY
Tel: (0803) 212338

Boddingtons Bitter	(H)
Guest Beer Regular	(H)

ME ML
Small cosy, one-bar, pub in the centre of
Torquay. Popular with youngsters on
Friday & Saturday nights.

DEVON DUMPLING (Map Ref E6)
11 - 2:30 ; 5:30 - 11. (M-Th, 11-3. F, 11-11 Sat)
108, SHIPHAY LANE, SHIPHAY,
TORQUAY, OS: SX893655
Tel: (0803) 613465

Courage Best Bitter	**(H)**
Courage Directors	**(H)**
John Smith's Bitter	**(H)**
Ruddles County	**(H)**
Wadworth 6X	**(H)**

DB ME ML RF
Good, out of town pub, with oak beamed
lounge bar and separate public bar.
Popular with locals and visitors. Extensive
bar menu.

HAYWAIN HOTEL (Map Ref E6)
47, SHERWELL VALLEY ROAD,
CHELSTON, TORQUAY
Tel: (0803) 605346

Furgusons Dartmoor Best Bitter	**(H)**
Furgusons Dartmoor Strong	**(H)**

HOP & GRAPES (Map Ref E6)
11 - 11. (M-S)
LOWER UNION LANE, TORQUAY
Tel: (0803) 296814

Courage Best Bitter	**(H)**
John Smith's Bitter	**(H)**
Wadworth 6X	**(H)**
Guest Beer Regular	**(H)**

BR (TORRE) FA LM ML OD
Traditional style pub, heavily into real ales.
'Happy hour' 5-7 each night, and all day
Sunday, also good value home - cooked
food. DJ entertainment every night.

JULE'S (Map Ref E6)
11 - 11. (M-S)
QUEENS HOTEL, THE STRAND,
TORQUAY
Tel: (0803) 292350

Wadworth 6X	**(H)**
Tetley Bitter	**(H)**

ME ML QP RM SN
Pleasantly decorated an furnished after
conversion from disco bar. Nightly live
entertainment during summer and
weekends rest of year.

KENTS CAVERN HOTEL (Map Ref E6)
11 - 11. (M-S)
1, ILSHAM ROAD, WELLSWOOD,
TORQUAY
Tel: (0803) 292522

Courage Best Bitter	**(H)**
Courage Directors	**(H)**
John Smith's Bitter	**(H)**
Wadworth 6X	**(H)**
Guest Beer Regular	**(H)**

FA LM ME ML OD PB PG QP
Friendly local situated in Wellswood
village, offering a good range of real ales,
home-cooked food, and a warm welcome.
Live jazz weekly. Ideally situated for a visit
to Kents Cavern or Babbacombe beach.

MASONS ARMS (Map Ref E6)
11 - 3:30 ; 6 - 11. (M-S) 110/112,
BABBACOMBE ROAD, TORQUAY
Tel: (0803) 329300

Boddingtons Bitter	**(H)**
Theakston XB (GUEST)	**(H)**
Flowers IPA	**(H)**

DF FA ME ML OD PB PG (QUIZ) QP
Wooden beamed, locals pub, popular with
tourists in summer.

OLD MARKET INN (Map Ref E6)
11 - 11. (M-S)
TORWOOD PLACE, TORWOOD STREET,
TORQUAY
Tel: (0803) 294334

Adnams Broadside	**(H)**
Batemans XXXB	**(H)**
Fullers London Pride	**(H)**
Fullers ESB	**(H)**
Greene King Abbot	**(H)**
Marston's Owd Rodger	**(H)**
Morland Old Speckled Hen	**(H)**
Palmers Tally Ho!	**(H)**
Smiles Brewery Bitter	**(H)**
Smiles Exhibition	**(H)**
Wadworth 6X	**(H)**

DF FA ML
The second Severn Inn's 'Cask Ale House'
in the south west, refurbished with fake
beams and masses of dark stained wood.
Up to 14 cask ales generally available or
settling, kept in fair condition, but at very
high prices. Basic, but sustaining food at
reasonable prices.

WIG & PEN (Map Ref E6)
11 - 11. (M-S)
170, UNION STREET, TORQUAY
Tel: (0803) 213848

Courage Best Bitter	(H)
Wadworth 6X	(H)
Guest Beer Regular	

BR (TORRE) ME ML
Modern pub, just off the main street,
popular for bar food.

TORRINGTON

BLACK HORSE INN (Map Ref B3)
11 - 3 ; 6 - 11. (M-F, 6.30-11 Sat)
HIGH STREET, TORRINGTON.
Tel: (0805) 22121

Courage Directors	(H)
John Smith's Bitter	(H)
Ushers Best Bitter	(H)
Wadworth 6X	(H)
Guest Beer Regular	(H)

AC FA ME ML PG RF (LOUNGE) RS
Tudor pub, reputed to be the oldest in
Torrington, where General Fairfax stayed
during the civil war. Excellent restaurant at
rear.

The Black Horse Inn

Torrington - North Devon
Tel: Torrington (0805) 22121

Reputed to be one of the oldest Inns
in North Devon, The Black Horse
has been in existence so long, no
precise records exist. It is known,
however, that the Inn was the
headquarters of General Fairfax
during the Civil War.

- En-suite accommodation
- Restaurant • Bar Snacks
- Fine Ales • Good Pub
Guide 1993 • Good Beer
Guide 1993

HUNTERS INN (Map Ref B3)
11 - 11. (M-S)
WELL STREET, TORRINGTON.
Tel: (0805) 23832

Boddingtons Bitter	(H)
Flowers IPA	(H)
Flowers Original	(H)
Guest Beer Regular	(H)

AC CP ME ML OD PG RF
Deservedly popular town pub, with a
medium sized L-shaped bar, and well kept
guest ales.

NEW MARKET INN (Map Ref B3)
11 - 3 ; 6:30 - 11. (M-F (W), 11-11 Sat. &
SUMMER)
SOUTH STREET, TORRINGTON.
Tel: (0805) 22289

Morland Old Speckled Hen	(H)
Guest Beer Regular (H)	

AC FA LM (OCCASIONALLY) ME ML OD
PB PG PL RF ST
Dimly lit pub with wooden floor. Pool
room to rear.

PUFFING BILLY (Map Ref B3)
11 - 3 ; 5:30 - 11. (M-S)
OLD STATION HOUSE, TORRINGTON.
ON A386 1MILE NORTH OF TOWN)
Tel: (0805) 23050

Greene King Abbot	(H)
Wadworth 6X	(H)

CC CP FA ME ML OD PG RF
Old railway station converted to a pub,
with the emphasis on food. 'Tarka Trail'
passes the door.

TORRINGTON ARMS (Map Ref B3)
11 - 2 ; 5:30 - 11. (M-S)
NEW STREET, TORRINGTON.
Tel: (0805) 22280

John Smith's Bitter	(H)

TOTNES

ALBERT INN (Map Ref D6)
11 - 3 ; 6 - 11. (M-F, 11-11 Th, Sat)
32, BRIDGETOWN, TOTNES
Tel: (0803) 863214

Draught Bass	(H)
Courage Best Bitter	(H)

BR (TOTNES) PB PG
American style pub, with occasional live
music.

Kingsbridge Inn

LEECHWELL STREET, TOTNES.
(Top of the Town).
★ Totnes Family Owned and Managed
★ Large adjoining car park
★ The oldest Totnes inn
★ Free House
★ Local Cider and Real Ales
★ Fresh Daily Home Cooked Food and Platters
★ Parties Catered For
★ Reservations Lunch and Evenings

Tel: TOTNES (0803) 863324

Paul and Rosemary Triggs   Martyn and Jane Canevali

CASTLE INN (Map Ref D6)
CASTLE STREET, TOTNES
Tel: (0803) 863274

Ruddles Best Bitter	(H)
Ruddles County	(H)
Ushers Best Bitter	(H)

KINGSBRIDGE INN (Map Ref D6)
11 - 2:30 ; 5:30 - 11. (M-S)
9, LEECHWELL STREET, TOTNES
Tel: (0803) 863324

Draught Bass	(H)
Courage Best Bitter	(H)
Courage Directors	(H)
Furgusons Dartmoor Best Bitter	(H)

BR (TOTNES) CI ME ML NS OD QP
Grade 2 listed, low ceilinged inn with many alcoves. The accent is on food but the pub has a very friendly and easy-going atmosphere.

STEAM PACKET INN (Map Ref D6)
11 - 11. (M-S)
48, ST. PETERS QUAY, TOTNES
Tel: (0803) 863880

Furgusons Dartmoor Best Bitter	(H)
Wadworth 6X	(H)
Guest Beer Regular	(H)

AC BR (TOTNES) CA CP FA GD LM ME ML OD PG QP RF
Tastefully modernised ground floor of a sizeable old warehouse building. British and international menu. Piano night - Wednesday, Jazz night - Friday. A mellow and relaxingly comfortable, riverside pub.

TRUSHAM

CRIDFORD INN (Map Ref E5)
11:30 - 2:30 ; 6:30 - 11: (M-S (W), 11-3, 6-11 (S))
TRUSHAM, Nr. CHUDLEIGH
Tel: (0626) 853694

Draught Bass	(G)
Brains SA	(H)
Butcombe Bitter	(H)
Cotleigh Old Buzzard	(G)
Flowers Original	(H)

AC CA CC CI CP DF FA GD ME ML OD QP RF RS
Reputed to be the oldest house in Devon, its history can be traced back to 825 AD. Since then it has been a nunnery and a farmhouse, before being converted into a pub in the mid 1980s. A date stone in the restaurant shows 1081, but it is not known if it is contemporaneous to this building. The pub still has old stained glass windows, and is said to be haunted by 2 ghosts. The floor is stone flagged, and the furniture consists of church pews and armchairs. 2 local farmhouse ciders are available.

TUCKENHAY

WATERMAN ARMS (MAP REF D7)
11 - 3 ; 6 - 11. (MS)
BOW BRIDGE, TUCKENHAY, TOTNES
Tel: (0803) 732214

Furgusons Dartmoor Best Bitter	(H)
Palmers IPA	(H)
Tetley Bitter	(H)

AC CA CC CI DF FA ME ML OD PB PG QP RF
Riverside pub with oak beams and oars hanging from the ceiling. Stained glass above the bar. Successful food orientated pub beside picturesque Bow Bridge, run by an ex-brewer. Two stone floored rooms around a U-shaped bar. Large car park. Outside seating area, beside the creek.

UFFCULME

OSTLER (Map Ref F3)
12 - 3 ; 5 - 11. (M-F. 11-11 Sat)
COMMERCIAL ROAD, UFFCULME.
Tel: (0884) 840260

Boddingtons Bitter	(H)

AC DF FA ME ML OD PB PG
The only remaining pub in the village.

UGBOROUGH

ANCHOR INN (Map Ref C7)
11- 3 ; 5 - 11 (M-S)
1, LUTTERBURN STREET, UGBOROUGH,
Nr. MODBURY

Tel: (0752) 892283
Draught Bass	(G)
Wadworth 6X	(H)
Guest Beer Regular	(H)

AC CP ME ML PG QP RF
Excellent stone-walled, wooden-floored
village bar to the left. Equally excellent
cuisine in the attractive lounge to the right.

SHIP INN (Map Ref C7)
11 - 3 ; 6 - 11. (M-S)
UGBOROUGH, Nr. MODBURY
Tel: (0752) 892565

Draught Bass	(H)
Wadworth 6X	(H)
Guest Beer Regular	(H)

ME ML OD PG QP RF
Traditional c16 pub, with excellent food
and an active darts team.

UMBERLEIGH

RISING SUN (Map Ref C3)
12 - 11. (M-S)
UMBERLEIGH, NR. BARNSTAPLE.
Tel: (0769) 60447

Ruddles County	(H)
Ushers Best Bitter	(H)

AC BR (UMBERLEIGH) CP FA ME ML OD
PB QP RF RS
Famous fishing hotel, now under new
management.

UPLYME

BLACK DOG HOTEL (Map Ref H4)
10:30 - 2 ; 6:30 - 11. (M-S (W), 10:30 - 3, 6-11
(S))
LYME ROAD, UPLYME, (ON A3070 ON
COUNTY BORDER WITH DORSET).
Tel: (0297) 442634

Palmers BB	(H)
Palmers IPA	(H)

AC CA CI CP DB DF FA GD LM ME ML
OD PG PL QP RF SN
Small but busy country type hotel.
Extensive menu, regular live music.
Lounge bar, restaurant and a beer garden
bar-b-que in summer.

NEW INN (Map Ref H4)
11 - 2 ; 7 - 11: (M-S (closed Mon
A.M.)11-3,7-11 (S))
LYME ROAD, UPLYME.
(ON A3070, BETWEEN TALBOT &
BLACK DOG HOTELS)
Tel: (0297) 443210

Palmers BB	(H)
Palmers IPA	(H)

AC CA CP DB FA GD ME ML
(not Mondays in Winter) OD PL SN ST
Cosy village pub catering for middle of
range custom.

TALBOT ARMS HOTEL
(Map Ref H4)
11:30 - 2:30 ; 6 - 11. (M-S)
LYME ROAD, UPLYME. (ON A3070 IN
MIDDLE OF VILLAGE)
Tel: (0297) 443136

Courage Directors	(H)
Fuller London Pride	(H)
Ruddle County	(E)

AC CA CC CP DB FA GD LM ME ML OD
PG QP RF SN ST
Cosy bar and riverside garden. Occasional
live music. Guest beers.

UPOTTERY

SIDMOUTH ARMS (Map Ref G4)
11 - 2:30 ; 6 - 11. (M-S)
UPOTTERY, Nr. HONITON.
Tel: (0404) 86252

Draught Bass	(H)
Flowers IPA	(H)

DF FA ME ML OD PG RF
Popular and busy village pub near A30.

WALKHAMPTON

WALKHAMPTON INN (Map Ref C6)
WALKHAMPTON, YELVERTON
Tel: (0822) 855556

Draught Bass	(H)
Furgusons Dartmoor Best Bitter	(H)
Furgusons Dartmoor Strong	(H)

WATERLOO CROSS

OLD COTTAGE INN (Map Ref F3)
11 - 11. (M-F. 11 - 2.30, 5.30 - 11 Sat.)
WATERLOO CROSS, UFFCULME.
Tel: (0884) 840328

Ind Coope Burton Ale (E)

AC BR (TIVERTON PARKWAY) CA
(CARAVAN PARK ADJOINING) CC CP
DF FA ME ML OD PG RF
Pleasant roadside inn with adjoining
caravan site. Popular for meals. BEWARE!
Beer dispensed by electric pump via
FALSE BARREL ENDS.

WATERMOUTH COVE

OLD SAWMILL INN (Map Ref C1)
12 - 2:30 ; 7 - 11. (M-S (W), VARIABLE IN
SUMMER)
CASTLE HILL, WATERMOUTH COVE,
BERRYNARBOR.
Tel: (0271) 882259

Draught Bass (H)

AC CA CP FA ME ML OD PG RS
Large, comfortable pub with separate
restaurant, close to Watermouth Castle.

WEARE GIFFORD

CYDER PRESSE (Map Ref B3)
WEARE GIFFORD, Nr. BIDEFORD,
Tel: (0237) 475640

Courage Best Bitter (H)
Ruddles County (H)

WELCOMBE

OLD SMITHY INN (Map Ref A3)
11 - 3 ; 7 - 11 (M-S (W), 11 - 11 (S), 12 - 2.30,
6 - 10.30 Sun)
WELCOMBE, HARTLAND, Nr.
BIDEFORD. (2 MILES OFF A39),
OS: SS232178
Tel: (028883) 305

Butcombe Bitter (H)
Marston's Pedigree (H)

(SUMMER ONLY) AC CA CC CP DF FA
ME ML OD RF
Thatched 13th century inn near windswept
cliffs. Attractive garden, family annexe,
popular food, good value accommodation,
recommended. Almost on the Cornwall
border.

WEMBURY

ODD WHEEL (Map Ref B7)
12 - 3 ; 6:30 - 11 (M-F; 12 - 11 Sat)
KNIGHTON ROAD, WEMBURY
Tel: (0752) 862287

Courage Best Bitter (H)
Ruddle Best Bitter (H)
Ruddles County (H)
Ushers Best Bitter (H)

CA CP DB DM FA ME ML OD PG QP RF
Large country pub 1 mile from the beach
on the main road through the village.

WEMBWORTHY

LYMINGTON ARMS (Map Ref C3)
11 - 3 ; 6 - 11. (M-S - SUPPER LICENSE TO
12pm)
LAMA CROSS, WEMBWORTHY, Nr.
CHULMLEIGH. (1/2 ml. FROM
WEMBWORTHY ON WINKLEIGH
ROAD), OS: SS664092
Tel: (0837) 83572

Eldridge Pope Hardy Country (H)
Royal Oak (H)
Palmers IPA (H)

AC CP ME ML OD PG RF
Extensively modernised Georgian
coaching inn with a luxurious lounge and
a pubby bar, set in idyllic rural
surroundings.

WEST ALVINGTON

RING OF BELLS (Map Ref D8)
11 - 3 ; 6 - 11 (M-S)
WEST ALVINGTON, KINGSBRIDGE
Tel: (0548) 2437

Draught Bass (H)
Worthington Best Bitter (H)

AC CA CP DF FA ME ML OD PB PG QP
RS
Large pub on main road from Kingsbridge
to Salcombe, very popular for it's carvery.
A locals pub with a friendly atmosphere,
and a collection of minature plates on the
walls.

WEST CHARLETON

ASHBURTON ARMS (Map Ref D8)
12 - 2:30 ; 6 - 11 (M-S)
WEST CHARLETON (A379)
Tel: (0548) 531242

Draught Bass	(H)
Furgusons Dartmoor Best Bitter	(H)

WEST DOWN

FOXHUNTERS INN (Map Ref B1)
WEST DOWN, Nr. BARNSTAPLE.
Tel: (0271) 863757

Draught Bass	(H)
Courage Directors	(H)

WEST LYN

BEGGARS ROOST INN (Map Ref D1)
7 - 11. (M-S (W), VARIABLE IN SUMMER)
WEST LYN, Nr. LYNTON.
Tel: (0598) 52404

Draught Bass	(H)
Ind Coope Burton Ale	(H)
Tetley Bitter	(H)

AC CA CP ME ML OD
Large roadside inn, named after the
nearby, famous, classic car trial section.

WESTCOTT

MERRY HARRIERS (Map Ref F4)
12 - 2:30 ; 7 - 11 (M-S. 12 - 2 Sun.)
WESTCOTT, CULLOMPTON.
(ON B3181 1ml SOUTH OF
CULLOMPTON.)
Tel: (0392) 881254

Draught Bass	(H)

CA CP DF ME ML MR OD QP RF ST
Friendly roadside inn with a skittle alley
cum function room and a separate
restaurant with a reputation for high
quality home cooked food.

WESTLEIGH

WESTLEIGH INN (Map Ref B2)
WESTLEIGH, Nr. BIDEFORD.
OS: SS472286
Tel: (0271) 860867

Ushers Best Bitter	(H)

WESTWARD HO!

PIG-ON-THE-HILL (Map Ref B2)
11 - 3 ; 6 - 11 (M-S)
PUSE HILL, WESTWARD HO!, Nr.
BIDEFORD.
Tel: (0237) 425889

Ind Coope Burton Ale	(H)

AC CA CP FA ME ML OD
Modern pub near popular tourist resort.

WHIDDON DOWN

POST INN (Map Ref D4)
11:30 - 3 ; 6 - 11 (M-S)
WHIDDON DOWN, Nr. OKEHAMPTON.
(TURN OF A30 AT ROUNDABOUT,
APPROX 1/4 ml. ON LEFT)
Tel: (0647) 23242

Draught Bass	(H)
Exe Valley Dob's Best Bitter	(H)
Furgusons Dartmoor Best Bitter	(H)
Flowers IPA	(H)

CA CI (INCH'S HARVEST STRONG) CP
DB DF DM FA LM (MONDAYS) ME ML
OD PG PL RF SH ST
Pleasant pub on side of OLD A30, catering
mainly for food.

WHIMPLE

NEW FOUNTAIN INN (Map Ref F4)
11 - 3 ; 6 - 11 (M-S. EVE.HRS LONGER IN
SUMMER)
CHURCH ROAD, WHIMPLE, Nr.
EXETER.
Tel: (0404) 822350

Furgusons Dartmoor Best Bitter	(H)
Oakhill Bitter	(H)
Tetley Bitter	(H)

BR (WHIMPLE) DB FA ME ML OD PB PG
RF
Family run local, with a warm friendly
atmosphere, and serving a varied menu of
good value home-cooked food.

PADDOCK INN (Map Ref F4)
11 - 2:30 ; 6 - 11. (M-S)
LONDON ROAD, WHIMPLE, Nr.
EXETER.
Tel: (0404) 822356

Exe Valley Bitter	**(H)**
Ind Coope Burton Ale	**(H)**

CA CP FA ME ML OD PG
Large, multi-roomed, inn on A30(T).
Formerly a farmhouse, now a well
furnished and comfortable inn serving
good value, home-cooked food with a
varied menu (including vegetarian). An
impressive range of bottled beers, from
around the world, is available. Guest cask
beers.

THIRSTY FARMER INN (Map Ref F4)
11 - 2:30 ; 6 - 11 (M-Th. 11 - 3 F, Sat)
WHIMPLE, Nr. EXETER.
Tel: (0404) 822287

Flowers IPA	**(H)**

WHITCHURCH

WHITCHURCH INN (Map Ref B6)
CHURCH HILL, WHITCHURCH
Tel: (0822) 615383

Draught Bass	**(H)**

WHITESTONE

TRAVELLERS REST (Map Ref E4)
11 - 2:30 ; 5:30 - 11. (M-F 6 - 11 Sat (W) 11 - 3
(S))
TEDBURN ROAD, WHITESTONE,
EXETER. OS: SX867930
Tel: (039281) 217

Draught Bass	**(H)**
Marston's Pedigree	**(H)**
Flowers Original	**(H)**

AC CP DB FA GD ME ML OD PG PL QP
RF RS
16th century coaching house with log fires
and old beams. A large bar area. The
separate restaurant serves all homemade
food and caters for vegetarians.

WIDECOMBE IN THE MOOR

RUGGLESTONE INN (Map Ref D5)
11 - 2:30 ; 6 - 11. (M-F, 11 - 3 Sat)
WIDECOMBE-IN-THE-MOOR.
NEWTON ABBOT, OS: SX721766
Tel: (0364) 2327

Draught Bass	**(G)**

CA CI ML OD PG QP RF SH
A superb example of a Dartmoor pub,
completely unspoilt. There is no bar; just a
door to the kitchen. Recently changed
ownership, but new owner promises to
keep it a classic rural pub.

WILLAND

HALFWAY HOUSE (Map Ref F3)
11 - 2:30 ; 6 - 11. ((S), 12 - 2.30 (W))
WILLAND, CULLOMPTON.
(ON B3181)
Tel: (0884) 820258

Courage Directors	**(H)**
John Smith's Bitter	**(H)**

CA CP DF FA ME ML OD PB
Roadside pub halfway between Exeter and
Taunton, hence its name.

WINKLEIGH

KINGS ARMS (Map Ref C4)
WINKLEIGH, Nr. TORRINGTON.
Tel: (0837) 83384

Ushers Best Bitter	**(H)**

WOODBURY

MALTSTERS ARMS, (Map Ref F5)
11 - 3 ; 6:30 - 11. (M-F (W), 11 - 11 (S))
GREENWAY, WOODBURY, EXETER. (IN
VILLAGE SQUARE NEAR CHURCH)
Tel: (0395) 32218

Marston's Pedigree	**(H)**

WHITE HART (Map Ref F5)
11 - 2:30 ; 6 - 11. (M-S)
CHURCH STILE LANE, WOODBURY,
EXETER. (OPPOSITE CHURCH IN
VILLAGE CENTRE.),
Tel: (0395) 32221

Draught Bass	(H)
Charrington IPA	(H)

CA CA CP CP DB DB FA FA GD GD ME
ME ML ML OD OD PB PB PG PG QP QP
RF RF SN SN ST ST
Former housing for builders of church,
500+ years old. Well known for its home
cooked food. Large, separate
games/function room.

WOODBURY SALTERTON

DIGGERS REST (Map Ref F5)
11 - 2:30 ; 6:30 - 11. (M-S, 12 - 2.30 SUN)
WOODBURY SALTERTON, EXETER.
(VILLAGE CENTRE, OPPOSITE
CHURCH)
Tel: (0395) 32375

Draught Bass	(H)
Flowers IPA	(H)

c14. thatched pub, well known for its food.
Large games room at rear.

WHITE HORSE INN (Map Ref F5)
11:30 - 2:30 ; 6 - 11. (M-S (W), 5 - 11 (S))
WOODBURY SALTERTON, EXETER. (ON
A3052, AT JUNCTION TO WOODBURY
SALTERTON.), OS: SY0290
Tel: (0395) 32244

Draught Bass	(H)
Flowers IPA	(H)
Flowers Original	(H)

CA CP DF FA GD ME ML OD QP SN
Roadside pub with large open bar.

WOODLAND

RISING SUN (Map Ref D6)
WOODLAND, ASHBURTON (1.5 MILES
FROM WOODLAND TURN ON A38, 1
MILE FROM WOODLAND), OS: SX790697
Tel: (0364) 52544

Draught Bass	(H)
Wadworth 6X	(H)

WOOLACOMBE

JUBILEE INN (Map Ref B1)
11 - 2:30 ; 6 - 11. (M-S (W), 11 - 11 (S))
SOUTH STREET, WOOLACOMBE.
Tel: (0271) 870487

Tetley Bitter	(H)

FA ME ML OD PG
Spacious, modern pub at back of shops,
only a short walk from one of Britain's
finest beaches.

**MILL AT OSSABOROUGH (Map Ref
B1)**
11 - 11. (M-S SUMMER ONLY)
OSSABOROUGH, WOOLACOMBE.
(400m FROM B3343,NEAR GOLDEN
COAST HOLIDAY VILLAGE.), OS:
SS481434
Tel: (0271) 870237

Flowers Original	(H)

WOOLFARDISWORTHY

FARMERS ARMS (Map Ref A3)
11 - 11. (M-S)
WOOLFARDISWORTHY, Nr. CLOVELLY,.
Tel: (0237) 431467

Tetley Bitter	(H)

CP ME ML OD PB PG RF
Popular local in a rapidly growing village.
Beer mat collection on bar ceiling.
Excellent food.

WRANGATON

COACH & HORSES (Map Ref C7)

Flowers IPA	(H)
Flowers Original	(H)

Massive barn with restaurant facilities

JOIN NOW

YARCOMBE

YARCOMBE INN (Map Ref G4)
11 - 11. (M-S)
YARCOMBE, Nr. HONITON.
Tel: (040486) 218

Boddingtons Bitter	(H)
Exmoor Ale	(H)
Marston's Pedigree	(H)
Flowers Original	(H)

AC CP FA ME ML OD PB PG
Lively village inn recently refurbished, on
A30 near Dorset boundary.

YARDE DOWN

POLTIMORE ARMS (Map Ref D2)
11:30 - 2:30 ; 6:30 - 11. (M-S)
YARDE DOWN, Nr. SOUTH MOLTON,
(TOP OF HILL, OUTSIDE BRAYFORD,
ON SIMONSBATH ROAD.), OS: SS725356
Tel: (0598) 710381

Cotleigh Tawny	(G)
Ruddles County	(H)

CC CP FA ME ML OD PG QP RF
Classic, unspoilt Exmoor pub, with a fine
reputation for food. Large roaring log fire
in winter.

YEALMPTON

ROSE & CROWN (Map Ref C7)
10:30 - 3 ; 5 - 11. (M-S)
MARKET STREET, YEALMPTON
Tel: (0752) 880223

Courage Best Bitter	(H)
Guest Beer Regular	(H)

AC CA CC CP FA ME ML OD PB PG
Massive roadhouse with a beer cellar
designed for a quiet country tavern -
hence only one permanent real ale.
Popular with locals and visitors,
well managed and frequently host to
antiques fairs etc. Regularly changing
guest ales.

VOLUNTEER INN (Map Ref C7)
11 - 2:30 ; 6 - 11. (M-S)
MARKET STREET, YEALMPTON
Tel: (0752) 880463

Courage Best Bitter	(H)

CD (EUCHRE) DM OD PG RF
The village local; comfortable lounge, and
a public bar with a interesting collection of
naval crests on the beams.

YELVERTON

DEVON TORS HOTEL (Map Ref B6)
11 - 11. (M-S)
YELVERTON, Nr. PLYMOUTH
Tel: (0822) 853604

Draught Bass	(H)
Charrington IPA	(H)

CH CP ME (NOT SUNDAY) ML PG RS
Spacious, basement bar with separate
restaurant and games/family room.

LEG O' MUTTON INN (Map Ref B6)
11 - 2:30 ; 5:30 - 10:30. (M-Th; 5 - 11 F, Sat
(W); 11 - 11 M-S (S))
YELVERTON, Nr. PLYMOUTH
Tel: (0822) 854195

Courage Best Bitter	(H)
Courage Directors	(H)

ROCK INN (Map Ref B6)
11 - 3 ; 5:30 - 11. (M-F; 11 - 11 Sat (W); 11 -
11 M-S (S))
YELVERTON, Nr. PLYMOUTH
Tel: (0822) 852022

Draught Bass	(H)
Charrington IPA	(H)
Boddingtons Bitter	(H)
St Austell HSD	(H)

CD CH CP DB DF FA GD ME ML OD PB
PG PL QP RF
Large, well run pub, with 3 bars. the
popular family room has videos for
children.

YEOFORD

MARE & FOAL (Map Ref D4)
YEOFORD, Nr. CREDITON,
Tel: (0363) 84348

Marston's Pedigree	(H)
Flowers IPA	(H)

ZEAL MONARCHORUM

WAIE INN (Map Ref D4)
11 - 2:30 ; 6 - 11 (M-S)
ZEAL MONARCHORUM, Nr. CREDITON
(SIGNPOSTED FROM VILLAGE)
Tel: (0363) 82348

Draught Bass	(E)

CA (AT PUB) CP DB DF (ACCESS ONLY)
FA GD ME ML MR OD PB PG PL QP
(LOUNGE) SK ST
Pleasant, modern, two-bar village pub,
with an accent on food. Sports centre at
rear of pub open all day.

Pubs Index

This is a list of all the Real Ale pubs known to CAMRA in Devon. Not all the pubs listed below are contained in the main body of this guide. Of the remainder, it is not known whether or not they sell real ale. The only information we have about the pubs is their name and address.

Pub Name	District	Map Ref	Pub Name	District	Map Ref
BUTCHER'S ARMS	PLYMOUTH	B7	COACH AND HORSES	HORNS CROSS	B3
BUTCHERS ARMS	ALSWEAR	D3	COACH HOUSE	PAIGNTON	E6
BUTCHERS ARMS	ABBOTSKERSWELL	E6	COACH HOUSE INN	ILFRACOMBE	B1
BUTLERS	EXETER	E5	COACH HOUSE INN	WRANGATON	C7
BUTTERLEIGH INN	BUTTERLEIGH	E4	COACHING HOUSE	CHUDLEIGH	E5
BYSTOCK HOTEL -			COCKFOSTERS INN	PAIGNTON	E6
STOCKS BAR.	EXETER	E5	COCKHAVEN		
			MANOR INN	BISHOPSTEIGNTON	E6
CADELEIGH ARMS	CADELEIGH	E4	COLCOMBE CASTLE	COLYTON	G4
CAFE ROYAL	TORQUAY	E6	COLEBROOK INN	PLYMPTON	C7
CALIFORNIA INN	CALIFORNIA CROSS	D7	COLONIAL	PLYMOUTH	B7
CAMBERLEY	WOOLACOMBE	B1	COMMERCIAL INN	PLYMOUTH	B7
CANNON INN	NEWTON POPPLEFORD	F5	COMPLEX	PLYMOUTH	B7
CARLTON	HONITON	F4	COMPTON INN	PLYMOUTH	B7
CAROUSEL BAR	ILFRACOMBE	B1	COOLINS WINE BAR	EXETER	E5
CARPENTERS ARMS	CROYDE	B2	COOMBE CELLARS	COOMBEINTEIGNHEAD	E6
CARPENTERS ARMS	ILSINGTON	D5	COOMBE HOUSE		
CARY ARMS	TORQUAY	E6	COUNTRY HOTEL	COLEFORD	D4
CASEY'S	PLYMOUTH	B7	COOMBE VIEW INN	HUNTSHAW CROSS	B3
CASTLE	STOKE GABRIEL	E7	COPPA DOLLA	BROADHEMPSTON	D6
CASTLE	TORQUAY	E6	COPPER KEY	NORTH TAWTON	C4
CASTLE INN	BRADNINCH	E4	CORNER HOUSE	BARNSTAPLE	C2
CASTLE INN	HOLCOMBE	E5	CORNER HOUSE	PLYMOUTH	B7
CASTLE INN	COMBE MARTIN	C1	CORNISH ARMS	TAVISTOCK	B6
CASTLE INN	LANDKEY	C2	CORNWALLS GATE	PLYMOUTH	B7
CASTLE INN	GEORGE NYMPTON	D2	CORNWOOD INN	CORNWOOD	C7
CASTLE INN	TOTNES	D6	COTT INN	DARTINGTON	D6
CASTLE INN	LYDFORD	B5	COTTAGE HOTEL	HOPE COVE	C8
CAT AND FIDDLE INN,	CLYST ST. MARY	E5	COTTAGE INN	MARSH	G4
CATHERINE WHEEL	HEMYOCK	F3	COTTAGE INN	TAVISTOCK	B6
CEDARS INN	BICKINGTON	C2	COUNTESS WEAR LODGE	EXETER	E5
CHAMPION OF WALES	APPLEDORE	B2	COUNTRY HOUSE	TORQUAY	E6
CHARFORD MANOR			COUNTRY HOUSE INN	EXETER	E5
COUNTRY HOTEL	DIPTFORD	D7	COUNTRY HOUSE INN,	EXMOUTH	F5
CHARLIES CIRCUS	PLYMOUTH	B7	COUNTRY MAN INN	NORTH TAWTON	C4
CHASER'S ARMS	STOKEINTEIGNHEAD	E6	COUNTRYMAN	BARNSTAPLE	C2
CHAUCERS INN	EXETER	E5	COUNTRYMAN	SAMPFORD COURTENAY	C4
CHELSTON MANOR	TORQUAY	E6	COURT FARM INN	ABBOTSKERSWELL	E6
CHERRY TREE	PLYMOUTH	B7	COURTENAY	NEWTON ABBOT	E6
CHERUB INN	DARTMOUTH	E7	COURTENAY ARMS	STARCROSS	E5
CHICHESTER ARMS	BISHOPS TAWTON	C2	COURTENAY HOTEL	TEIGNMOUTH	E6
CHICHESTER ARMS	MORTEHOE	B1	COURTLANDS HOTEL	TORQUAY	E6
CHICHESTER ARMS	BARNSTAPLE	C2	COVERDALE HOTEL	PAIGNTON	E6
CHICHESTER ARMS	CHILLATON	B5	COWICK BARTON INN	EXETER	E8
CHILCOT ARMS	CHAWLEIGH	D3	COWLEY BRIDGE INN	EXETER	E5
CHILLINGTON INN	CHILLINGTON	D8	CRAB SHELL INN	KINGSBRIDGE	D8
CHINA HOUSE	PLYMOUTH	B7	CRABSHELL		
CHIPSHOP INN	CHIPSHOP	B6	MOTOR LODGE	KINGSBRIDGE	D8
CHURCH HOUSE INN	CHURCHSTOW	D7	CRANFORD INN	ST. GILES-IN-THE-WOOD	C3
CHURCH HOUSE INN	HARBERTON	D7	CRAWFORD	EXETER	E5
CHURCH HOUSE INN	HOLNE	D6	CREALOCK ARMS	LITTLEHAM (N)	B3
CHURCH HOUSE INN	MARLDON	E6	CREDITON INN	CREDITON	D4
CHURCH HOUSE INN	PAIGNTON	E6	CRICKET INN	BEESANDS	D8
CHURCH HOUSE INN	RATTERY	D6	CRIDFORD INN	TRUSHAM	E5
CHURCH HOUSE INN	STOKE GABRIEL	E7	CROMWELL ARMS	BOVEY TRACEY	D5
CHURCH HOUSE INN	STOKE-IN-TEIGNHEAD	E6	CROOKED SPIRE	ERMINGTON	C7
CHURCH HOUSE INN	STOKENHAM	D8	CROSS HOTEL	COPPLESTONE	D4
CHURCH HOUSE INN	TORBRYAN	D6	CROSS KEYS	TIVERTON	E3
CHURCH HOUSE INN	TORQUAY	E6	CROSSWAYS INN	FOLLY GATE	C4
CLARENCE	TORQUAY	E6	CROSSWAYS TAVERN	HELE	E4
CLARENCE HOTEL	BARNSTAPLE	C2	CROW'S NEST	CROCKERNWELL	D5
CLARENCE HOTEL	PLYMOUTH	B7	CROWN	WEST DOWN	B1
CLAYCUTTERS ARMS	CHUDLEIGH K'TON	E5	CROWN & SCEPTRE	TORQUAY	E6
CLEAVE	LUSTLEIGH	D5	CROWN AND ANCHOR	BRIXHAM	E7
CLIFFORD ARMS	SHALDON	E6	CROWN AND SCEPTRE	EXETER	E5
CLIFTON HOTEL	TORQUAY	E6	CROWN AND SCEPTRE	NEWTON ST. CYRES	E4
CLIFTON HOTEL	PLYMOUTH	B7	CROWN AND SCEPTRE	HOLSWORTHY	A4
CLIFTON INN	EXETER	E5	CROWN HOTEL	LYNTON	D1
CLINTON ARMS	FRITHELSTOCK	B3	CRUWYS ARMS	PENNYMOOR	E3
CLIPPER	TORQUAY	E6	CULM VALLEY INN	CULMSTOCK	F3
CLIPPER	PLYMOUTH	B7	CYDER PRESS	TORQUAY	E6
CLODAGH'S BAR	PAIGNTON	E6	CYDER PRESSE	WEARE GIFFORD	B3
CLOVELLY INN	BRATTON CLOVELLY	B5			
COACH & HORSES	APPLEDORE	B2	DART BRIDGE INN	BUCKFASTLEIGH	D6
COACH & HORSES	WRANGATON	C7	DART MARINA HOTEL	DARTMOUTH	E7
COACH AND HORSES	BUCKLAND BREWER	B3	DARTM'R HALFWAY INN	BICKINGTON (SD)	D6

Pub Name	District	Map Ref	Pub Name	District	Map Ref
DARTMOOR INN	BOVEY TRACEY	D5	EXETER ARMS	OKEHAMPTON	C4
DARTMOOR INN	LYDFORD	B5	EXETER ARMS MOTEL	EXETER	E5
DARTMOOR INN	PRINCETOWN	C6	EXETER INN	BAMPTON	E3
DARTMOOR RAILWAY	CREDITON	D4	EXETER INN	CLYST HONITON	E4
DARTMOOR UNION INN	HOLBETON	C7	EXETER INN	DAWLISH	E5
DARTMOUTH	TOTNES	D6	EXETER INN	NEWTON POPPLEFORD	F5
DARTMOUTH ARMS	DARTMOUTH	E7	EXETER INN	THORVERTON	E4
DARTMOUTH INN	NEWTON ABBOT	E6	EXETER INN	TOPSHAM	E5
DAWLISH INN	TEIGNMOUTH	E6	EXETER INN	BARNSTAPLE	C2
DEER LEAP	EXMOUTH	F5	EXETER INN	CHITTLEHAMHOLT	C3
DEER PARK INN	STOKE FLEMING	E7	EXETER INN	ASHBURTON	D6
DENLEY'S	TOPSHAM	E5	EXETER INN	MODBURY	C7
DEVILS ELBOW HOTEL	PRINCETOWN	C6	EXMOOR SANDPIPER INN	COUNTISBURY	D1
DEVILS STONE INN	SHEBBEAR	B3	EXMOUTH ARMS	EXMOUTH	F5
DEVON ARMS	NEWTON ABBOT	E6			
DEVON ARMS	TEIGNMOUTH	E6	FAGIN'S TAVERN	BARNSTAPLE	C2
DEVON ARMS	TORQUAY	E6	FAIRMILE INN	FAIRMILE	F4
DEVON ARMS HOTEL	KENTON	E5	FALCON	PLYMOUTH	B7
DEVON DUMPLING	TORQUAY	E6	FALCON HOTEL	TORQUAY	E6
DEVON TORS HOTEL	YELVERTON	B6	FALSTAFF	PLYMOUTH	B7
DEVON YEOMAN	EXETER	E5	FAMOUS OLD GEORGE	SEATON	G5
DEVONPORT ARMS	PAIGNTON	E6	FAMOUS OLDE BARREL	EXMOUTH	F5
DEVONPORT INN,	EXETER	E5	FAMOUS SHIP	EXMOUTH	F5
DEVONSHIRE	STICKLEPATH	C4	FAREHAM INN	PLYMOUTH	B7
DEWDROP INN	KINGSTEIGNTON	E6	FARMERS ARMS	WOOLFARDISWORTHY	A3
DIGGERS REST	WOODBURY SALTERTON	F5	FARMHOUSE INN	EXMOUTH	F5
DISTILLERY	PLYMOUTH	B7	FEATHERS HOTEL	BUDLEIGH SALTERTON	F5
DITTISHAM INN	DITTISHAM	E7	FELLOWSHIP INN	PLYMOUTH	B7
DODBROOKE INN	KINGSBRIDGE	D8	FENNY BRIDGES INN	FENNY BRIDGES	F4
DOG & DUCK	TORQUAY	E6	FERRY BOAT INN	DITTISHAM	E7
DOG & DUCK	PLYMOUTH	B7	FERRY HOUSE INN	PLYMOUTH	B7
DOLPHIN	BOVEY TRACEY	D5	FERRY INN	SALCOMBE	D8
DOLPHIN	TORQUAY	E6	FERRYBOAT INN	SHALDON	E6
DOLPHIN HOTEL	BEER	G5	FERRYBOAT INN	PLYMOUTH	B7
DOLPHIN HOTEL	THORVERTON	E4	FIESTA INN	PAIGNTON	E6
DOLPHIN HOTEL	PLYMOUTH	B7	FIRST & LAST	PLYMOUTH	B7
DOLPHIN INN	KENTON	E5	FIRST & LAST (TALBOT)	TEIGNMOUTH	E6
DOLPHIN INN	COMBE MARTIN	C1	FIRST & LAST INN	ERMINGTON	C7
DOLPHIN INN	KINGSTON	C7	FIRST IN, LAST OUT	BIDEFORD	B2
DOUBLE LOCKS	EXETER	E5	FISHERMAN'S ARMS	PLYMOUTH	B7
DOVE INN	SIDMOUTH	F5	FISHERMAN'S REST	AVETON GIFFORD	D7
DRAKE MANOR INN	BUCKLAND		FISHERMANS COT	BICKLEIGH	E3
	MONACHORUM	B6	FISHERMANS INN	SEATON	G5
DRAKES DRUM	PLYMSTOCK	B7	FIVE BELLS INN	CLYST HYDON	F4
			FLEECE & FIRKIN	ASHBURTON	D6
DRAKES TAVERN	TORQUAY	E6	FLINTLOCK INN	MARSH	G4
DREWE ARMS	BROADHEMBURY	F4	FLOATING BRIDGE INN	DARTMOUTH	E7
DREWE ARMS	DREWSTEIGNTON	D5	FLYING HORSE	EXETER	E5
DRUM INN	COCKINGTON	E6	FOCSLE INN	COMBE MARTIN	C1
DUKE OF MARLBOROUGH			FORAYS	TORQUAY	E6
HOTEL	SIDMOUTH	F5	FORCES TAVERN	BLACKAWTON	D7
DUKE OF SOMERSET	PLYMOUTH	B7	FORD HOTEL	PLYMOUTH	B7
DUKE OF YORK	CLYST HONITON	E4	FOREST INN	PRINCETOWN	C6
DUKE OF YORK	CREDITON	D4	FORTESCUE ARMS	WOOLACOMBE	B1
DUKE OF YORK	EXETER	E5	FORTESCUE ARMS	EAST ALLINGTON	D7
DUKE OF YORK	IDDESLEIGH	C4	FORTESCUE ARMS HOTEL	KINGS NYMPTON	C3
DURANT ARMS	ASHPRINGTON	D7	FORTESCUE HOTEL	PLYMOUTH	B7
EAGLE TAVERN	EXETER	E5	FORTESCUE INN	SALCOMBE	D8
EAGLE TAVERN	PLYMOUTH	B7	FORTUNE O' WAR	TORQUAY	E6
			FOSTERS		
EAST DART HOTEL	POSTBRIDGE	C5	INTERNATIONAL PUB	PLYMOUTH	B7
EBBERLEY ARMS	BARNSTAPLE	C2	FOUNTAIN HEAD	BRANSCOMBE	G5
RINGTON ARMS	KNOWLE	B2	FOUNTAIN HOTEL	OKEHAMPTON	C4
EDDYSTONE INN	HEYBROOK BAY	B7	FOUNTAIN INN	NORTH TAWTON	C4
EDGCOMBE HOTEL	PLYMOUTH	B7	FOUR IN HAND	TIVERTON	E3
EDGCUMBE ARMS	MILTON ABBOT	B5	FOX & HOUNDS	BRIDESTOWE	B5
EDGCUMBE HOTEL	BERE ALSTON	B6	FOX AND GOOSE INNE	PARRACOMBE	C1
ELBURTON HOTEL	PLYMSTOCK	B7	FOX AND HOUNDS	FREMINGTON	B2
ELEPHANTS NEST	HORNDON	B5	FOX AND HOUNDS HOTEL	EGGESFORD	D3
ELIZABETHAN INN	LUTON	E5	FOX INN	NEWTON ABBOT	E6
ELLACOMBE INN	TORQUAY	E6	FOXHOUND INN	BRIXTON	C7
EMBASSY TAVERN	PAIGNTON	E6	FOXHUNTERS INN	WEST DOWN	B1
ENDEAVOUR	TEIGNMOUTH	E6	FREDDIE'S BAR	PLYMOUTH	B7
EWE	EXETER	E5	FRIENDSHIP INN		
EXCHANGE	CREDITON	D4	(KEYHAM)	PLYMOUTH	B7

Pub Name	District	Map Ref
FRIENDSHIP INN (NORTH HILL)	PLYMOUTH	B7
FROG & FRIGATE	PLYMOUTH	B7
FROUDE ARMS	EAST ANSTEY	E2
GANNET	BIDEFORD	B2
GEORGE	TORQUAY	E6
GEORGE & DRAGON	DARTMOUTH	E7
GEORGE AND DRAGON	CLYST ST. GEORGE	E5
GEORGE AND DRAGON	ILFRACOMBE	B1
GEORGE COACH INN	PLYMOUTH	B7
GEORGE HOTEL	AXMINSTER	G4
GEORGE HOTEL	HATHERLEIGH	C4
GEORGE HOTEL	SOUTH MOLTON	D2
GEORGE INN	CHARDSTOCK	G4
GEORGE INN	BRAUNTON	B2
GEORGE INN	BLACKAWTON	D7
GEORGE INN	BUCKFASTLEIGH	D6
GEORGE'S TAVERNA	TORQUAY	E6
GERRARD ARMS	COLYTON	G4
GLEN	PLYMOUTH	B7
GLOBE	EXETER	E5
GLOBE	BEAFORD	C3
GLOBE	CHULMLEIGH	D3
GLOBE	LYNTON	D1
GLOBE	NEWTON ABBOT	E6
GLOBE	PAIGNTON	E6
GLOBE HOTEL	TOPSHAM	E5
GLOBE HOTEL	TORRINGTON	B3
GLOBE HOTEL	CHAGFORD	D5
GLOBE HOTEL	BRIXHAM	E7
GLOBE INN	LYMPSTONE	E5
GLOBE INN	SAMPFORD PEVERELL	F3
GLOBE INN	CHUDLEIGH	E5
GLOBE INN	FROGMORE	D8
GLOBE INN	TOTNES	D6
GLOBE INN	BUCKFASTLEIGH	D6
GLOBE INN	BUCKFASTLEIGH	D6
GOLDEN FLEECE	HOLSWORTHY	A4
GOLDEN HIND	MUSBURY	G4
GOLDEN HIND	WOOLACOMBE	B1
GOLDEN HIND	PLYMOUTH	B7
GOLDEN HINDE	BIDEFORD	B2
GOLDEN INN	HIGHAMPTON	B4
GOLDEN LION	NORTHAM	B2
GOLDEN LION	BRIXHAM	E7
GOLDEN LION	NEWTON ABBOT	E6
GOLDEN LION HOTEL	ASHBURTON	D6
GOLDEN LION INN	TIPTON ST. JOHN	F5
GOLDEN LION INN	HIGH BICKINGTON	C3
GOLDEN LION INN	TEIGNMOUTH	E6
GOLDEN LION TAP	BARNSTAPLE	C2
GOOD COMPANIONS	PLYMOUTH	B7
GOOD KNIGHT INN	CHERITON BISHOP	D4
GRAMPUS	LEE	B1
GRAND DUCHESS	PLYMOUTH	B7
GRAND HOTEL	PLYMOUTH	B7
GRAND HOTEL (PULLMAN BAR)	TORQUAY	E6
GREAT WESTERN HOTEL	EXETER	E5
GREEN DRAGON	LANGTREE	B3
GREEN DRAGON	NORTH TAWTON	C4
GREEN DRAGON	NORTHLEW	C4
GREEN DRAGON	STOKE FLEMING	E7
GREEN GABLES	EXETER	E5
GRENVILLE ARMS	WESTWARD HO!	B2
GRENVILLE HOTEL	PLYMOUTH	B7
GREYHOUND INN	FENNY BRIDGES	F4
GROVE	EXMOUTH	F5
GROVE INN	KINGS NYMPTON	C3
GUNFIELD HOTEL	DARTMOUTH	E7
HALF MOON	CHERITON FITZPAINE	E4
HALF MOON	CLYST ST. MARY	E5
HALF MOON	TIVERTON	E3
HALF MOON	SHEEPWASH	B4
HALF MOON	PAIGNTON	E6
HALF MOON	TEIGNMOUTH	E6
HALF MOON INN	CLAYHIDON	F3
HALF MOON INN	EXETER	E5
HALF MOON INN	PLYMOUTH	B7
HALFWAY HOUSE	WILLAND	F3
HALFWAY HOUSE INN	AYLESBEARE	F5
HALFWAY HOUSE INN	GRENOFEN	B6
HALLSANDS HOTEL	HALLSANDS	D8
HARBOUR INN	AXMOUTH	G5
HARE & HOUNDS	KINGSKERSWELL	E6
HARE AND HOUNDS	SIDBURY	F4
HARE AND HOUNDS	TIVERTON	E3
HARRIS ARMS	PORTGATE	B5
HART INN	HARTLAND	A3
HARTLAND QUAY HOTEL	HARTLAND QUAY	A2
HARTNOLL COUNTRY HOUSE	BOLHAM	E3
HAVELOCK	TORQUAY	E6
HAYWAIN	BURLESCOMBE	F3
HAYWAIN HOTEL	TORQUAY	E6
HEART OF OAK	EXETER	E5
HEARTS OF OAK	BARNSTAPLE	C2
HEATHFIELD	HONITON	F4
HEAVITREE ARMS	EXMOUTH	F5
HEAVITREE ARMS	BIDEFORD	B2
HEAVITREE ARMS	NEWTON ABBOT	E6
HELE ARMS	PLYMPTON	C7
HELE BAY HOTEL	ILFRACOMBE	B1
HENRY'S BAR	PAIGNTON	E6
HERBERT	PLYMOUTH	B7
HERMITAGE	KINGSBRIDGE	D8
HERON HOUSE HOTEL	THURLESTONE	C8
HIGHWAYMAN'S HAUNT	CHUDLEIGH	E5
HIGHWEEK INN	NEWTON ABBOT	E6
HILL PARK HOTEL	PLYMOUTH	B7
HOB NOBS	TEIGNMOUTH	E6
HOLE IN THE WALL	EXETER	E5
HOLE IN THE WALL	TORQUAY	E6
HOLE-IN-THE-WALL	BRIXHAM	E7
HOLLY TREE	EXMOUTH	F5
HONITON INN	EXETER	E5
HOOK AND PARROT	SEATON	G5
HOOPS INN	HORNS CROSS	B3
HOP & GRAPES	TORQUAY	E6
HOPE & ANCHOR INN	HOPE COVE	C8
HORSE & GROOM	BITTAFORD	C7
HORSE AND DRAY	EXETER	E5
HORSE AND GROOM	EXETER	E5
HORSE AND GROOM	BARNSTAPLE	C2
HUNGRY FOX	BROADCLYST	E4
HUNTERS INN	NEWTON TRACEY	C2
HUNTERS INN	PARRACOMBE	C1
HUNTERS INN	TORRINGTON	B3
HUNTERS LODGE	AXMINSTER	G4
HUNTERS LODGE INN	CORNWORTHY	D7
HUNTSMAN	HOLSWORTHY	A4
HUNTSMAN INN	IDE	E5
HYDE PARK HOTEL	PLYMOUTH	B7
ILMINSTER STAGE	CULMSTOCK	F3
ILSINGTON HOTEL	ILSINGTON	D5
IMPERIAL HOTEL	EXETER	E5
IMPERIAL HOTEL	EXMOUTH	F5
IMPERIAL HOTEL	BARNSTAPLE	C2
IMPERIAL HOTEL	ILFRACOMBE	B1
IMPERIAL HOTEL	TORQUAY	E6
IMPERIAL INN	IVYBRIDGE	C7
INDIAN INN	PLYMOUTH	B7
INN ON THE GREEN	PAIGNTON	E6
INN ON THE STRAND	BARNSTAPLE	C2
IVY HOUSE	TEIGNMOUTH	E6

Pub Name	District	Map Ref	Pub Name	District	Map Ref
JACK OF BOTH SIDES	BIDEFORD	B2	LEY ARMS	KENN	E5
JACK RUSSELL	SWIMBRIDGE	C2	LIFEBOAT INN	TEIGNMOUTH	E6
JACK-IN-THE-GREEN	ROCKBEARE	F4	LIFEBOAT INN	PLYMOUTH	B7
JAMES STREET			LIGHTER INN	TOPSHAM	E5
SPIRIT VAULTS	PLYMOUTH	B7	LINNEY	COFFINSWELL	E6
JOHN BULL	TORQUAY	E6	LION INN	COMBE MARTIN	C1
JOINERS ARMS	BIDEFORD	B2	LITTLE HOUSE	TORQUAY	E6
JOLLY ABBOT	NEWTON ABBOT	E6	LITTLE MUTTON		
JOLLY FARMER	NEWTON ABBOT	E6	MONSTER	PLYMOUTH	B7
JOLLY MILLER	PLYMOUTH	B7	LIVE AND LET LIVE	LANDSCOVE	D6
JOLLY PORTER	EXETER	E5	LOBSTER POT INN	HOPE COVE	C8
JOLLY SAILOR	TEIGNMOUTH	E6	LOCOMOTIVE	NEWTON ABBOT	E6
JOLLY SAILOR INN	EAST OGWELL	E6	LODDISWELL INN	LODDISWELL	D7
JOURNEY'S END INN	RINGMORE	C7	LONDON & PARIS	ILFRACOMBE	B1
JUBILEE INN	WEST ANSTEY	E2	LONDON HOTEL	OKEHAMPTON	C4
JUBILEE INN	WOOLACOMBE	B1	LONDON HOTEL	ASHBURTON	D6
JULE'S	TORQUAY	E6	LONDON HOTEL	SOUTH BRENT	D7
JUNCTION INN	HALWILL JUNCTION	B4	LONDON INN	MORCHARD BISHOP	D4
			LONDON INN	OTTERY ST. MARY	F4
KANGAROO	TEIGNMOUTH	E6	LONDON INN	BRAUNTON	B2
KEEPERS COTTAGE INN	KENTISBEARE	F4	LONDON INN	MOLLAND	D2
KENTS CAVERN HOTEL	TORQUAY	E6	LONDON INN	COMBE MARTIN	C1
KESTOR INN	MANATON	D5	LONDON INN	SHALDON	E6
KESTREL	BIDEFORD	B2	LONDON INN	STOKE FLEMING	E7
KEYBERRY HOTEL	NEWTON ABBOT	E6	LONDON INN	HORRABRIDGE	B6
KING OF PRUSSIA	BOVEY TRACEY	D5	LONDON INN	PLYMPTON	C7
KING OF PRUSSIA	KINGSBRIDGE	D8	LONG BAR	BRIXHAM	E7
KING WILLIAM IV	BUDLEIGH SALTERTON	F5	LONGBRIDGE INN	MEMBURY	G4
KING WILLIAM IV	TOTNES	D6	LOOK OUT BAR	EAST PORTLEMOUTH	D8
KING WILLIAM IV HOTEL	TEIGNMOUTH	E6	LOPES ARMS	PLYMOUTH	B7
KINGFISHER	COLYTON	G4	LORD BERESFORD	PLYMOUTH	B7
KINGS ARMS	BOW	D4	LORD HALDON	DUNCHIDEOCK	E5
KINGS ARMS	EXETER	E5	LORD HIGH ADMIRAL	PLYMOUTH	B7
KINGS ARMS	OTTERTON	F5	LORD NELSON	TOPSHAM	E5
KINGS ARMS	SEATON	G5	LORD NELSON	KINGSKERSWELL	E6
KINGS ARMS	STOCKLAND	G4	LORD NELSON INN	DARTMOUTH	E7
KINGS ARMS	BIDEFORD	B2	LORD NELSON INN	TOTNES	D6
KINGS ARMS	HARTLAND	A3	LOUNGE	PLYMOUTH	B7
KINGS ARMS	HOLSWORTHY	A4	LUGGER	PLYMOUTH	B7
KINGS ARMS	OKEHAMPTON	C4	LUPPITT INN	LUPPITT	F4
KINGS ARMS	SOUTH MOLTON	D2	LYMINGTON ARMS	WEMBWORTHY	C3
KINGS ARMS	WINKLEIGH	C4	LYNEHAM INN	PLYMPTON	C7
KINGS ARMS	GEORGEHAM	B2			
KINGS ARMS	KINGSBRIDGE	D8	MACBETHS	TORQUAY	E6
KINGS ARMS	KINGSTEIGNTON	E6	MALT SCOOP	MERTON	C3
KINGS ARMS	SALCOMBE	D8	MALTHOUSE	PLYMOUTH	B7
KINGS ARMS	STRETE	D7	MALTSCOOP INN	LAPFORD	D3
KINGS ARMS	TEIGNMOUTH	E6	MALTSTERS ARMS	CLYST ST. MARY	E5
KINGS ARMS	BUCKFASTLEIGH	D6	MALTSTERS ARMS	HARBETON FORD	D7
KINGS ARMS	PLYMOUTH	B7	MALTSTERS ARMS	TUCKENHAY	D7
KINGS ARMS	PLYMSTOCK	B7	MALTSTERS ARMS,	WOODBURY	F5
KINGS ARMS (TAMERTON)	PLYMOUTH	B7	MANOR	TORQUAY	E6
KINGS ARMS HOTEL	TEDBURN ST. MARY	D4	MANOR HOUSE HOTEL	CULLOMPTON	F4
KINGS ARMS HOTEL	SOUTH ZEAL	C4	MANOR HOUSE HOTEL	TORQUAY	E6
KINGS HEAD	CULLOMPTON	F4	MANOR HOUSE INN	CROYDE	B2
KINGS HEAD	PLYMOUTH	B7	MANOR INN	LOWER ASHTON	E5
KINGSBRIDGE INN	TOTNES	D6	MANOR INN	ASHWATER	B4
KINGSBRIDGE			MANOR INN	TORQUAY	E6
WINE LODGE	KINGSBRIDGE	D8	MANOR INN	BRIXHAM	E7
KINGSLEY INN	NORTHAM	B2	MANOR INN	GALMPTON	C8
			MANOR INN	LYDFORD	B5
LAMB	BIDEFORD	B2	MARE & FOAL	YEOFORD	D4
LAMB & FLAG	OTTERY ST. MARY	F4	MARINE HOTEL	DAWLISH	E5
LAMB INN	AXMINSTER	G4	MARINE HOTEL	SALCOMBE	D8
LAMB INN	LONGDOWN	E5	MARINERS ARMS	BRAUNTON	B2
LAMB INN	SILVERTON	E4	MARISCO TAVERN	LUNDY ISLAND	A1
LAMB INN	SANDFORD	D4	MARITIME	BRIXHAM	E7
LANDSDOWNE	TORQUAY	E6	MARKET HOUSE INN	DARTMOUTH	E7
LANGDON COURT HOTEL	DOWN THOMAS	B7	MARKET HOUSE INN	NEWTON ABBOT	E6
LANSDOWNE HOTEL	DAWLISH	E5	MARKET HOUSE INN,	CULLOMPTON	F4
LAURELS	PETROCKSTOWE	C4	MARKET INN	BARNSTAPLE	C2
LAVENDOR MANOR	BERRY POMEROY	D6	MARKET INN	HATHERLEIGH	C4
LEAPING SALMON INN	HORRABRIDGE	B6	MARKET INN	TAVISTOCK	B6
LEG O' MUTTON INN	YELVERTON	B6	MARSHALLS	BARNSTAPLE	C2
LENNARDS BAR	EXMOUTH	F5	MARY TAVY INN	MARY TAVY	B5

Pub Name	District	Map Ref	Pub Name	District	Map Ref
PASSAGE INN	TOPSHAM	E5	QUAY	INSTOW	B2
PATCH 'N' PARROT	BIDEFORD	B2	QUAY	KINGSBRIDGE	D8
PEACOCKS	TORQUAY	E6	QUEEN & CONSTITUTION	PLYMOUTH	B7
PEAR TREE INN	PLYMOUTH	B7	QUEEN VICTORIA	EXETER	E5
PEN & PARCHMENT	PLYMOUTH	B7	QUEENS	ILFRACOMBE	B1
PENN INN	NEWTON ABBOT	E6	QUEENS ARMS	DARTINGTON	D6
PENNYCOMEQUICK	PLYMOUTH	B7	QUEENS ARMS	SLAPTON	D7
PETER TAVY INN	PETER TAVY	B5	QUEENS DOCK TAVERN	PLYMOUTH	B7
PHOENIX TAVERN	PLYMOUTH	B7	QUEENS HEAD	TIVERTON	E3
PIAZZA	TORQUAY	E6	QUEENS HEAD	HARTLAND	A3
PICKWICK	TORQUAY	E6	QUEENS HEAD	BARNSTAPLE	C2
PICKWICK INN	PAIGNTON	E6	QUEENS HEAD HOTEL	EXETER	E5
PICKWICK INN	ST ANN'S CHAPEL	C7	QUEENS HEAD HOTEL	TAVISTOCK	B6
PIED PIPER	KINGSKERSWELL	E6	QUEENS HOTEL	LYNTON	D1
PIER HOTEL	ILFRACOMBE	B1	QUEENS HOTEL	NEWTON ABBOT	E6
PIER INN	PAIGNTON	E6	QUEENS HOTEL	TORQUAY	E6
PIG & WHISTLE	LITTLEHEMPSTON	D6	QUEENS HOTEL	BRIXHAM	E7
PIG AND TRUFFLE	EXETER	E5			
PIG'S EAR	BRADWORTHY	A3	RACEHORSE	TIVERTON	E3
PIG-ON-THE-HILL	WESTWARD HO!	B2	RADWAY	SIDMOUTH	F5
PIGS NOSE INN	EAST PRAWLE	D8	RAILWAY	HONITON	F4
PILCHARD INN	BURGH ISLAND	C8	RAILWAY	DAWLISH	E5
PLOUGH & HARROW	NEWTON ABBOT	E6	RAILWAY	TORQUAY	E6
PLOUGH INN	BICKINGTON	C2	RAILWAY INN	NORTH TAWTON	C4
PLOUGH INN	IPPLEPEN	E6	RAILWAY INN	NEWTON ABBOT	E6
PLUME OF FEATHERS	OTTERY ST. MARY	F4	RAILWAY INN	PLYMOUTH	B7
PLUME OF FEATHERS	OKEHAMPTON	C4	RALEIGH BAR &		
PLUME OF FEATHERS	PRINCETOWN	C6	RESTAURANT	DARTMOUTH	E7
PLYMOUTH	MORETONHAMPSTEAD	D5	RAMS HEAD	DOLTON	C3
PLYMOUTH INN	CREDITON	D4	RED COW	EXETER	E5
PLYMSTOCK INN	PLYMSTOCK	B7	RED COW	HONITON	F4
POACHERS INN	IDE	E5	RED HOUSE HOTEL	EXETER	E5
POACHERS POCKET	BURLESCOMBE	F3	RED LION	AXMINSTER	G4
POLE ARMS HOTEL	SEATON	G5	RED LION	SIDBURY	F5
POLSHAM ARMS	PAIGNTON	E6	RED LION	CHULMLEIGH	D3
POLTIMORE ARMS	EXETER	E5	RED LION	CLOVELLY	A3
POLTIMORE ARMS	NORTH MOLTON	D2	RED LION	EXBOURNE	C4
POLTIMORE ARMS	YARDE DOWN	D2	RED LION	ASHBURTON	D6
PONY AND TRAP	CULLOMPTON	F4	RED LION HOTEL	OAKFORD	E3
PORT LIGHT HOTEL	MALBOROUGH	D8	RED LION INN	BROADCLYST	E4
PORT ROYAL INN,	EXETER	E5	RED LION INN	SHOBROOKE	E4
PORTOBELLO INN	BIDEFORD	B2	RED LION INN	DITTISHAM	E7
PORTSMOUTH ARMS	PORTSMOUTH ARMS	C3	REDWING	LYMPSTONE	E5
PORTSMOUTH ARMS	BURRINGTON	C3	REDWOODS INN	UPLOWMAN	F3
POST HORN	TORQUAY	E6	REFORM INN	BARNSTAPLE	C2
POST INN	WHIDDON DOWN	D4	REVENUE INN	PLYMOUTH	B7
POST OFFICE INN	PLYMPTON	C7	RIDGEWAY INN	SMALLRIDGE	G4
PRETORIA WINE VAULTS	OKEHAMPTON	C4	RING O' BELLS	CHERITON FITZPAINE	E4
PREWLEY MOOR ARM	SOURTON	C5	RING O' BELLS	BIDEFORD	B2
PRINCE ALBERT	DAWLISH	E5	RING O' BELLS	LANDKEY	C2
PRINCE ALBERT	EXETER	E5	RING O' BELLS	NORTH TAWTON	C4
PRINCE ALBERT	ILFRACOMBE	B1	RING O'BELLS	CHAGFORD	D5
PRINCE ALBERT BAR	TORQUAY	E6	RING OF BELLS	NORTH BOVEY	D5
PRINCE ALFRED	PLYMOUTH	B7	RING OF BELLS	WEST ALVINGTON	D8
PRINCE BLUCHER	TIVERTON	E3	RING OF BELLS	BISHOPSTEIGNTON	E6
PRINCE MAURICE	PLYMOUTH	B7	RING OF BELLS	MORETONHAMPSTEAD	D5
PRINCE OF			RINGS ASH INN	ASHREIGNEY	C3
ORANGE HOTEL	TORQUAY	E6	RISING SUN	SIDFORD	F5
PRINCE OF WALES	HOLCOMBE ROGUS	F3	RISING SUN	BARNSTAPLE	C2
PRINCE OF WALES	ILFRACOMBE	B1	RISING SUN	BARNSTAPLE	
PRINCE OF WALES HOTEL	PRINCETOWN	C6		(NEWPORT)	C2
PRINCE OF WALES INN	DAWLISH	E5	RISING SUN	UMBERLEIGH	C3
PRINCE REGENT	TIVERTON	E3	RISING SUN	WOODLAND	D6
PRINCE REGENT	PLYMOUTH	B7	RISING SUN HOTEL	LYNMOUTH	D1
PRINTERS ELBOW	TORQUAY	E6	RISING SUN INN	SOUTH ZEAL	C4
PRINTERS PIE	EXETER	E5	RISING SUN INN	BRIXHAM	E7
PROSPECT INN	EXETER	E5	RISING SUN INN	PLYMOUTH	B7
PROVIDENCE INN	EAST PRAWLE	D8	RIVERSIDE HOTEL	WRAFTON	B2
PROVIDENCE INN	PLYMOUTH	B7	RIVERSIDE INN	BOVEY TRACEY	D5
PUB	TORQUAY	E6	RIVIERA HOTEL	SIDMOUTH	F5
PUFFING BILLY	EXTON	E5	ROCK HOUSE HOTEL	THURLESTONE	C8
PUFFING BILLY	TORRINGTON	B3	ROCK INN	GEORGEHAM	B2
PYM ARMS	PLYMOUTH	B7	ROCK INN	HAYTOR VALE	D5
PYNE ARMS	EAST DOWN	C1	ROCK INN	YELVERTON	B6

Pub Name	District	Map Ref	Pub Name	District	Map Ref
ROCKFORD INN	ROCKFORD	D1	SEYMOUR ARMS	PLYMOUTH	B7
ROLLE ARMS	EAST BUDLEIGH	F5	SHIP	CREDITON	D4
ROLLE QUAY INN	BARNSTAPLE	C2	SHIP	WESTWARD HO!	B2
ROSE & CROWN	CALVERLEIGH	E3	SHIP	KINGSWEAR	E7
ROSE & CROWN	YEALMPTON	C7	SHIP	PAIGNTON	E6
ROSE AND CROWN	SANDFORD	D4	SHIP & PLOUGH	KINGSBRIDGE	D8
ROSE AND CROWN	BARNSTAPLE	C2	SHIP AGROUND	MORTEHOE	B1
ROSE GRANGE	TORQUAY	E6	SHIP AND PELICAN	EXETER	E5
ROSE OF BABBACOMBE	TORQUAY	E6	SHIP AND PILOT INN	ILFRACOMBE	B1
ROUGEMENT HOTEL -			SHIP IN DOCK INN	DARTMOUTH	E7
DRAKE'S BAR	EXETER	E5	SHIP INN	AXMOUTH	G5
ROYAL ALBERT			SHIP INN	COCKWOOD	E5
BRIDGE INN	PLYMOUTH	B7	SHIP INN	EXETER	E5
ROYAL AT BABBACOMBE	TORQUAY	E6	SHIP INN	CHUDLEIGH	E5
ROYAL BEACON HOTEL	EXMOUTH	F5	SHIP INN	NEWTON ABBOT	E6
ROYAL BRITANNIA HOTEL	ILFRACOMBE	B1	SHIP INN	TEIGNMOUTH	E6
ROYAL CASTLE HOTEL	LYNTON	D1	SHIP INN	PLYMOUTH	B7
ROYAL CASTLE HOTEL	DARTMOUTH	E7	SHIP INN	UGBOROUGH	C7
ROYAL CLARENCE	PLYMOUTH	B7	SHIP ON LAUNCH	BIDEFORD	B2
ROYAL CLARENCE HOTEL	EXETER	E5	SHIPS TAVERN &		
ROYAL DART HOTEL	KINGSWEAR	E7	KINGS HEAD	PLYMSTOCK	B7
ROYAL EXCHANGE	BARNSTAPLE	C2	SHIPWRIGHTS ARMS	SALCOMBE	D8
ROYAL EXCHANGE	TORRINGTON	B3	SHIPWRIGHTS ARMS	SHALDON	E6
ROYAL EXCHANGE	LEWDOWN	B5	SHIPWRIGHTS ARMS	PLYMOUTH	B7
ROYAL FORTESCUE	BARNSTAPLE	C2	SHORE INN	WESTWARD HO!	B2
ROYAL GEORGE	APPLEDORE	B2	SHUTE ARMS	SEATON JUNCTION	G4
ROYAL HOTEL	APPLEDORE	B2	SIDMOUTH ARMS	UPOTTERY	G4
ROYAL HOTEL	TORQUAY	E6	SILVERTON INN	SILVERTON	E4
ROYAL INN	HORSEBRIDGE	B6	SIPPERS	PLYMOUTH	B7
ROYAL MAIL	BIDEFORD	B2	SIR JOSHUA REYNOLDS	PLYMPTON	C7
ROYAL MARINE INN	COMBE MARTIN	C1	SIR RICHARD GRANVILLE	BIDEFORD	B2
ROYAL OAK	DUNKESWELL	F4	SIR WALTER RALEIGH	EAST BUDLEIGH	F5
ROYAL OAK	DUNSFORD	D5	SIX BELLS	PAYHEMBURY	F4
ROYAL OAK	EXETER	E5	SKIPPER	BRIXHAM	E7
ROYAL OAK	EXMINSTER	E5	SKYLARK	CLEARBROOK	B6
ROYAL OAK	NADDERWATER	E4	SLEEPER	SEATON	G5
ROYAL OAK	CHAWLEIGH	D3	SLOOP	KINGSKERSWELL	E6
ROYAL OAK	DOLTON	C3	SLOOP INN	BANTHAM	C7
ROYAL OAK	ASHBURTON	D6	SMOKEY HOUSE INN	PAIGNTON	E6
ROYAL OAK	IDEFORD	E5	SMUGGLERS INN	HOLCOMBE	E5
ROYAL OAK	MALBOROUGH	D8	SMUGGLERS INN	TOTNES	D6
ROYAL OAK	SOUTH BRENT	D7	SNOOTY FOX	TORQUAY	E6
ROYAL OAK	BIGBURY	C7	SOUTH DEVON INN	DAWLISH	E5
ROYAL OAK	PLYMSTOCK	B7	SOUTH PACIFIC	TEIGNMOUTH	E6
ROYAL OAK INN	BRIDESTOWE	B5	SOUTH SANDS HOTEL	SALCOMBE	D8
ROYAL OAK INN	MEAVY	C6	SPANISH CELLAR	TEIGNMOUTH	E6
ROYAL SEVEN STARS	TOTNES	D6	SPINNING WHEEL	PAIGNTON	E6
ROYAL SOVEREIGN	PLYMOUTH	B7	SPORTSMANS	TORQUAY	E6
ROYAL STANDARD	TORQUAY	E6	SPORTSMANS ARMS	BLACKAWTON	D7
ROYAL STANDARD	MARY TAVY	B5	SPORTSMANS INN	IVYBRIDGE	C7
ROYAL STANDARD HOTEL	SHALDON	E6	SPRAT & MACKEREL	BRIXHAM	E7
ROYAL UNION INN	DARTMOUTH	E7	ST. ANNS WELL BREWERY	EXETER	E5
RUFFWELL HOTEL	THORVERTON	E4	ST. LEVAN INN	PLYMOUTH	B7
RUGGLESTONE INN	WIDECOMBE -IN		STAFFORD HOTEL	OTTERY ST. MARY	F4
	-THE MOOR	D5	STAG & STABLE BAR	LYNTON	D1
RUMOUR	TOTNES	D6	STAG INN	RACKENFORD	D3
			STAGHUNTERS INN	BRENDON	D1
SALTERTON ARMS	BUDLEIGH SALTERTON	F5	STAGS HEAD	BARNSTAPLE	C2
SALUTATION	TOPSHAM	E5	STAGS HEAD	FILLEIGH	C2
SANDPIPER INN	ILFRACOMBE	B1	STAPLECROSS INN	HOCKWORTHY	F3
SANDS	WESTWARD HO!	B2	STAR	HONITON	F4
SANDY PARK INN	SANDY PARK	D5	STAR	LIVERTON	D6
SANDYGATE INN	KINGSTEIGNTON	E6	STAR OF THE WEST	PLYMOUTH	B7
SARACENS HEAD	NEWTON ABBOT	E6	START BAY INN	TORCROSS	D8
SAWYERS ARMS	EXETER	E5	STEAM PACKET	TOPSHAM	E5
SEA TROUT INN	STAVERTON	D6	STEAM PACKET INN	DARTMOUTH	E7
SEAGATE HOTEL	APPLEDORE	B2	STEAM PACKET INN	KINGSWEAR	E7
SEALE ARMS	DARTMOUTH	E7	STEAM PACKET INN	TOTNES	D6
SEVEN STARS	EXETER	E5	STEAM PACKET INN	PLYMOUTH	B7
SEVEN STARS	KENNFORD	E5	STEAMERS	EXETER	E5
SEVEN STARS	TIVERTON	E3	STOKE ARMS	EXETER	E5
SEVEN STARS	WINKLEIGH	C4	STOKE CANNON INN	STOKE CANNON	E4
SEVEN STARS	DARTMOUTH	E7	STOKE INN	PLYMOUTH	B7
SEVEN STARS	KINGSBRIDGE	D8	STOKE VAULTS	PLYMOUTH	B7
SEVEN STARS INN	SOUTH TAWTON	C4	STONE MASONS ARMS	PLYMOUTH	B7
SEVEN STARS INN	PLYMOUTH	B7	STOPFORD ARMS	PLYMOUTH	B7

Pub Name	District	Map Ref	Pub Name	District	Map Ref
STOWEY ARMS	EXMINSTER	E5	TORS INN	BELSTONE	C4
STRAND BAR	TORQUAY	E6	TOWER INN	SLAPTON	D7
STUMBLE INN	TORQUAY	E6	TOWN & COUNTRY	BARNSTAPLE	C2
SUN INN	BUCKFASTLEIGH	D6	TOWN ARMS	SOUTH MOLTON	D2
SWAN HOTEL	BAMPTON	E3	TOWN CRIER	EXMOUTH	F5
SWAN INN	LYMPSTONE	E5	TOWN HOUSE	PLYMOUTH	B7
SWAN INN	SIDMOUTH	F5	TRADE WINDS	BIDEFORD	B2
SWAN INN	DAWLISH	E5	TRADESMANS ARMS	SCORRITON	D6
SWAN INN	BIDEFORD	B2	TRADESMANS ARMS	STOKENHAM	D8
SWAN INN	MONKOKEHAMPTON	C4	TRADESMANS ARMS	PLYMOUTH	B7
SWAN INN	NEWTON ABBOT	E6	TRAFALGAR HOTEL	DARTMOUTH	E7
SWAN INN	NOSS MAYO	C7	TRAFALGAR INN	PLYMOUTH	B7
SWAN INN	PLYMOUTH	B7	TRAVELLERS REST	WHITESTONE	E4
SWANS NEST	EXMINSTER	E5	TRAWLER	BRIXHAM	E7
SYMPHONY'S WINE BAR	DARTMOUTH	E7	TREBY ARMS	SPARKWELL	C7
			TRELAWNY HOTEL	PLYMOUTH	B7
TALATON INN	TALATON	F4	TROUT INN		
TALBOT	BIDEFORD	B2	(CLOSED 15/1/93)	BICKLEIGH	E3
TALBOT ARMS HOTEL	UPLYME	H4	TUCKERS ARMS	DALWOOD	G4
TALLY HO!	EXETER	E5	TUDOR ROSE	SIDMOUTH	F5
TALLY HO!	LITTLEHEMPSTON	D6	TURF HOTEL	EXMINSTER	E5
TALLY HO! INN	HATHERLEIGH	C4	TURKS HEAD	EXETER	E5
TAMAR HOTEL	PLYMOUTH	B7	TWISTED OAK	IDE	E5
TANTON'S HOTEL	BIDEFORD	B2	TWO BRIDGES HOTEL	PRINCETOWN	C6
TAP & BARREL	PLYMOUTH	B7	TWO MILE OAK	ABBOTSKERSWELL	E6
TAP AND BARREL	EXETER	E5	TWO TREES	PLYMOUTH	B7
TAPPERS BAR	SIDMOUTH	F5			
TAVERN IN THE TOWN	BARNSTAPLE	C2	UNICORN	PLYMPTON	C7
TAVERNERS	AVETON GIFFORD	D7	UNION	BARNSTAPLE	C2
TAVISTOCK INN	POUNDSGATE	D6	UNION	TORQUAY	E6
TAVISTOCK INN	TAVISTOCK	B6	UNION INN	DOLTON	C3
TAW RIVER INN	STICKLEPATH	C4	UNION INN	STIBB CROSS	B3
TEIGN BREWERY	TEIGNMOUTH	E6	UNION INN	CHILLINGTON	D8
TEIGN HOUSE INN	CHRISTOW	D5	UNION INN	DENBURY	D6
TEIGNMOUTH INN	DAWLISH	E5	UNION INN	MORETONHAMPSTEAD	D5
TEN TORS INN	KINGSTEIGNTON	E6	UNION INN	NEWTON ABBOT	E6
TERMINUS	BIDEFORD	B2	UNION INN	PLYMPTON	C7
TERMINUS HOTEL	PLYMOUTH	B7	UNION INN	TAVISTOCK	B6
THATCHED BARN INN	CROYDE	B2	UNITY	PLYMOUTH	B7
THATCHED HOUSE INN	EXETER	E5	UPTON VALE	TORQUAY	E6
THATCHED TAVERN	MAIDENCOMBE	E6			
THE BANK,	EXMOUTH	F5	VALENTINES	TEIGNMOUTH	E6
THE EXCHANGE	EXETER	E5	VALLETORT INN	PLYMOUTH	B7
THE GIBBONS	TORQUAY	E6	VALLIANT SOLDIER	EXETER	E5
THE GISSONS ARMS,	KENNFORD	E5	VICTORIA	ILFRACOMBE	B1
THE LAMB	ILFRACOMBE	B1	VICTORIA & ALBERT	STOKE GABRIEL	E7
THE MALL	PLYMOUTH	B7	VICTORIA HOTEL	DARTMOUTH	E7
THE TWYFORD	TIVERTON	E3	VICTORIA HOTEL	PAIGNTON	E6
THELBRIDGE CROSS INN	THELBRIDGE	D3	VICTORIA INN	EXETER	E5
THIRSTY FARMER INN	WHIMPLE	F4	VICTORIA INN	ASHBURTON	D6
THISTLE PARK TAVERN	PLYMOUTH	B7	VICTORIA INN	SALCOMBE	D8
THREE CROWNS	CHAGFORD	D5	VICTORIA,	EXMOUTH	F5
THREE CROWNS	PLYMOUTH	B7	VICTUALLING OFFICE		
THREE ELMS	BRIXHAM	E7	TAVERN	PLYMOUTH	B7
THREE FERRETS	PLYMOUTH	B7	VILLAGE	BRIXHAM	E7
THREE HORSESHOES INN	BRANSCOMBE	G5	VILLAGE INN	EXETER	E5
THREE LITTLE PIGS	CREDITON	D4	VILLAGE INN	THURLESTONE	C8
THREE PIGEONS	BISHOPS TAWTON	C2	VILLAGE INN AT		
THREE TUNS	HONITON	F4	LYNMOUTH	LYNMOUTH	D1
THREE TUNS	SILVERTON	E4	VINE HOTEL	PLYMOUTH	B7
THREE TUNS	BARNSTAPLE	C2	VINE INN	HONITON	F4
TIDES REACH HOTEL	SALCOMBE	D8	VINES	EXETER	E5
TIVERTON ARMS	SOUTH MOLTON	D2	VIRTUOUS LADY	TAVISTOCK	B6
TIVERTON INN	BAMPTON	E3	VOLUNTEER	HONITON	F4
TOBY JUG INN	BICKINGTON (SD)	D6	VOLUNTEER	OTTERY ST. MARY	F4
TOM COBLEY INN	PAIGNTON	E6	VOLUNTEER	SIDMOUTH	F5
TOM COBLEY TAVERN	SPREYTON	D4	VOLUNTEER INN	YEALMPTON	C7
TOP GEORGE INN	COMBE MARTIN	C1			
TORBAY ST	PAIGNTON	E6	WAIE INN	ZEAL MONARCHORUM	D4
TORCROSS HOTEL	TORCROSS	D8	WALKHAMPTON INN	WALKHAMPTON	C6
TORRE ABBEY HOTEL	TORQUAY	E6	WALRUS	PLYMOUTH	B7
TORRIDGE	BIDEFORD	B2	WARREN HOUSE INN	POSTBRIDGE	C5
TORRIDGE INN	BLACK TORRINGTON	B4	WATERFRONT	TORQUAY	E6
TORRIDGE INN	TORRINGTON	B3	WATERLOO INN	PLYMOUTH	B7
TORRINGTON ARMS	TORRINGTON	B3	WATERMANS ARMS	BRIXHAM	E7

Pub Name	District	Map Ref	Pub Name	District	Map Ref
WATERMANS ARMS	BUCKFASTLEIGH	D6	WHITE HART INN	BRIDESTOWE	B5
WATERMANS ARMS	TOTNES	D6	WHITE HART INN	NEWTON ABBOT	E6
WATERMANS ARMS	TUCKENHAY	D7	WHITE HART INN (1)	TORQUAY	E6
WATERSIDE HOTEL	PAIGNTON	E6	WHITE HART INN (2)	TORQUAY	E6
WAVERLEY	ILFRACOMBE	B1	WHITE HORSE	TIVERTON	E3
WAYFARER	INSTOW	B2	WHITE HORSE	BARNSTAPLE	C2
WEARY TRAVELLER,	CULLOMPTON	F4	WHITE HORSE	MORETONHAMPSTEAD	D5
WELCOME INN	EXETER	E5	WHITE HORSE HOTEL	CHURSTON FERRERS	E7
WELCOME INN	HALBERTON	F3	WHITE HORSE INN	BAMPTON	E3
WELCOME STRANGER	LIVERTON	D6	WHITE HORSE INN	WOODBURY	
WELL HOUSE	EXETER	E5		SALTERTON	F5
WELLINGTON	IPPLEPEN	E6	WHITE LION	HONITON	F4
WELLINGTON ARMS	ILFRACOMBE	B1	WHITE LION	BRAUNTON	B2
WELLINGTON HOTEL	PLYMOUTH	B7	WHITE THORN INN	SHAUGH PRIOR	C6
WEST OF ENGLAND	TORRINGTON	B3	WHO'D HAVE		
WESTCOUNTRY INN	BURSDON MOOR	A3	THOUGHT IT	MILTON COOMBE	B6
WESTERN HOTEL	PLYMOUTH	B7	WIG & PEN	TORQUAY	E6
WESTERN MILL HOTEL	PLYMOUTH	B7	WILD GOOSE	COOMBEINTEIGNHEAD	E6
WESTLEIGH INN	WESTLEIGH	B2	WILLIAMS ARMS	WRAFTON	B2
WHEEL INN	ILFRACOMBE	B1	WINDJAMMER	DARTMOUTH	E7
WHEELWRIGHT INN	COLYFORD	G4	WINDMILL INN	PLYMOUTH	B7
WHIPTON VILLAGE INN	EXETER	E5	WINDSOR ARMS	BARNSTAPLE	C2
WHITCHURCH INN	WHITCHURCH	B6	WINDSOR CASTLE	EXETER	E5
WHITE BALL	TIVERTON	E3	WINKLEIGH HOTEL	WINKLEIGH	C4
WHITE COTTAGE HOTEL	COLYTON	G4	WINSTONS	EXETER	E5
WHITE HART	BOW	D4	WOLBOROUGH INN	NEWTON ABBOT	E6
WHITE HART	COLYFORD	G4	WOOD COUNTRY	SOUTH TAWTON	C4
WHITE HART	CULLOMPTON	F4	WOODACOTT ARMS	THORNBURY	B3
WHITE HART	DAWLISH	E5	WOODFORD		
WHITE HART	WOODBURY	F5	BRIDGE HOTEL	WOODFORD BRIDGE	B3
WHITE HART	DAWLISH	E5	WOODLAND FORT INN	PLYMOUTH	B7
WHITE HART	BRATTON FLEMING	C2	WOODPECKER INN	AVONWICK	D7
WHITE HART	HOLSWORTHY	A4	WOODSIDE	PLYMOUTH	B7
WHITE HART	NORTH TAWTON	C4	WREY ARMS	STICKLEPATH	
WHITE HART	CHUDLEIGH	E5		(BARNSTAPLE)	C2
WHITE HART	KINGSBRIDGE	D8	WYNDHAM ARMS	KENTISBEARE	F4
WHITE HART	MORETONHAMPSTEAD	D5			
WHITE HART	TORQUAY	E6	YARCOMBE INN	YARCOMBE	G4
WHITE HART BAR	DARTINGTON	D6	YE OLDE SADDLERS ARMS,	LYMPSTONE	E5
WHITE HART HOTEL	EXETER	E5	YE OLDE SNARE &		
WHITE HART HOTEL	OKEHAMPTON	C4	GINTRAP	BISHOPS NYMPTON	D3
WHITE HART INN	BIDEFORD	B2	YORK	TORQUAY	E6

CAMRA LOCALLY

Programmes and events are announced monthly in CAMRA's national newspaper What's Brewing, and include branch meetings, socials, brewery visits, pub crawls and surveys, visits to neighbouring festivals and joint meetings.

Each year in the middle of June we hold the Exeter Beer Festival, with a Winter Ale Festival during January. Other events occur from time to time.

Local Contacts are:

Regional Director:	Peter Bridle 10 Cornwall Road Bishopston Bristol BS7 8LH (0272) 248894
Exeter and East Devon:	Andy Hurst 49 Oxford Road St Thomas, Exeter (0392) 432139
Plymouth and West Devon:	Ian Daniels 28 Buddle Close Tavistock PL19 OEG (0822) 616861
South Devon:	Roger Adams 5 St Leonard's Road Newton Abbot TQ12 1JY (0626) 66933
North Devon:	Mick Gullick 1 Rose Mount Hill Top Road Bideford (0805) 22663

CAMRA NATIONALLY

OK. You've read the guide from cover to cover (well almost).

You've tried a few of the recommendations. You may even have tried a pint or two. So... are you coming to join CAMRA, or are we going to have to fit you up with a concrete swimsuit?

More seriously ...

If you believe in the value of freedom of choice, traditional British pubs and tarditional British beer, there is only one thing to do - join the organisation that is fighting to preserve them - CAMRA, by completing the form on the next page. We have a small full time staff at our national headquarters in St Albans. Most of CAMRA's campaigning work, including the publishing of national and local beer guides, is performed by our 30,000 plus members who give invaluable time and effort as unpaid volunteers.

PROTECT YOUR PLEASURE

JOIN CAMRA NOW

Just fill in the form below and send, with a cheque for £10 (payable to CAMRA Ltd) to **Carol Couch, CAMRA, 34 Alma Road, St. Albans, Herts AL1 3BW.**

APPLICATION FORM

Name ....

Address ....

....

...........................Post Code ....

I wish to join the Campaign for Real Ale, and agree to abide by the Memorandum and Articles of Association. I enclose a cheque for **£10 (£14** if overseas).

Signed ....Date ....